Name _____

Middle School Math Solution

MATHbook

COURSE 1 · STUDENT EDITION

4th Edition

AUTHORING TEAM

Sandy Bartle Finocchi   **Amy Jones Lewis**

Josh Fisher   **Janet Sinopoli**   **Victoria Fisher**

501 Grant Street, Suite 1075
Pittsburgh, PA 15219
Phone: 888-851-7094
Customer Service Phone: 412-690-2444

www.carnegielearning.com

Foundation Authors (2010)

William S. Hadley,
Algebra and Proportional Reasoning

Mary Lou Metz,
Data Analysis and Probability

Mary Lynn Raith,
Number and Operations

Janet Sinopoli,
Algebra

Jaclyn Snyder,
Geometry and Measurement

Contributors

Sarah Galasso

Acknowledgments

- The members of the Carnegie Learning Production Team—Sara Kozelnik, Sara Schmidt Boldon, Laura Norris, Mary Travis, Jaana Bykonich, Michelle Rohm, and Bob Dreas

- The members of Carnegie Learning Cognitive Scientist Team—John Connelly, Bob Hausmann, and Martina Pavelko—for their insight in learning science and collaboration on MATHia Software.

- **Primary Design:** Abbe Eckstein

- **Design Support:** Madison Kalo, Douglas Fuchs, and Heather Greenwood

- **Production Vendors:** Paul Leveno, BizeeWorks, LLC, Lumina Datamatics, LTD, and Trivium Education Services

Credits: Art and Photo Credits are at the end of the Index.

ISBN: 978-1-68459-726-0

Student Edition

Printed in the United States of America

1 2 3 4 5 6 7 8 9 BAB 25 24 23 22 21

Cover Design by Anne Milliron and Moncur (thinkmoncur.com)

LONG + LIVE + MATH

Mathematics is so much more than memorizing rules. It is learning to reason, to make connections, and to make sense of the world. Focus on the journey and the process.

No matter where you are starting from, your effort will lead to improvement.

We believe in Learning by Doing™ — and we believe in YOU!

Introducing Carnegie Learning's Middle School Math Solution

You will develop a deep understanding of key mathematical ideas by actively engaging with them in various ways — in print and online, together and individually, through concept and application.

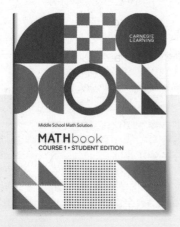

60/40

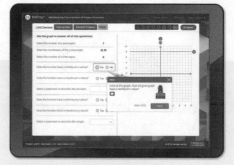

LEARN
TOGETHER WITH

MATHbook

When you work in this textbook, you'll collaborate, create, communicate, and problem-solve together with your peers.

LEARN
INDIVIDUALLY WITH

MATHia

When you work in this software, you'll work at your own pace and receive 1-to-1 coaching that adapts to your needs as you go.

EXPLORE FAMILY RESOURCES ONLINE
www.carnegielearning.com/home-connection

Table of Contents

Download MATHia progress trackers!

www.carnegielearning.com/login

MODULE 1 Composing and Decomposing

TOPIC 1 Factors and Multiples

📖 MATHbook	📷 MATHia

MATHbook

MATHia

**Writing Equivalent Expressions Using the
Distributive Property**
- Commutative and Associative Properties
- Exploring the Distributive Property with Numeric Expressions
- Using the Distributive Property with Numeric Expressions

Identifying Common Factors and Common Multiples
- Prime Factorization
- Determining the LCM or GCF of Two Numbers
- Using the GCF to Rewrite the Sum of Two Numbers

Multiplying Fractions
- Multiplying by Fractions to Increase or Decrease Quantities

Fraction by Fraction Division
- Representing Fraction Division
- Interpreting Remainders Using Models
- Developing the Fraction Division Algorithm
- Multiplying and Dividing Rational Numbers

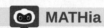
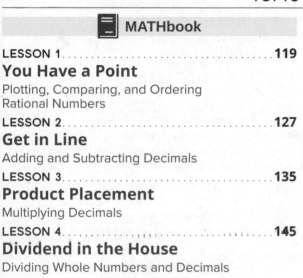

MODULE 2 Relating Quantities

MODULE 3 Determining Unknown Quantities

TOPIC 1 Expressions

🤖 MATHia

Evaluating Numeric Expressions
- Writing and Evaluating Exponent Expressions
- Order of Operations
- Applying the Order of Operations
- Using Order of Operations to Evaluate Numeric Expressions

Introduction to Algebraic Expressions
- Writing Expressions from Verbal Descriptions
- Patterns and One-Step Expressions
- Identifying Parts of Simple Algebraic
- Evaluating Algebraic Expressions

Equivalent Algebraic Expressions
- Modeling Equivalent Algebraic Expressions
- Exploring the Distributive Property with Algebraic Expressions
- Using Order of Operations to Rewrite Algebraic Expressions

Using Algebraic Expressions to Analyze and Solve Problems
- Using Picture Algebra

TOPIC 2 Equations

🤖 MATHia

Reasoning with Algebraic Expressions
- Using Substitution to Identify Solutions to Equations

Solving One-Step Addition and Subtraction Equations
- Exploring One-Step Equations with Double Number Lines
- Using Double Number Lines to Solve One-Step Addition Equations
- Solving with Addition and Subtraction

Solving One-Step Multiplication and Division Equations
- Using Double Number Lines to Solve One-Step Multiplication Equations
- Solving with Multiplication and Division
- Solving One-Step Equations

Solving One-Step Equations with Decimals and Fractions
- Solving One-Step Equations with Decimals
- Solving One-Step Equations with Fractions

Solutions to Inequalities
- Using Substitution to Identify Solutions to Inequalities
- Graphing Inequalities with Positive Rational Numbers
- Writing Inequalities from Real-World Situations

Table of Contents Continued

MODULE 4 Moving Beyond Positive Quantities

MODULE 5 Describing Variability of Quantities

TOPIC 1 The Statistical Process

📖 MATHbook

🤖 MATHia

Understanding the Statistical Process
- Analyzing Distributions with Shape, Center, and Spread

Analyzing Numerical Data Displays
- Creating Dot Plots
- Interpreting Dot Plot

Using Histograms to Display Data
- Introduction to Histograms
- Creating Histograms
- Exploring Histograms

TOPIC 2 Numeric Summaries of Data

📖 MATHbook

🤖 MATHia

Analyzing Data Using Measures of Center
- Calculating Mean, Median, Mode, and Range
- Determining Measures of Center
- Measuring the Effects of Changing Data Sets

Displaying the Five-Number Summary
- Introduction to Box Plots
- Creating Box Plots
- Exploring Box Plots
- Interpreting Box Plots

Mean Absolute Deviation
- Calculating Mean Absolute Deviation
- Using Mean Absolute Deviation

Choosing Appropriate Measures
- Choosing Appropriate Measures

Let's Get Started!

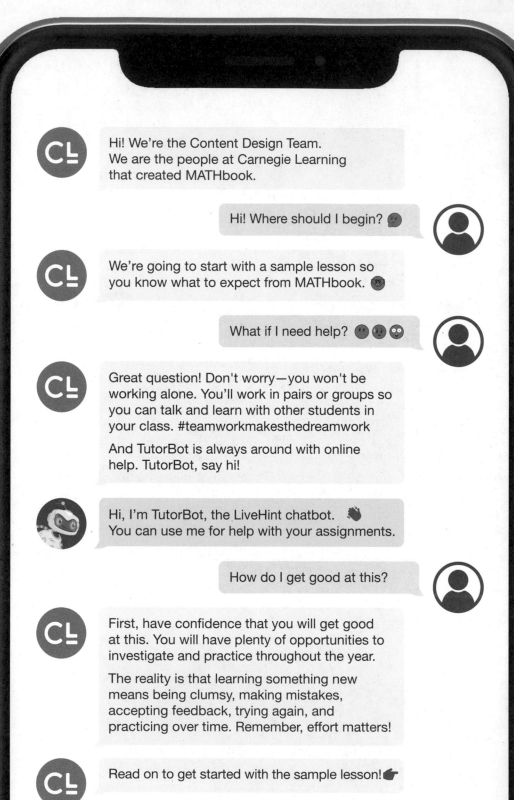

CL: Hi! We're the Content Design Team. We are the people at Carnegie Learning that created MATHbook.

User: Hi! Where should I begin? 🤔

CL: We're going to start with a sample lesson so you know what to expect from MATHbook. 🙂

User: What if I need help? 😮😟😳

CL: Great question! Don't worry—you won't be working alone. You'll work in pairs or groups so you can talk and learn with other students in your class. #teamworkmakesthedreamwork

And TutorBot is always around with online help. TutorBot, say hi!

TutorBot: Hi, I'm TutorBot, the LiveHint chatbot. 👋 You can use me for help with your assignments.

User: How do I get good at this?

CL: First, have confidence that you will get good at this. You will have plenty of opportunities to investigate and practice throughout the year.

The reality is that learning something new means being clumsy, making mistakes, accepting feedback, trying again, and practicing over time. Remember, effort matters!

CL: Read on to get started with the sample lesson! 👉

User: Let's do it! 💪😀

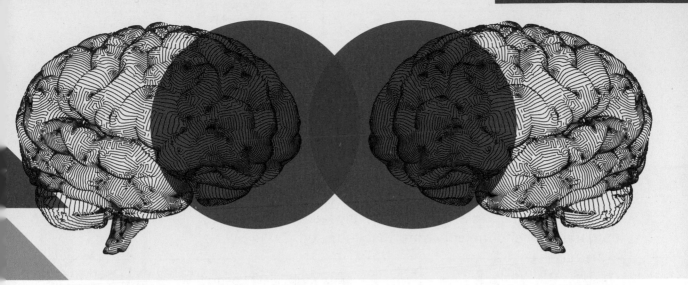

A Meeting of the Minds

An Introduction to MATHbook and Your Learning Resources

KEY TERMS

yet

Learning Goals

- Establish a community of learners.
- Preview the contents of MATHbook.
- Consider how you will interact with MATHbook to make your learning visible.
- Understand how MATHia software supports each MATHbook Topic.
- Set personal goals to take ownership of your learning.

REVIEW (1–2 minutes)

> These questions review a skill you will need in the lesson. Answer each question.

1. Why is it helpful to review what you already know before learning something new?

TAKE NOTE . . .
Each lesson opens with a statement that connects what you have learned with a question to ponder.

In previous math classes, you have analyzed patterns and relationships, learned about numbers and operations in base ten and fractions, measurement and data, and geometry.

How can you use MATHbook and MATHia software to meet the goals of this course?

You Already Know A Lot

Each Lesson in this book begins with a Getting Started that gives you the opportunity to use what you know about the world and what you have learned in previous math classes. You know a lot from a variety of learning experiences.

❯ Think back to how you learn something new.

1 List three different skills that you recently learned. Then, describe why you wanted to learn that skill and the strategies that you used.

Motivation to Learn the New Skill	New Skill	Strategies I Used to Learn This Skill

One learning strategy is to talk with your peers. In this course, you will work with your classmates to solve problems, discuss strategies, and learn together.

❯ Compare and discuss your list with a classmate.

2 Which strategies do you have in common? Which strategies does your classmate have that you did not think of on your own?

ASK YOURSELF . . .
How do your strategies change based on what you are learning and what you already know about it?

THINK ABOUT . . .
Listening well, cooperating with others, and appreciating different perspectives are essential life skills.

❯ Be prepared to share your list of learning strategies with the class.

Learning Together with MATHbook

In this course, you will learn new math concepts by exploring and investigating ideas, reading, writing, and talking to your classmates. You will even learn by making mistakes with concepts you haven't mastered yet.

> Flip through the first Module of your MATHbook.

1 What do you find interesting? Does anything look familiar?

2 Compare the title and subtitle of several lessons. **What do you notice?**

3 Describe the icons you see within the lessons.

> **HABITS OF MIND**
> • Make sense of problems and persevere in solving them.

THINK ABOUT . . .
Using the word **yet** should remind you that the process is more important than answer-getting. So, take risks!

You will encounter different problem types as you work through activities.

Worked Example	Thumbs Up	Thumbs Down	Who's Correct
WORKED EXAMPLE			

When you see one of these problem types, take your time and read through it. Question your own understanding, think about the connections between steps, consider why the method is correct, or analyze what error was made.

4 Search through the different Activities in Module 1 and locate a Worked Example, Thumbs Up, Thumbs Down, or Who's Correct.

(a) What Topic, Lesson, and Activity are you in? **How do you know?**

5 How do you see these problem types helping you learn?

In MATHbook, you can mark up the pages in any way that is helpful to you as you take ownership of your learning.

> Analyze a page from Brody's MATHbook.

6 What strategies did Brody use to make sense of the key term and diagram?

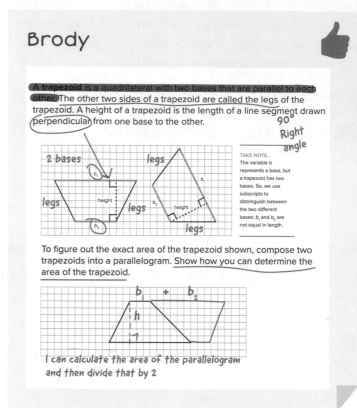

Brody 👍

A **trapezoid** is a quadrilateral with two bases that are parallel to each other. The other two sides of a trapezoid are called the legs of the trapezoid. A height of a trapezoid is the length of a line segment drawn perpendicular from one base to the other.

90°
Right angle

TAKE NOTE...
The variable b represents a base, but a trapezoid has two bases. So, we use subscripts to distinguish between the two different bases: b_1 and b_2 are not equal in length.

2 bases   legs
legs   height   legs b_1 height
b_2 legs

To figure out the exact area of the trapezoid shown, compose two trapezoids into a parallelogram. Show how you can determine the area of the trapezoid.

b_1 + b_2
h

I can calculate the area of the parallelogram and then divide that by 2

7 Locate the word **trapezoid** in the glossary. What page is it on?

Through the process of writing, you clarify your understanding and improve your communication skills. The Academic Glossary on Page FM-20 is your guide as you engage with the kind of thinking you do as you are learning the content.

8 Locate the word **show** in the Academic Glossary. Which of the Ask Yourself questions should Brody have asked himself to answer Question 1?

TAKE NOTE . . .
Tear out the **Habits of Mind** and **Academic Glossary** pages. Keep them close by as you are working through the course.

It is not just about what mathematical content you are learning, but how you are learning it. Notice the Habits of Mind beside each Activity title. The full list is located on Page FM-19.

9 What is the Habit of Mind for this **Using MATHbook** activity? **How will developing this habit help you?**

Learning Individually with MATHia

To learn the concepts in each topic, you will work with your classmates to complete the lessons within MATHbook, and you will work individually to complete workspaces in the MATHia software.

> Watch the animation about MATHia.

1 How are supports included to help you solve problems within MATHia?

You will notice that there are MATHia Connections at the start of some Activities.

> Analyze this worked example.

WORKED EXAMPLE

ACTIVITY 1
MATHia CONNECTION
• Commutative and Associative Properties
• Exploring the Distributive Property with Numeric Expressions
• Using the Distributive Property with Numeric Expressions

The MATHia Connection indicates the workspaces that have similar content to this activity. In the workspaces listed, you will practice the skills you are developing in a lesson.

TAKE NOTE . . .
If you are without access to MATHia, a Skills Practice workbook is available for you to practice each topic's skills and mathematical concepts.

---

2 How many workspaces are associated with Topic 1 *Factors and Multiples*?

TALK THE TALK

LESSON 0 — Getting Started · ⌐ Activity ¬ 1 · 2 · **Talk the Talk**

So, Give It a Shot!

The Talk the Talk activity is your opportunity to reflect on the main ideas of the lesson.

- Be honest with yourself.
- Ask questions to clarify anything you don't understand yet.
- Show what you know!

REMEMBER . . .

1 Why is it important to take time to reflect on your progress?

2 Describe the different ways you will learn math this year.

3 It is important to set personal and academic goals for the year. List three goals for this school year.

- _____

- _____

- _____

There are resources to assist you as you review the concepts in each topic. See Page FM-18 for *Your Tools for Review*.

4 Where do you locate a Topic Summary? How can you use this resource to prepare for an assessment?

FM-16 Middle School Math Solution > Intro Lesson

INTRO LESSON ASSIGNMENT

> Use a separate piece of paper for your Journal entry.

REMEMBER

In this course, you will connect ratio and rate to whole number multiplication and division, extend your understanding of number and operation to the system of rational numbers, use expressions and equations to solve problems, and develop an understanding of statistical thinking.

PRACTICE

> Share the Home Connection for Topic 1 *Factors and Multiples* with an adult.

1 Follow this QR code or URL to access the digital file.

ONLINE RESOURCES FOR FAMILIES
www.carnegielearning.com/home-connection

2 What information does the Home Connection provide?

As you complete the Practice section of each Assignment, LiveHint is your textbook assistant. LiveHint allows you to obtain real-time hints from any device on questions through the TutorBot. With LiveHint, you never have to navigate through assignments on your own.

> Go to **LiveHint.com**.

LiveHint™

3 Follow the instructions to access hints to this question.

- First hint: _____

- Second hint: _____

- Third hint: _____

STRETCH Optional

Why do you think Module 1 is titled *Composing and Decomposing*?

Your Tools for Review

There are topic-level resources to assist you as you review the concepts and prepare for an assessment.

MIXED PRACTICE

At the end of each topic, a **Mixed Practice** worksheet provides practice with skills from previous topics and this topic.

Spaced Review
Fluency and problem solving from previous topics

End of Topic Review
Review problems from this topic

 Log in to MyCL for a version with **additional space** for you to write your answers.

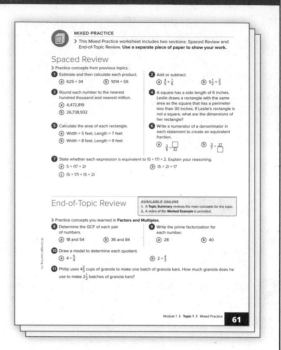

TOPIC SUMMARY

A **Topic Summary** is available online for review of the key terms and main ideas of each lesson.

ASK YOURSELF . . .
- Do I know the meaning of each key term?
- Do I remember the main concepts of each lesson?
- Do I understand the strategy used to solve the worked example?

 Log in to MyCL to download the **Topic Summary**.

Watch a video of each **Worked Example**.

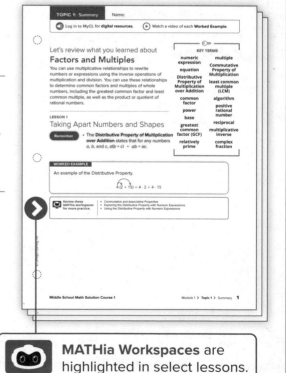

 MATHia Workspaces are highlighted in select lessons.

HABITS OF MIND

> Tear out this page and use it as a guide as you engage with the the kind of thinking you do as you are learning the content.

Mathematical Practices

The types of activities within this book require you to make sense of mathematics and to demonstrate your reasoning through problem solving, writing, discussing, and presenting.

FOR ALL LESSONS . . .

Make sense of problems and persevere in solving them.

ASK YOURSELF . . .

- What is this problem asking and what is my plan for answering it?
- What tools do I need to solve this problem?
- Does my answer make sense?

TAKE NOTE . . .

To help develop these habits of mind ask yourself the types of questions listed as you work.

Each activity denotes the practice or pair of practices intentionally being developed. With practice you can develop the habits of mind of a productive mathematical thinker.

WHEN YOU SEE . . .	ASK YOURSELF . . .	WHAT DOES THIS MEAN FOR YOU?
HABITS OF MIND • Reason abstractly and quantitatively. • Construct viable arguments and critique the reasoning of others.	• What representation can I use to solve this problem? • How can this problem be represented with symbols and numbers? • How can I explain my thinking? • How does my strategy compare to my partner's?	
HABITS OF MIND • Model with Mathematics. • Use appropriate tools strategically.	• What expression or equation could represent this situation? • What tools would help me solve this problem? • What representations best show my thinking? • How does this answer make sense in the context of the original problem?	
HABITS OF MIND • Attend to precision.	• Is my answer accurate? • Did I use the correct units or labels? • Is there a more efficient way to solve this problem? • Is there more sophisticated vocabulary that I could use in my explanation?	
HABITS OF MIND • Look for and make use of structure. • Look for and express regularity in repeated reasoning.	• What characteristics of this expression or equation are made clear through this representation? • How can I use what I know to explain why this works? • Can I develop a more efficient method? • How could this problem help me to solve another problem?	

ACADEMIC GLOSSARY

There are important terms you will encounter throughout this book.

Knowing what is meant by these terms and using these terms will help you think, reason, and communicate your ideas. You will often see these phrases in highlighted questions throughout each activity.

TERM	DEFINITION	ASK YOURSELF	RELATED PHRASES
Analyze	To study or look closely for patterns. Analyzing can involve examining or breaking a concept down into smaller parts to gain a better understanding of it.	• Do I see any patterns? • Have I seen something like this before? • What happens if the shape, representation, or numbers change?	**Examine** **Evaluate** **Determine** **Observe** **Consider** **Investigate** **What do you notice?** **What do you think?** **Sort and match**
Explain Your Reasoning	To give details or describe how to determine an answer or solution. Explaining your reasoning helps justify conclusions.	• How should I organize my thoughts? • Is my explanation logical? • Does my reasoning make sense? • How can I justify my answer to others?	**Show your work** **Explain your calculation** **Justify** **Why or why not?**
Represent	To display information in various ways. Representing mathematics can be done using words, tables, graphs, or symbols.	• How should I organize my thoughts? • How do I use this model to show a concept or idea? • What does this representation tell me? • Is my representation accurate?	**Show** **Sketch** **Draw** **Create** **Plot** **Graph** **Write an equation** **Complete the table**
Estimate	To make an educated guess based on the analysis of given data. Estimating first helps inform reasoning.	• Does my reasoning make sense? • Is my solution close to my estimation?	**Predict** **Approximate** **Expect** **About how much?**
Describe	To represent or give an account of in words. Describing communicates mathematical ideas to others.	• How should I organize my thoughts? • Is my explanation logical? • Did I consider the context of the situation? • Does my reasoning make sense?	**Demonstrate** **Label** **Display** **Compare** **Determine** **Define** **What are the advantages?** **What are the disadvantages?** **What is similar?** **What is different?**

Composing and Decomposing

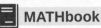
MATHia

Writing Equivalent Expressions Using the Distributive Property
- Commutative and Associative Properties
- Exploring the Distributive Property with Numeric Expressions
- Using the Distributive Property with Numeric Expressions

Identifying Common Factors and Common Multiples
- Prime Factorization
- Determining the LCM or GCF of Two Numbers
- Using the GCF to Rewrite the Sum of Two Numbers

Multiplying Fractions
- Multiplying by Fractions to Increase or Decrease Quantities

Fraction by Fraction Division
- Representing Fraction Division
- Interpreting Remainders Using Models
- Developing the Fraction Division Algorithm
- Multiplying and Dividing Rational Numbers

Area of Triangles and Quadrilaterals
- Calculating Area of Rectangles
- Developing Area Formulas
- Calculating Area of Various Figures

Composite Figures
- Solving Area Problems
- Calculating Area of Composite Figures

Deepening Understanding of Volume
- Determining Volume Using Unit Fraction Cubes
- Calculating Volume of Right Rectangular Prisms

Surface Area of Rectangular Prisms and Pyramids
- Determining Surface Area Using Nets
- Calculating Surface Area of Prisms and Pyramids Using Nets

Adding and Subtracting Decimals
- Adding and Subtracting Decimals
- Decimal Sums and Differences

Multiplying Decimals
- Exploring Decimal Facts
- Patterns with Products and Quotients
- Multiplying Decimals
- Decimal Products

Dividing Decimals
- Dividing Decimals
- Whole Number and Decimal Quotients
- Solving Real-World Problems Using Decimal Operations

Getting Ready for Module 1
Composing and Decomposing

You will investigate strategies to identify factors and multiples and explore methods for multiplying and dividing fractions. You will continue working with area and volume and develop strategies to determine surface area. Building on your work with decimals, you will develop standard algorithms for each decimal operations.

The lessons in this module build on your prior experiences with area and multiplying with fractions.

Review these key terms and strategies for multiplying fractions to get ready to compose and decompose numbers and shapes.

KEY TERMS

area

The number of square units needed to cover a two-dimensional shape or the surface of an object is called the area.

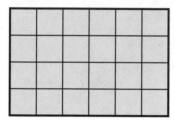

The rectangle has an area of 24 square units.

decimal notation

Decimal notation is an equivalent form of a number using a decimal point.

Fraction
$$\frac{107}{100} = 1 + \frac{7}{100}$$
$$= 1 + 0.07 = 1.07$$
Decimal Notation

SKILLS YOU WILL NEED

Multiply a Whole Number by a Fraction

For example, $3 \times \frac{3}{4}$.

You can think about $3 \times \frac{3}{4}$ as 3 groups of $\frac{3}{4}$.

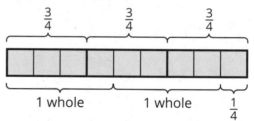

You can add the pieces together to get $2\frac{1}{4}$.

The final result is:

$$3 \times \frac{3}{4} = \frac{3}{1} \times \frac{3}{4}$$
$$= \frac{9}{4} = 2\frac{1}{4}$$

 REVIEW

> Calculate each product.

1 $12 \times \frac{1}{3}$

2 $\frac{7}{11} \times 5$

3 $4 \times \frac{5}{9}$

4 $\frac{1}{8} \times \frac{1}{5}$

Answers are in the Appendix on page 719.

 **MATHia**

Brush up on your skills.
If you need more practice with these skills, ask your teacher for access to corresponding workspaces in MATHia.

LESSON 1

Taking Apart Numbers and Shapes

Writing Equivalent Expressions Using the Distributive Property

Learning Goals

- Write, read, and evaluate equivalent numeric expressions.

- Identify the adjacent side lengths of a rectangle as factors of the area value.

- Identify parts of an expression, such as the product and the factors.

- Write equivalent numeric expressions for the area of a rectangle by decomposing one side length into the sum of two or more numbers.

- Apply the Distributive Property to rewrite the product of two factors.

REVIEW ▶ (1–2 minutes)

❯ Calculate the area of each rectangle. **Show your work.**

1 6 in.

15 in. ▭

2 9 yd

12 yd ▭

You know how to operate with numbers using different strategies. Taking apart numbers before you operate can highlight important information or make calculations easier.

How can you use these strategies to express number sentences in different ways?

GETTING STARTED

Factors and
Multiples

TOPIC 1   LESSON 1

Getting
Started

Activity
1

Talk
the Talk

Break It Down to Build It Up

Callie is installing a rectangular walkway up to her house. The width of the walkway is 5 feet and the length is 27 feet. She needs to calculate the area of the walkway to determine the amount of materials needed to build it.

1 Mark and label 2 different ways you could divide an area model to determine the area of the walkway.

2 Determine the areas of each of the subdivided parts of your models.

3 What is the total area of the walkway?

ACTIVITY 1
MATHia CONNECTION
- Commutative and Associative Properties
- Exploring the Distributive Property with Numeric Expressions
- Using the Distributive Property with Numeric Expressions

Connecting Area Models and the Distributive Property

The numeric expression of 5 × 27 represents the area of the walkway from the Getting Started. A **numeric expression** is a mathematical phrase that contains numbers and operations.

The equation 5 × 27 = 135 shows that the expression 5 × 27 is equal to the expression 135.

An **equation** is a mathematical sentence that uses an equals sign to show that two expressions are the same as one another.

> **HABITS OF MIND**
> - Look for and make use of structure.
> - Look for and express regularity in repeated reasoning.

TOPIC 1

THINK ABOUT...
What are other ways you could take apart one of the factors and write a corresponding equation? What would the equation look like if you divided the model into more than two regions?

❯ Reflect on the different ways you can rewrite the product of 5 and 27.

1 Select one of your area models to complete the example.

How did you take apart the side length of 27?   5 × 27 = 5(____ + ____)

What are the factors of each smaller region?   = (5 · ____) + (5 · ____)

What is the area of each smaller region?   = ____ + ____

What is the total area?   = ____

You just used the *Distributive Property*!

The **Distributive Property of Multiplication over Addition** states that for any numbers a, b, and c, the equation $a(b + c) = ab + ac$ is true.

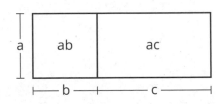

2 Explain the Distributive Property using the area model shown.

WORKED EXAMPLE

An example of the Distributive Property.

$$4(2 + 15) = 4 \cdot 2 + 4 \cdot 15$$

TAKE NOTE...

You can also use grouping symbols to show that you need to multiply each set of factors before you add them, $(4 \cdot 2) + (4 \cdot 15)$.

You can read and describe the expression $4(2 + 15)$ in different ways. For example, you can say:

- four times the quantity of two plus fifteen,
- four times the sum of two and fifteen, or
- the product of four and the sum of two and fifteen.

You can describe the expression $4(2 + 15)$ as a product of two factors.

The quantity $(2 + 15)$ is both a single factor and a sum of two terms.

3 Fill in the missing addend in each box that makes the equation true.

   (a) $7 (\underline{\hspace{1cm}} + 10) = 21 + 70$ (b) $3 (\underline{\hspace{1cm}} + 15) = 36 + 45$

   (c) $8 (2 + \underline{\hspace{1cm}}) = 16 + 56$ (d) $5 (6 + \underline{\hspace{1cm}}) = 30 + 45$

4 Rewrite one of the factors as the sum of two terms in each expression and use the Distributive Property to verify each product.

   (a) $4 \times 17 = 68$ (b) $9 \times 34 = 306$

   (c) $3 \times 29 = 87$

5 Identify each statement as true or false. If the statement is false, show how you could rewrite it to make it a true statement.

(a) True   False $3(2 + 4) = 3.2 + 4$

(b) True   False $6(10 + 5) = 6.10 + 6.5$

(c) True   False $7(20 + 8) = 7 + 20 \cdot 8$

(d) True   False $4(5 + 10) = 20 + 10$

(e) True   False $2(6 + 11) = 12 + 22$

TALK THE TALK

Factors and Multiples

TOPIC 1 — LESSON 1

Getting Started

Activity 1

Talk the Talk

The Floor Is Yours

You can apply the Distributive Property to solve real-world problems.

❯ Consider the situation.

Tyler is setting up the gym floor for an after-school program. He wants to include a rectangular area for playing volleyball and another for dodgeball. He also wants to have an area for kids who like to play board games or just sit and read. The gym floor is 50 feet by 84 feet, or 4200 square feet.

1 Create a diagram to show how you would divide up the gym floor. Represent your diagram using the Distributive Property and write an explanation for the areas assigned to each activity.

> Use a separate piece of paper for your Journal entry.

JOURNAL

Explain the Distributive Property in terms of composing and decomposing numbers.

REMEMBER

There are many ways to rewrite equivalent expressions using properties. The Distributive Property of Multiplication over Addition states that for any numbers a, b, and c, $a(b + c) = ab + ac$.

PRACTICE

> Divide each rectangle into two or three smaller rectangles to demonstrate the Distributive Property. Then write each area in the form $a(b + c) = ab + ac$.

1

|— 122 —|

3

2

|— 122 —|

6

3

|— 244 —|

6

❯ Evaluate each expression using the Distributive Property. Show your work.

4 6(12 + 4)

5 10 + 4(2 + 20)

6 7(4 + 19)

STRETCH Optional

❯ Decompose each rectangle into smaller rectangles to demonstrate the Distributive Property. Write each area in the form $a(b + c) = ab + ac$ and then determine the total area.

1

$6\frac{1}{2}$

$\frac{1}{2}$

2

$9\frac{1}{6}$

$\frac{1}{3}$

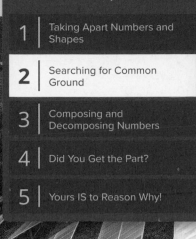

LESSON 2

Searching for Common Ground

Identifying Common Factors and Common Multiples

Learning Goals

- Use powers and exponents to write the prime factorization of a number.

- Determine the greatest common factor of two whole numbers less than or equal to 100.

- Rewrite the sum of two whole numbers with a common factor as a product using the Distributive Property.

- Determine the least common multiple of two whole numbers less than or equal to 12.

REVIEW (1–2 minutes)

❯ In the array of numbers shown, circle the prime numbers, cross out the composite numbers, and use a box to identify any number that is neither prime nor composite.

1	2	3	4	5	6	7	8	9	10
11	12	13	14	15	16	17	18	19	20

Just as you can compose and decompose shapes, you can compose and decompose numbers using factors and multiples.

How can you use shapes to see relationships between numbers?

How Many Rectangles Can You Build?

Understanding the area of rectangles is helpful when learning about factors. A rectangular area model is one way to represent multiplication.

You and your partner will create area models for the numbers 12 and 16.

Number assigned to me _____   Number assigned to my partner _____

❯ Use the grid paper located on page 23 to create and cut out as many unique rectangles as possible with the area of your assigned number.

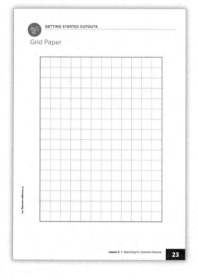

ASK YOURSELF...

How do you know whether you have created all of the possible rectangles with the given area?

1 Label each rectangle with its dimensions. List the dimensions of all of the rectangles that you created for your assigned number.

2 How are factors and factor pairs represented in your rectangles?

3 List all of the factors of 12 and 16.

> Together with your partner, combine one of your rectangles and one of your partner's rectangles to make a larger rectangle. Use this method to create additional rectangles.

4 Complete the table with the information for each larger rectangle that you and your partner created.

Dimensions of Smaller Rectangle 1	Dimensions of Smaller Rectangle 2	Dimensions of the Larger Rectangle	Area of the Larger Rectangle as a Sum of the Smaller Rectangles	Total Area of Larger Rectangle
$l \times w_1$	$l \times w_2$	$l(w_1 + w_2)$	$A_1 + A_2$	

5 How are the dimensions of the larger rectangle related to its total area?

6 For each larger rectangle you and your partner created, write a numeric expression that relates the dimensions of the larger rectangle to the sum of the areas of the smaller rectangles.

> Consider any factors shared between your number and your partner's number.

7 How are the common factors represented in the larger rectangles that you and your partner created?

TAKE NOTE...
Common factors are the factors shared between the numbers.

8 How are the common factors represented in the numeric expressions that you and your partner wrote?

9 List the common factors of the two numbers.

Prime Factors

You just determined factors by cutting out rectangles with a given area. You used common factors to create larger rectangles. Suppose you wanted to determine factors for a larger number and did not want to cut out rectangles? How would you know whether you had a complete list of factors?

In this activity, you will write numbers as the product of its prime factors. This is also known as writing the prime factorization.

A factor tree is a way to organize the prime factorization of a number. You can choose any factor pair to get started.

DID YOU KNOW?

You can express any whole number as a product of primes, only primes, and nothing else.

WORKED EXAMPLE

Use a factor tree to write the prime factorization for 30.

• Begin with the number 30.

• Pick any whole number factor pair of 30, other than 1 and 30.

• Draw a branch from 30 to each factor, 2 and 15.

• Since both of the factors are not prime, you are not finished.

• Use branches to write a factor pair for 15.

• Because 2, 3, and 5 are all prime, this factor tree is complete.

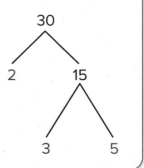

1 Use the factor tree to write the prime factorization of 30.

30 = _____

The factor tree in the Worked Example is not the only factor tree that you can create for 30.

2 Create a different factor tree for 30. How many factor trees can you create?

3 Create a factor tree and write the prime factorization for each number.

    (a) 24   (b) 81   (c) 96

You may have noticed that each prime factorization in Question 3 had repeat factors. You can represent repeated multiplication as a *power*. A **power** has two elements: the base and the exponent.

$$2 \times 2 \times 2 \times 2$$

$$\text{base} \longrightarrow 2^4 \longleftarrow \text{exponent}$$

$$\underbrace{}_{\text{power}}$$

The **base** of a power is the factor multiplied by itself repeatedly, and the **exponent** of the power is the number of times you use the base as a factor.

4 Identify the base and exponent in each power. Then, write each power in words.

    (a) 7^5 (b) 4^8

> **TAKE NOTE...**
> You can read
> a power in
> different ways:
> "2 to the fourth
> power"
> "2 raised to the
> fourth power"

5 Write the prime factorization for each number in Question 3 using powers.

    (a) 24   (b) 81   (c) 96

ACTIVITY 2
MATHia CONNECTION
• Prime Factorization

Factors and
Multiples

TOPIC 1   LESSON 2

Getting
Started   1   Activity
2   3   4   Talk
the Talk

Common Factors

In the Getting Started you used your rectangles to determine the common factors of two numbers. Is there another way to determine common factors?

HABITS OF MIND
• Model with mathematics.
• Use appropriate tools strategically.

WORKED EXAMPLE

One way to determine common factors is to use prime factorization. Start by writing each number as a product of its prime factors.

$56 = 2 \cdot 2 \cdot 2 \cdot 7$

$42 = 2 \cdot 3 \cdot 7$

Organize the prime factors into a table. Only list shared factors in the same column.

Number	Prime Factors				
56	2	2	2		7
42	2			3	7

The common factors of the two numbers are the numbers that are in both rows and the product of the numbers that are in both rows.

The common factors of 56 and 42 are 2, 7, and 14.

1 How do you know that 14 is a common factor of 56 and 42?

2 Why is there a space between 2 and 7 in the top row of the table?

3 Consider the numbers 54 and 84.

   ⓐ Create a table of prime factors.

   ⓑ Identify all of the common factors of 54 and 84.

   ⓒ Of the common factors, which factor is the largest?

The **greatest common factor (GCF)** is the largest factor two or more numbers have in common.

4 Rewrite each sum using the GCF and the Distributive Property.

   ⓐ 56 + 42

   ⓑ 54 + 84

TAKE NOTE...
Two numbers are **relatively prime** when the only common factor they share is 1.

TOPIC 1

ACTIVITY 3

Factors and
Multiples

TOPIC 1   LESSON 2

Getting   Activity   Talk
Started   1   2   3   4   the Talk

Common Multiples

You can use rectangular arrays to determine multiples and common multiples.

WORKED EXAMPLE

Consider the area model for 6 · 8 = 48.

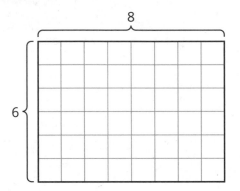

One way to think about the area model is to analyze the collection of columns.

The addition of each new column creates a multiple of 6.

- The first column is a 6 × 1 rectangle representing the first multiple of 6, or 6.

- The first and second columns together are a 6 × 2 rectangle representing the second multiple of 6, or 12.

- The whole rectangle represents 6 × 8, or 48.

TAKE NOTE...

A **multiple** is the product of a given whole number and another whole number.

1 List the first eight multiples of 6 by labeling each column of the area model in the worked example.

Next, think about the area model as a collection of 6 rows. The first row alone creates an 8 × 1 rectangle, which represents the first multiple of 8, or 8. Including all rows of the 8 × 6 rectangle represents the sixth multiple of 8, or 48.

TAKE NOTE...

The **Commutative Property of Multiplication** states that for any numbers a and b, the product $a \cdot b$ is equal to the product $b \cdot a$.

2 List the first six multiples of 8 by labeling each row of the area model in the worked example.

While 48 is a multiple shared by both 6 and 8, it is not the *least common multiple*. The **least common multiple (LCM)** is the smallest multiple (other than zero) that two or more numbers have in common.

> Analyze the multiples of 6 and 8 that you labeled on the area model.

3 Identify the least common multiple of 6 and 8.

LCM(6, 8) = _____

As demonstrated by the rectangular array, for any two whole numbers *a* and *b*, a common multiple is $a \cdot b$. However, this number may not be the *least* common multiple of *a* and *b*.

4 Determine the least common multiple of 6 and 9.

    ⓐ List the first 9 multiples of 6.

    ⓑ List the first 6 multiples of 9.

    ⓒ What is the least common multiple of 6 and 9?

5 Determine the least common multiple of 7 and 8.

LCM(7, 8) = _____

6 Using prime factorization, how can you determine whether the least common multiple of two numbers is the product of the two numbers or is less than the product of the two numbers?

ACTIVITY 4
MATHia CONNECTION
• Determining GCF and LCM
• Using the GCF to Rewrite the Sum of Two Numbers

Factors and
Multiples
TOPIC 1   LESSON 2

Getting   ——— Activity ———   Talk
Started   1   2   3   4   the Talk

Using Prime Factors to Determine LCM

Suppose you want to determine the LCM of 56 and 42 without drawing an area model. Is there another way?

HABITS OF MIND
• Look for and make use of structure.
• Look for and express regularity in repeated reasoning.

WORKED EXAMPLE

Organize the prime factors into a table. Only list shared factors in the same column.

Number	Prime Factors				
56	2	2	2		7
42	2			3	7

Determine the prime factors that the numbers share: 2, 7

Determine the prime factors that the numbers *do not* share: 2, 2, 3

The least common multiple of the two numbers is the product of their shared prime factors and non-shared prime factors: $2 \cdot 2 \cdot 2 \cdot 3 \cdot 7 = 168$

LCM(56, 42) = 168

---

1 For each pair of numbers, determine their product. Then, use a factor table to determine their least common multiple and their greatest common factor.

   (a) 12 and 10

ⓑ 9 and 15

ⓒ 9 and 10

ⓓ 5 and 9

2 Write a sentence to describe the relationship between the product, GCF, and LCM.

Bringing It Back Around

You have composed and decomposed numbers using factors and multiples.

> Use the relationship between factors and multiples to answer each question.

1 Consider the sum $36 + 24$.

   (a) Express the sum $36 + 24$ as many ways as possible as the product $a(b + c)$.

   (b) How can you use factors to determine whether you have listed all possible products $a(b + c)$ that are equivalent to $36 + 24$?

2 Can you always determine the greatest common factor of any two numbers? **Explain your reasoning.**

3 When the greatest common factor of two numbers is 1, what can you say about the numbers?

4 Can you always determine the least common multiple of any two numbers? **Explain your reasoning.**

5 When the least common multiple of two numbers is the product of those numbers, what can you say about the two numbers?

Grid Paper

Why is this page blank?

So you can cut out your rectangles on the other side.

LESSON 2 ASSIGNMENT

> Use a separate piece of paper for your Journal entry.

REMEMBER

You can decompose numbers into a product of their prime factors. You can compose numbers into multiples. You can relate numbers using their greatest common factor and their least common multiple.

PRACTICE

1 Create a factor tree and write the prime factorization for each number.

(a) 70

(b) 90

2 Consider the numbers 18 and 30.

(a) List all of the factors of 18.

(b) List all of the factors of 30.

(c) What factors do 18 and 30 have in common?

(d) What is the greatest common factor of 18 and 30?

3 Consider the numbers 54 and 72.

    ⓐ Create a table of prime factors of 54 and 72.

    ⓑ Identify the common factors of 54 and 72.

    ⓒ Identify the greatest common factor of 54 and 72.

4 For each pair of numbers, determine the least common multiple and at least one other common multiple.

    ⓐ 3 and 5   ⓑ 4 and 6   ⓒ 8 and 12

STRETCH Optional

❯ Determine the LCM or GCF for each.

1 GCF(8, 27, 35)   **2** GCF(20, 90, 50)

3 LCM(4, 8, 14)   **4** LCM(9, 15, 18)

LESSON 3

Composing and Decomposing Numbers

Least Common Multiple and Greatest Common Factor

Learning Goals

- Use greatest common factors and least common multiples to solve problems.

- Determine the greatest common factor of two whole numbers less than or equal to 100.

- Determine the least common multiple of two whole numbers less than or equal to 12.

REVIEW (1–2 minutes)

❯ Write the prime factorization of each number.

1 21

2 30

3 42

4 19

You have identified the least common multiple and greatest common factor of pairs of numbers.

How can you use LCM and GCF to solve problems?

We Have That in Common

You can solve real-world problems that involve common factors or common multiples by thinking about the question you are trying to answer.

❯ Consider each scenario. Determine whether you would use either a common factor or a common multiple to solve the problem. **Explain your reasoning.**

1 Hot dogs come in packs of 8 and hot dog buns come in packs of 6. What is the least number of hot dogs packs you can buy when you want to have the same number of hot dogs and buns?

2 Zev has 36 pencils and 45 erasers. He wants to use all of the pencils and erasers to make identical packages for his friends. What is the greatest number of packages Zev can make?

3 There are 40 sixth graders and 24 seventh graders in an afterschool program. The director wants to create groups where each group has the same number of sixth graders, and each group has the same number of seventh graders. What is the greatest number of groups she can make?

4 Every time Sariyah babysits, she saves $12 of her earnings. Every time Aaron babysits, he saves $9 of his earnings. After babysitting a number of times, Sariyah and Aaron have saved the exact same amount of earnings. What is the least possible amount of savings they could each have?

Using GCF and LCM to Solve Problems

> Consider each situation. Solve each using either the greatest common factor or the least common multiple.

Emily has three bags of different types of beads. She wants to split up the beads into mixed packages to share with her friends. She wants each package to have exactly the same number of each type of bead with no beads left over.

SPACERS
40 COUNT

ROUND BEADS
72 COUNT

RECTANGULAR BEADS
24 COUNT

REMEMBER...
Common factors help you think about how to divide, or share things equally. Common multiples help you think about how things with different cycles can occur at the same time.

1 What is the greatest number of packages that Emily can assemble? Describe the collection of beads in each package.

A cyclist completes a lap around a track in 12 minutes. A second cyclist completes a lap around the same track in 9 minutes.

2 If both riders begin at the starting line at the same time and maintain their speed, after how many minutes will they meet again at the starting line?
Explain your reasoning.

Finishing Where We Started

You have used LCM and GCF to solve real-world problems in this lesson.

❯ Revisit the situations from the Getting Started. Solve each one using either GCF or LCM.

1 Hot dogs come in packs of 8 and hot dog buns come in packs of 6. What is the least number of hot dog packs you can buy when you want to have the same number of hot dogs and buns?

2 Zev has 36 pencils and 45 erasers. He wants to use all of the pencils and erasers to make identical packages for his friends. What is the greatest number of packages Zev can make?

3 There are 40 sixth graders and 24 seventh graders in an after-school program. The director wants to create groups where each group has the same number of sixth graders, and each group has the same number of seventh graders. What is the greatest number of groups she can make?

4 Every time Sariyah babysits, she saves $12 of her earnings. Every time Aaron babysits, he saves $9 of his earnings. After babysitting a number of times, Sariyah and Aaron have saved the exact same amount of earnings. What is the least possible amount of savings they could each have?

LESSON 3 ASSIGNMENT

> Use a separate piece of paper for your Journal entry.

REMEMBER

Common factors help determine how to divide or share things equally. Common multiples help determine how things with different cycles can occur at the same time.

PRACTICE

> Read and solve each problem.

1 Two machines in a car parts factory mold different parts that will eventually be put together in an assembly plant. The first machine makes a part every 12 seconds, and the second machine makes a part every 45 seconds. The quality control engineer tests these parts each time they both come out of the machines at the same time. How often does she test the parts? Show your work and express your answer in minutes.

2 Mr. Ellis runs an after-school program for nine- and ten-year-olds. Each day the children participate in an activity or sport and receive a snack. One afternoon, 56 nine-year-olds and 42 ten-year-olds attend the after-school program.

(a) Mr. Ellis wants to divide the group into basketball teams so that each team has the same number of nine-year-olds, and each team has the same number of ten-year-olds. How many different ways can he divide the group?

(b) What is the greatest number of teams Mr. Ellis can make so each team has the same number of 9-year-olds and the same number of 10-year-olds?

(c) Do you think Mr. Ellis should make the greatest number of teams he can? Explain your reasoning.

Go to LiveHint.com for help on the **PRACTICE** questions.

3 Dr. Abramson is working on 3 different experiments using water. Each experiment lasts for 15 minutes. For the first experiment, she checks the water level every 12 seconds. For the second experiment, she checks every 30 seconds. For the third experiment, she checks every 36 seconds. List the time in minutes that Dr. Abramson will check all 3 experiments at the same time.

4 The students in an art class have blue cloth that is 60 inches long, gold cloth that is 48 inches long, and white cloth that is 72 inches long. They want to cut all the cloth into pieces of equal length for a project.

(a) What is the greatest possible length of the pieces without having any cloth left over? Explain your reasoning.

(b) How many pieces of each color cloth will they have?

5 Boxes that are 16 inches tall are being stacked next to boxes that are 20 inches tall.

(a) What is the shortest height at which the two stacks will be the same height? Explain your reasoning.

(b) How many boxes will be in each stack?

STRETCH Optional

An amusement park gives away gifts to celebrate its grand opening. Every 2nd visitor will receive a sticker, every 5th visitor will receive a hat, every 8th visitor will receive a T-shirt, and every 50th visitor will receive a ticket to use on a return visit. How often will a visitor receive all four gifts?

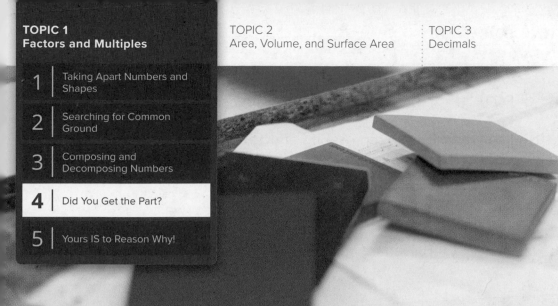
LESSON 4

Did You Get the Part?

Multiplying Fractions

🔑 **KEY TERM**
algorithm

Learning Goals

- Multiply two fractions using the standard algorithm.
- Calculate the products of fractions in real-world and mathematical problems.

REVIEW (1–2 minutes)

❯ Plot each value on the number line shown.

1 2   **2** $\frac{1}{4}$ **3** $4\frac{1}{3}$ **4** $\frac{7}{2}$

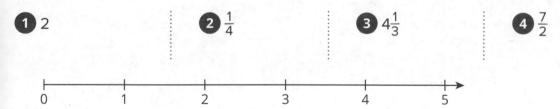

You have multiplied whole numbers by fractions and fractions by fractions.

How can you connect an area model to the procedure for multiplying two fractions?

A Part of a Part

Previously, you used an area model to represent products, to determine factors, and to list multiples of given numbers. In the same way that area models represent whole number multiplication, area models can represent fraction multiplication.

❯ Consider the expression $\frac{1}{4} \times \frac{1}{2}$ represented in the area model shown.

1 How are the factors $\frac{1}{4} \times \frac{1}{2}$ represented in the model?

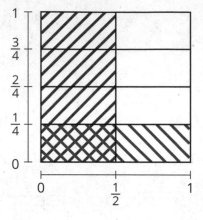

2 What is the product of $\frac{1}{4} \times \frac{1}{2}$? **Describe how the product is represented in the model.**

> Consider the expression $\frac{2}{3} \times \frac{3}{5}$.

3 Model the expression and determine the product.

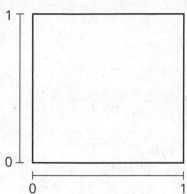

TAKE NOTE...

An **algorithm** is a process or description of steps you can follow to complete a mathematical calculation.

TOPIC 1

4 Show how the *algorithm* for multiplying two fractions less than 1 gives the same product as the model.

ACTIVITY 1

Factors and
Multiples

TOPIC 1 — LESSON 4

Getting
Started

Activity
1   2

Talk
the Talk

Using Area Models to Multiply Mixed Numbers

You can also use a model to represent the multiplication of mixed numbers.

> Bree is tiling the top of a table that measures $3\frac{1}{2}$ feet by $2\frac{1}{2}$ feet. She has 12 ceramic tiles that each measure 1 foot by 1 foot.

❯ Consider the 4 × 3 area model that represents the 12 tiles Bree will use.

1 Create a model to represent the dimensions of the table.

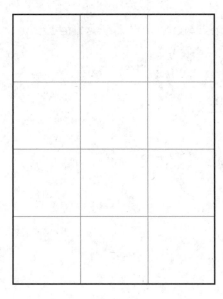

2 What portion of the tiles will Bree use to cover the table top?

> Suppose Bree doesn't want to cut the 1 ft × 1 ft tiles. Instead, she wants to buy smaller sized square tiles that she can use to cover the entire tabletop.

3 Redraw your $3\frac{1}{2} \times 2\frac{1}{2}$ model and divide that into smaller equal-sized tiles. **Describe your model.**

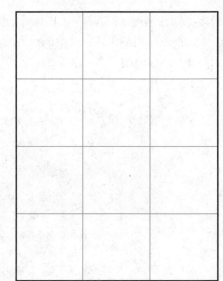

4 What size tile should she buy?

5 How many tiles of that size does she need?

6 Verify that your answer in Question 5 covers the same area as in Question 2.

ACTIVITY 2
MATHia CONNECTION
• Multiplying by Fractions to Increase or Decrease Quantities

Factors and
Multiples
TOPIC 1 — LESSON 4

Getting
Started — Activity — Talk
1   2   the Talk

Multiplying Mixed Numbers

You can use the standard algorithm to multiply a whole number and a mixed number or two mixed numbers when solving problems.

HABITS OF MIND
• Reason abstractly and quantitatively.
• Construct viable arguments and critique the reasoning of others.

The teachers at Riverside Middle School decide to make trail mix for an upcoming field trip. Ms. Hadley shares her Hawaiian Trail Mix Extravaganza recipe with the other teachers. The recipe shown is for 1 batch.

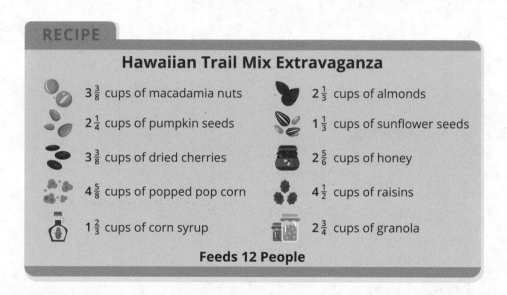

RECIPE

Hawaiian Trail Mix Extravaganza

$3\frac{3}{8}$ cups of macadamia nuts $2\frac{1}{3}$ cups of almonds

$2\frac{1}{4}$ cups of pumpkin seeds $1\frac{1}{3}$ cups of sunflower seeds

$3\frac{3}{8}$ cups of dried cherries $2\frac{5}{6}$ cups of honey

$4\frac{5}{8}$ cups of popped pop corn $4\frac{1}{2}$ cups of raisins

$1\frac{2}{3}$ cups of corn syrup $2\frac{3}{4}$ cups of granola

Feeds 12 People

1 Megan and CJ determined the number of cups of almonds it will take to make 3 batches.

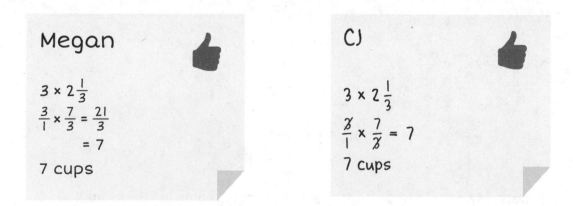

Megan 👍

$3 \times 2\frac{1}{3}$

$\frac{3}{1} \times \frac{7}{3} = \frac{21}{3}$

$= 7$

7 cups

CJ 👍

$3 \times 2\frac{1}{3}$

$\frac{\cancel{3}}{1} \times \frac{7}{\cancel{3}} = 7$

7 cups

How is CJ's strategy different from Megan's?

2 Determine the number of cups of each ingredient it will take to make $4\frac{1}{2}$ batches.
Show your work.

    (a) raisins   (b) sunflower seeds   (c) pumpkin seeds

3 Calculate each product. Write your answer as a mixed number. **Show your work.**

    (a) $2\frac{2}{5} \times 3\frac{2}{5}$ (b) $2\frac{2}{3} \times 4\frac{1}{4}$

    (c) $1\frac{3}{4} \times 2\frac{2}{5}$ (d) $1\frac{1}{2} \times \frac{5}{6}$

    (e) $3\frac{3}{4} \times 2$ (f) $2\frac{5}{8} \times 3$

TALK THE TALK

Factors and
Multiples

TOPIC 1   LESSON 4

Getting
Started   ⌐ Activity ⌐   Talk
           1   2   the Talk

Going in a General Direction

❯ Look back at the factors and products in this lesson. **What generalizations can you make about the multiplication of fractions?**

1 Determine whether each statement is *always*, *sometimes*, or *never* true. **Provide examples.**

    ⓐ If a fraction between 0 and 1 is multiplied by another fraction between 0 and 1, the product is less than 1.

    ⓑ If a fraction between 0 and 1 is multiplied by a mixed number, the product is greater than 1.

2 Describe the algorithm for multiplying any two fractions or mixed numbers.

❯ Use a separate piece of paper for your Journal entry.

Explain how to use the standard algorithm to calculate the product of two mixed numbers.

REMEMBER

To multiply any two fractions or mixed numbers, first rewrite mixed numbers as improper fractions. Then multiply the numerators and denominators of the fractions.

PRACTICE ▶

❯ Read and solve each problem.

1 Sara has an exercise routine that includes swimming, cycling, and running. The table shows the distances of each portion of her routine.

Exercise	Distance
Swimming	$\frac{2}{3}$ miles
Cycling	$10\frac{1}{2}$ miles
Running	$5\frac{3}{4}$ miles

ⓐ If Sara completes her routine each day this week, how many miles will she swim?

ⓑ If Sara completes her routine each day this week, how many miles will she cycle?

 Go to LiveHint.com for help on the **PRACTICE** ▶ questions.

Lesson 4 ❯ Did You Get the Part? **41**

2 Tristan is putting new sod down in his rectangular yard. His yard measures $6\frac{1}{5}$ meters by $8\frac{1}{3}$ meters. What is the area of the yard?

> Calculate each product. **Show your work.**

3 $3\frac{1}{2} \times 4\frac{5}{8}$

4 $12 \times 2\frac{2}{3}$

5 $7\frac{1}{5} \times 1\frac{5}{6}$

6 $2\frac{4}{5} \times 7$

7 $8\frac{1}{3} \times 3\frac{2}{5}$

8 $5\frac{3}{4} \times 4\frac{1}{10}$

STRETCH Optional

> Give an example of two mixed numbers whose product is a whole number. Describe how you determined the factors.

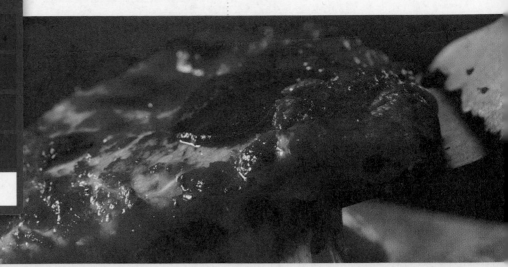

LESSON 5

Yours IS to Reason Why!

Fraction by Fraction Division

Learning Goals

- Model the division of fractions using bar models and number lines.
- Compute and interpret quotients of fractions and interpret remainders in real-world problems.
- Divide with mixed numbers.

KEY TERMS

positive rational number

reciprocal

multiplicative inverse

complex fraction

 **REVIEW** (1–2 minutes)

> Write the multiplication-division fact family for each rectangular array.

1

2

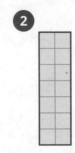

You know how to multiply fractions by fractions. You also know how to divide whole numbers by fractions.

How can you apply what you know to divide two fractions?

All in the Fact Family

You can write a multiplication-division fact family using fractions.

WORKED EXAMPLE

❯ Consider the unit square model divided into 5 equal rows and 4 equal columns.

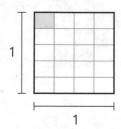

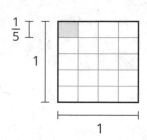

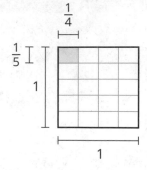

The shaded area represents the fraction $\frac{1}{20}$, because 1 rectangle is shaded of the 20 total rectangles.

The height of the shaded rectangle is $\frac{1}{5}$ of the height of the model.

The width of the shaded rectangle is $\frac{1}{4}$ of the width of the model.

So, the shaded area of the rectangle represents the product $\frac{1}{5} \times \frac{1}{4} = \frac{1}{20}$.

1 Write a multiplication-division fact family for the model.

TAKE NOTE...

The fractions in this lesson are part of a larger set of numbers called *positive rational numbers*. A **positive rational number** is a number you can write in the form $\frac{a}{b}$, where a and b are both whole numbers greater than zero.

2 Describe how the model shows the division of fractions.

3 Draw a diagram to model the multiplication of two different fractions. Write a multiplication-division fact family with fractions for your diagram. **Show your work.**

Whole Number ÷ Fraction

Division is the process of breaking a number up into an equal number of parts.

HABITS OF MIND
- Look for and make use of structure.
- Look for and express regularity in repeated reasoning.

WORKED EXAMPLE

The model shows $6 \div 2$. The expression asks, "How many groups of two are in 6?"

There are 3 groups of 2 in 6, so $6 \div 2 = 3$.

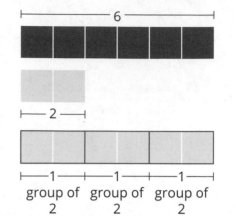

When you divide with fractions, you are asking the same question.

WORKED EXAMPLE

The model shows $6 \div \frac{1}{2}$. The expression asks, "How many halves, or groups of $\frac{1}{2}$, are in 6?"

There are twelve $\frac{1}{2}$–parts in 6, so $6 \div \frac{1}{2} = 12$.

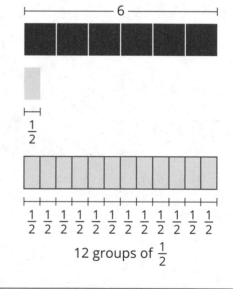

12 groups of $\frac{1}{2}$

1 Identify the dividend, divisor, and quotient in each model.

REMEMBER...
The dividend is the number divided into equal groups, the divisor is the number that divides the dividend, and the quotient is the result of the division.

❯ Consider each situation.

Suppose you are creating snack-sized portions from 4 cups of trail mix.

2 Determine the number of portions you can make if you use different measuring scoops. **Draw a diagram and write the appropriate number sentence.**

THINK ABOUT...
How can you use what you know about multiplication-division fact families to check your work?

ⓐ $\frac{1}{2}$ cup measuring scoop

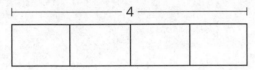

ⓑ $\frac{1}{4}$ cup measuring scoop

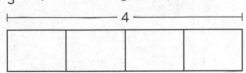

ⓒ $\frac{1}{3}$ cup measuring scoop

ⓓ How did the number of portions change as the size of the measuring scoop changed?

ⓔ Analyze the three number sentences you wrote. Consider the relationship between the dividend, divisor, and quotient in each model. **What patterns do you notice? Explain your reasoning.**

Suppose you are organizing games for a field day event that lasts 4 hours.

3 Determine how many games you can organize for the event if each game lasts the given amount of time. **Draw a diagram and write the appropriate number sentence.**

(a) $\frac{2}{3}$ hour

(b) $\frac{2}{5}$ hour

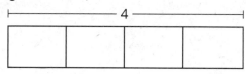

(c) $\frac{4}{5}$ hour

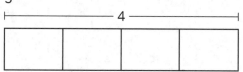

(d) Consider the relationship between the dividend, divisor, and quotient in each number sentence. How do these number sentences compare to the ones you wrote in Question 2? **What patterns do you notice? Explain your reasoning.**

❯ Consider the relationships between the different division statements that you just modeled.

4 How is the quotient of $4 \div \frac{1}{3}$ related to the quotient of $4 \div \frac{2}{3}$? **Explain your reasoning.**

5 From a previous example, you know that $6 \div \frac{1}{2} = 12$. Use reasoning to determine each quotient.

   ⓐ $6 \div \frac{1}{4}$ ⓑ $6 \div \frac{1}{8}$ ⓒ $6 \div \frac{1}{16}$

6 Jamilla is throwing a small party. She has 4 pizzas and decides that everyone at her party should receive a serving size that is $\frac{3}{5}$ of a pizza. Jamilla says she has $6\frac{2}{3}$ servings, but Devon says she has $6\frac{2}{5}$ servings. Draw a diagram of the situation, and solve for the quotient to determine who is correct. **Explain why the other person is not correct.**

7 Jonathon has 4 pizzas and decides that everyone at his party should receive a serving size that is $\frac{3}{4}$ of a pizza. Draw a diagram and determine the number of servings he will have for his party.

ACTIVITY 2
MATHia CONNECTION
- Representing Fraction Division
- Interpreting Remainders Using Models

Fraction ÷ Fraction

In this activity, you will use a number line model to determine a quotient when the dividend and divisor are both fractions.

HABITS OF MIND
- Model with mathematics.
- Use appropriate tools strategically.

> You want to determine how many $\frac{1}{4}$-inch pieces are in $\frac{3}{4}$ inch.

WORKED EXAMPLE

The model shows $\frac{3}{4} \div \frac{1}{4}$.

The division expression asks, "How many $\frac{1}{4}$s are in $\frac{3}{4}$?"

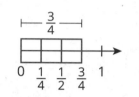

THINK ABOUT...
How can you partition the number line into equal-sized intervals?

---

1 What is the quotient $\frac{3}{4} \div \frac{1}{4}$ represented by the model in the worked example? **Interpret the quotient in terms of the situation.**

2 Write a question to describe what each division expression is asking. Then, draw a model to determine the quotient. **Write a sentence to describe your answer.**

ⓐ $\frac{1}{2} \div \frac{1}{8}$

ⓑ $\frac{3}{4} \div \frac{3}{8}$

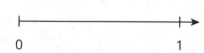

❯ Create a model to represent each situation and then answer the question.

3 Mason has $\frac{2}{3}$ of a foot of ribbon. He needs to divide the ribbon into $\frac{1}{6}$-foot pieces. How many pieces can he cut from the ribbon?

4 Niquelle places signposts along a trail that is $4\frac{1}{2}$ miles long. The signposts divide the trail into sections that are $\frac{3}{4}$ mile long. How many sections does Niquelle create along the trail?

5 Aster has a board that is $3\frac{1}{3}$ feet long. She needs to cut the board into $\frac{5}{12}$-foot pieces. Into how many pieces can she cut the board?

Moving From the Model to a Procedure

You have drawn models to answer "How many groups of a certain size are in a number?"

In this activity, you will analyze a few models that you drew to develop an efficient way to perform
division of fractions without a model.

❯ Revisit the strategy to draw a model for $4 \div \frac{1}{3} = 12$ and $4 \div \frac{2}{3} = 6$.

WORKED EXAMPLE

To create the model $4 \div \frac{1}{3}$, you partitioned 4 wholes to create twelve $\frac{1}{3}$-parts, so $4 \div \frac{1}{3} = 12$.

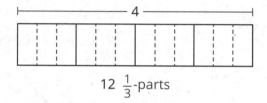

12 $\frac{1}{3}$-parts

Notice there is one step to this process.

STEP 1
The denominator of the divisor is 3.
Partition each whole into $\frac{1}{3}$-parts.

This is the same as $4 \cdot 3 = 12$.

To create the model $4 \div \frac{2}{3}$, you partitioned 4 units to create twelve $\frac{1}{3}$-parts and then grouped 2 $\frac{1}{3}$-parts together, so $4 \div \frac{2}{3} = 6$.

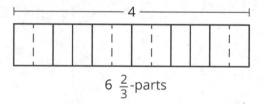

6 $\frac{2}{3}$-parts

Notice there are two steps to this process.

STEP 1
The denominator of the divisor is 3.
Partition each whole into $\frac{1}{3}$-parts.

This is the same as $4 \cdot 3 = 12$.

STEP 2
The numerator of the divisor is 2.

Group two of the $\frac{1}{3}$-parts together to create $\frac{2}{3}$-parts.

This is the same as $12 \div 2 = 6$.

The combination of steps is the same as $4 \cdot 3 \div 2 = 6$.

You can rewrite a fraction as division or division as a fraction: $\frac{a}{b} = a \div b$.

So, you can rewrite the final number sentence, $4 \cdot 3 \div 2 = 6$, as $4 \cdot \frac{3}{2} = 6$.

TOPIC 1

1 Compare the resulting equivalent number sentences from the worked examples. **What do you notice?**

- $4 \div \frac{1}{3} = 12$ and $4 \cdot 3 = 12$
- $4 \div \frac{2}{3} = 6$ and $4 \cdot \frac{3}{2} = 6$

You just developed a rule you can use to rewrite any division sentence as multiplication. You can rewrite any division sentence as multiplication by taking the reciprocal of the divisor.

$$\frac{a}{b} \div \frac{c}{d} = \frac{a}{b} \cdot \frac{d}{c}$$

2 Rewrite each division sentence as a multiplication sentence and then calculate the quotient.

(a) $5 \div \frac{1}{4}$

(b) $\frac{1}{8} \div 2$

(c) $\frac{4}{5} \div \frac{1}{3}$

(d) $\frac{3}{10} \div \frac{1}{3}$

> **TAKE NOTE...**
> A **reciprocal**, or *multiplicative inverse*, is one of a pair of numbers whose product is 1. The **multiplicative inverse** of the number $\frac{a}{b}$ is the number $\frac{b}{a}$, where a and b are nonzero numbers.

3 Explain why Alexa is incorrect and provide the correct reciprocal.

> **Alexa**
> The reciprocal of $3\frac{8}{5}$ is $3\frac{5}{8}$.

> Solve each problem. **Show your work and label your answer.**

4 If you have $5\frac{2}{3}$ pounds of trail mix, how many bags can you make so that each bag contains $1\frac{5}{6}$ pounds?

5 A cook in a restaurant made $47\frac{1}{2}$ cups of mashed potatoes. If there are $1\frac{1}{4}$ cups of mashed potatoes in a serving, how many servings did he make?

6 The hiking trail through Glacier Gorge in Rocky Mountains National Park is $9\frac{3}{5}$ miles round trip. If you hike $1\frac{3}{5}$ miles an hour, how many hours will the round trip take?

ACTIVITY 4
MATHia CONNECTION
• Developing the Fraction Division Algorithm
• Multiplying and Dividing Rational Numbers

Factors and Multiples

TOPIC 1   LESSON 5

Getting Started   1   Activity 2 3 4   Talk the Talk

TOPIC 1

Different Strategies to Divide Numbers

HABITS OF MIND
• Look for and make use of structure.
• Look for and express regularity in repeated reasoning.

You have learned that one way to divide two fractions is to rewrite the division problem as multiplication by the reciprocal of the divisor.

In this activity, you will consider two other strategies for dividing fractions.

In the same way that you can "multiply across," or multiply the numerators and multiply the denominators, to determine the product of two fractions, you can also "divide across" to determine the quotient of two fractions.

WORKED EXAMPLE

Determine the quotient $\frac{7}{8} \div \frac{1}{2}$.

Divide the numerators. Then divide the denominators.

$$\frac{7}{8} \div \frac{1}{2} = \frac{7 \div 1}{8 \div 2}$$
$$= \frac{7}{4}$$

1 Divide across to determine each quotient.

(a) $\frac{3}{8} \div \frac{1}{4}$

(b) $\frac{4}{9} \div \frac{2}{3}$

(c) $\frac{2}{5} \div \frac{1}{5}$

(d) $\frac{1}{4} \div \frac{3}{4}$

2 Think about the structure of the fractional parts of each dividend and divisor. What was special about the numbers that made dividing across a good strategy?

Kareem is trying to use the dividing across strategy to determine the quotient for the expression $\frac{6}{7} \div \frac{2}{3}$ but gets stuck.

$$\frac{6}{7} \div \frac{2}{3} = \frac{6 \div 2}{7 \div 3} = \frac{3}{7 \div 3}$$

3 Analyze Stella's reasoning to help Kareem. Explain why Stella's reasoning is not correct.

Stella

This is still a fraction, and I know that 3 divided by 3 is 1. So, the answer is $\frac{1}{7}$.

$$\frac{\cancel{3}^1}{7 \div \cancel{3}_1} = \frac{1}{7}$$

❯ Analyze Catherine's reasoning to help Kareem.

Catherine

We know how to rewrite a division sentence as a fraction.

$$\frac{3}{7 \div 3} = \frac{3}{\frac{7}{3}}$$

We also want the denominator to be 1, so we will need to use multiplicative inverses.

$$\frac{3}{7 \div 3} = \frac{3}{\frac{7}{3}} \cdot \frac{\frac{3}{7}}{\frac{3}{7}} = \frac{3 \cdot \frac{3}{7}}{1}$$

$$= \frac{9}{7}$$

So the answer is $\frac{9}{7}$.

REMEMBER...
The definition of division is that $a \div b = \frac{a}{b}$.

4 Explain how Catherine maintained equivalent fractions when she multiplied by $\frac{\frac{3}{7}}{\frac{3}{7}}$.

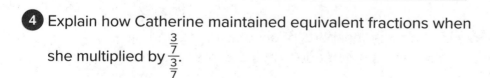

DID YOU KNOW?
A **complex fraction** is a fraction that has a fraction in either the numerator, the denominator, or both the numerator and denominator.

You can use multiplicative inverses to rewrite any division sentence as multiplication.

WORKED EXAMPLE

$$\frac{5}{8} \div \frac{3}{4} = \frac{\frac{5}{8}}{\frac{3}{4}}$$

Rewrite the division expression as a complex fraction.

$$= \frac{\frac{5}{8}}{\frac{3}{4}} \cdot \frac{\frac{4}{3}}{\frac{4}{3}}$$

Multiply the numerator and denominator by the multiplicative inverse of $\frac{3}{4}$.

$$= \frac{\frac{5}{8} \cdot \frac{4}{3}}{\frac{3}{4} \cdot \frac{4}{3}} = \frac{\frac{5}{8} \cdot \frac{4}{3}}{1}$$

Perform multiplication and rewrite the denominator as 1.

$$= \frac{5}{\underset{2}{8}} \cdot \frac{\cancel{4}}{3} = \frac{5}{6}$$

---

5 Use any method to determine each quotient.

(a) $\dfrac{9}{10} \div \dfrac{1}{3}$

(b) $\dfrac{5}{6} \div \dfrac{1}{3}$

(c) $\dfrac{4}{9} \div \dfrac{1}{2}$

(d) $\dfrac{3}{8} \div \dfrac{1}{2}$

(e) $\dfrac{7}{9} \div \dfrac{3}{7}$

(f) $\dfrac{5}{2} \div \dfrac{2}{3}$

ASK YOURSELF...

How can you, a savvy mathematician, look at the structure of a division problem and choose the most efficient strategy?

TALK THE TALK

Factors and
Multiples

TOPIC 1   LESSON 5

Getting
Started   Activity   Talk
              1   2   3   4   the Talk

Going (Almost) Numberless

> Look back at the dividends, divisors, and quotients in this lesson. **What generalizations can you make about the division of fractions?**

1 Complete each statement with *greater than*, *less than*, or *the same as*.

    ⓐ When you divide a quantity greater than 1 by a value between 0 and 1, the quotient is _____ the original quantity.

    ⓑ When you divide a quantity between 0 and 1 by a value greater than 1, the quotient is _____ the original quantity.

    ⓒ When you divide a quantity between 0 and 1 by a value between 0 and 1, the quotient is _____ the original quantity.

2 Complete each statement with *always*, *sometimes*, or *never*.

    ⓐ When you divide a mixed number by another mixed number, the quotient is _____ greater than 1.

    ⓑ When you mulitply a fraction between 0 and 1 by another fraction between 0 and 1, the product is _____ less than 1.

    ⓒ When you divide a whole number by a fraction between 0 and 1, the quotient is _____ less than 1.

    ⓓ When you multiply a fraction between 0 and 1 by a mixed number, the product is _____ greater than 1.

3 Consider the quotients $\frac{5}{6} \div \frac{1}{2}$ and $\frac{5}{6} \div 2$. Describe how these quotients are different.

LESSON 5 ASSIGNMENT

> Use a separate piece of paper for your Journal entry.

JOURNAL

Explain how to use a model to represent the division of two fractions.

REMEMBER

One way to divide two fractions is to rewrite the division problem as multiplication by the reciprocal of the divisor.

PRACTICE

1 Calculate each quotient.

(a) $\frac{2}{5} \div \frac{1}{3}$

(b) $\frac{7}{8} \div \frac{1}{4}$

(c) $\frac{3}{4} \div \frac{1}{6}$

(d) $\frac{15}{16} \div \frac{3}{4}$

(e) $\frac{7}{12} \div \frac{1}{3}$

(f) $1\frac{1}{8} \div \frac{5}{6}$

(g) $5\frac{3}{8} \div \frac{1}{4}$

(h) $7\frac{1}{3} \div 1\frac{2}{3}$

2 The top of a rectangular table has an area of 21 square feet. The width of the table is $3\frac{1}{2}$ feet. What is the length of the table?

3 The area of a triangular pendant on a necklace is $\frac{3}{4}$ square inch. The height of the triangle is $1\frac{1}{4}$ inches. What is the length of the base of the triangle?

STRETCH Optional

❯ Write a word problem that you can model by the quotient $2\frac{1}{2} \div \frac{3}{4}$.

> This Mixed Practice worksheet includes two sections: Spaced Review and End-of-Topic Review. **Use a separate piece of paper to show your work.**

Spaced Review

> Practice concepts from previous topics.

1 Estimate and then calculate each product.

(a) 625×34

(b) 1014×59

2 Add or subtract.

(a) $\frac{4}{5} + \frac{1}{6}$

(b) $5\frac{1}{2} + \frac{2}{3}$

3 Round each number to the nearest hundred thousand and nearest million.

(a) $4{,}472{,}819$

(b) $26{,}738{,}932$

4 A square has a side length of 6 inches. Leslie draws a rectangle with the same area as the square that has a perimeter less than 30 inches. If Leslie's rectangle is not a square, what are the dimensions of her rectangle?

5 Calculate the area of each rectangle.

(a) Width = 5 feet, Length = 7 feet

(b) Width = 8 feet, Length = 9 feet

6 Write a numerator of a denominator in each statement to create an equivalent fraction.

(a) $\frac{3}{8} = \frac{\square}{32}$

(b) $\frac{3}{7} = \frac{27}{\square}$

7 State whether each expression is equivalent to $(5 \times 17) \times 2$. Explain your reasoning.

(a) $5 \times (17 \times 2)$

(b) $(5 \times 2) \times 17$

(c) $(5 \times 17) + (5 \times 2)$

End-of-Topic Review

AVAILABLE ONLINE

1. A **Topic Summary** reviews the main concepts for the topic.
2. A video of the **Worked Example** is provided.

> Practice concepts you learned in **Factors and Multiples**.

8 Determine the GCF of each pair of numbers.

(a) 18 and 54

(b) 36 and 84

9 Write the prime factorization for each number.

(a) 28

(b) 40

10 Draw a model to determine each quotient.

(a) $4 \div \frac{5}{4}$

(b) $2 \div \frac{4}{3}$

11 Philip uses $4\frac{2}{3}$ cups of granola to make one batch of granola bars. How much granola does he use to make $2\frac{1}{2}$ batches of granola bars?

12 Use a factor table to determine the LCM of each pair of numbers.

(a) 8 and 12

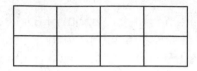

(b) 6 and 9

13 Ling is a camp counselor at a local summer camp. She is in charge of the weekly craft activity for 40 campers. She plans to make fabric-covered frames that each require $\frac{1}{6}$ yard of fabric.

The camp director gave her $6\frac{2}{3}$ yards of fabric remnants for this project. Does Ling have enough fabric for her craft activity? Show your work.

14 Consider the numbers 18 and 28.

(a) Sketch all distinct area models for the number 18.

(b) Sketch all distinct area models for the number 28.

(c) Use your area models and the Distributive Property to rewrite the expression 18 + 28.

TOPIC 1
Factors and Multiples

TOPIC 2
Area, Volume, and Surface Area

1 | All About That Base...and Height

2 | Slicing and Dicing

3 | Length, Width, and Depth

4 | Breaking the Fourth Wall

TOPIC 3
Decimals

LESSON 1

All About That Base...and Height

Area of Triangles and Quadrilaterals

Learning Goals

- State and compare the attributes of different figures.

- Explain that the area of a parallelogram is the same as the area of a rectangle with the same base length and height.

- Derive the formulas for the areas of triangles, parallelograms, and trapezoids by composing or decomposing the various figures into rectangles and triangles.

- Solve real-world and mathematical problems by composing and decomposing figures.

REVIEW (1–2 minutes)

❯ Write 3 different numeric expressions to describe the total area of the rectangle shown.

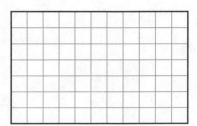

You can take a figure apart and put it back together in a different way without changing its area.

How can you compose and decompose rectangles to reason about the areas of common figures?

In the 20s

> Consider each two-dimensional figure.

1 Name each figure and describe the attributes.

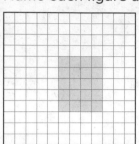

Name: _____
Attributes:

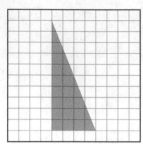

Name: _____
Attributes:

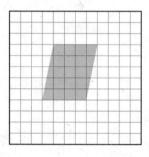

Name: _____
Attributes:

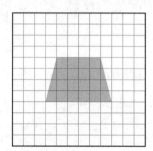

Name: _____
Attributes:

2 Each shaded figure shown has an area of exactly 20 square units.
Show how you know.

ACTIVITY 1
MATHia CONNECTION
• Calculating Area of Rectangles

Area, Volume, and Surface Area

TOPIC 2   **LESSON 1**

Getting Started

Activity
1 2 3 4

Talk the Talk

Investigating the Area of a Parallelogram

In this activity, you will investigate the area of a *parallelogram* using what you know about the area of a rectangle. A **parallelogram** is a four-sided figure with two pairs of parallel sides and opposite sides that are equal in length.

❯ Cut out a parallelogram from the grid located on page 73.

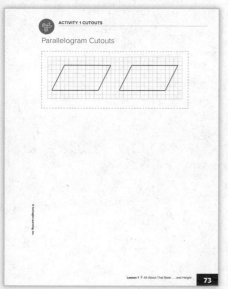

REMEMBER...
A rectangle is a special type of parallelogram.

1 Cut your parallelogram into pieces so that you can reassemble it to form a rectangle. Tape your rectangle in the space provided.

Parallelogram   **Rectangle**

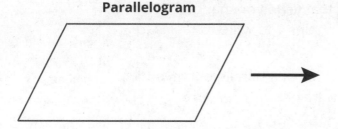

In a parallelogram, you can label any of the four sides as the base. The height, represented by a line segment, is the perpendicular distance from a base to its opposite side.

2 Label the base and height of the parallelogram and rectangle.

TAKE NOTE...
A right angle symbol indicates that lines or sides are perpendicular.

❯ Compare the attributes of the parallelogram and the rectangle you composed.

3 How does the height of the parallelogram relate to the height of the rectangle? How does the length of the base of the parallelogram relate to the length of the base of the rectangle? **Explain your reasoning.**

ASK YOURSELF...
When you write a sentence to explain your reasoning, be sure to express a complete idea. If you cover up the question, does your sentence make sense?

4 Describe the relationship between the areas of a parallelogram and rectangle that have the same base and height.

5 Use the terms *base* and *height* to describe how to calculate the area of a parallelogram.

When you want to represent a quantity that varies or changes, you can use a *variable*. The use of variables helps you write formulas to express relationships.

TAKE NOTE...
A **variable** is a letter used to represent a number.

6 Write the formulas to calculate the areas of a parallelogram and a rectangle. Use *b* for base and *h* for height.

Investigating the Area of a Triangle

In this activity, you will investigate the area of a triangle using what you know about the area of a parallelogram.

❯ Consider each triangle shown.

Triangle 1

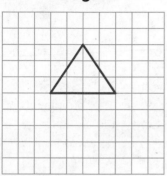

Triangle 2

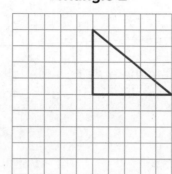

Triangle 3

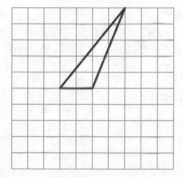

1 Use a separate piece of patty paper to trace each triangle.

   ⓐ Rotate the patty paper to create a parallelogram composed of two identical triangles.

   ⓑ Draw the parallelogram you created on your patty paper and label its base and height.

2 For each triangle, compose a second parallelogram using a different side of the triangle.

3 Determine the area of each parallelogram you created.

4 How does the area of each triangle relate to the area of the parallelogram?

5 Write a formula to calculate the area of a triangle using the formula for the area of a parallelogram. Use *b* for base and *h* for height.

REMEMBER...
The formula for the area of a parallelogram is $A = bh$.

WORKED EXAMPLE

As with the base of a parallelogram, the base of a triangle can be any of its sides. The height of a triangle, represented by a line segment, is the perpendicular distance from a vertex to the line containing the base.

Triangle ABC is shown in three different positions.

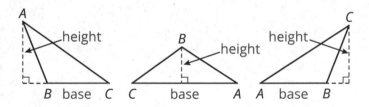

6 Analyze the worked example. What general statement can you make about determining the area of a triangle? **Explain your reasoning.**

ACTIVITY 3

Area, Volume, and Surface Area

TOPIC 2 LESSON 1

Getting Started 1 2 3 4

Activity

Talk the Talk

Investigating the Area of a Trapezoid

You have seen that decomposing and composing can help you think about shapes differently to determine their areas. In this activity, you will use the same strategy to determine the formula for calculating the area of a trapezoid.

A **trapezoid** is a quadrilateral with two bases that are parallel to each other. The other two sides of a trapezoid are called the legs of the trapezoid. A height of a trapezoid is the length of a line segment drawn perpendicular from one base to the other.

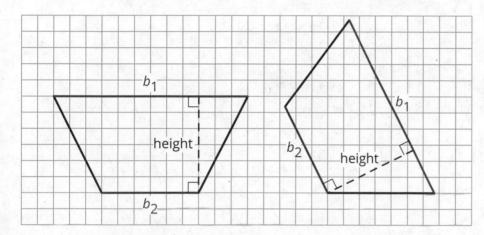

TAKE NOTE...
The variable b represents a base, but a trapezoid has two bases. So, we use subscripts to distinguish between the two different bases: b_1 and b_2 are not equal in length.

TOPIC 2

1 To figure out the exact area of the trapezoid shown, compose two trapezoids into a parallelogram. **Show how you can determine the area of the trapezoid.**

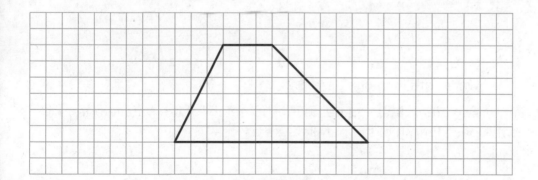

2 Describe how to calculate the area of any trapezoid in terms of the two bases and the height.

ACTIVITY 4
MATHia CONNECTION
• Developing Area Formulas
• Calculating Area of Various Figures

Area, Volume, and Surface Area
TOPIC 2 — LESSON 1

Getting Started   Activity   Talk
                1   2   3   4   the Talk

Calculating Areas of Figures

> Calculate the area of each figure.

1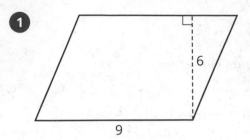

6

9

2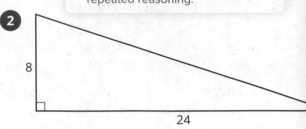

8

24

3

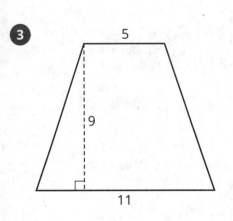

5

9

11

4

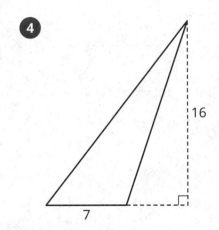

16

7

> Determine the unknown length in each figure.

5 A parallelogram has an area of 63 square units. The height of the parallelogram is 7 units. What is the base length of the parallelogram?

6 A triangle has an area of 24 square units. The base length of the triangle is 4 units. What is the height of the triangle?

❯ Solve each area problem.

7 Sanjay has enough material to build a rectangular dance floor with an area of 200 square feet. The greatest width the dance floor can be is $12\frac{1}{2}$ feet. What would be the length of this dance floor?

TOPIC 2

8 Determine the area of each object.

ⓐ

$\frac{4}{5}$ in.

$\frac{9}{10}$ in.

ⓑ

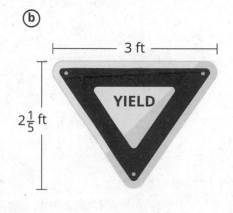

3 ft

$2\frac{1}{5}$ ft

YIELD

9 Tara has enough garden soil to make a garden bed with an area of 6 square yards. She wants to build the garden bed in the corner of her yard so it is the shape of a right triangle. Because of the location of her patio, one leg of the triangle must be $1\frac{1}{3}$ yards long. Determine the length of the other leg of the triangle.

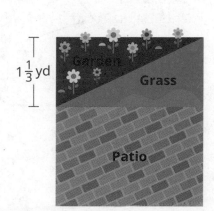

$1\frac{1}{3}$ yd

Garden

Grass

Patio

Figure 'Em Out!

You have decomposed and composed parallelograms in this lesson to derive the formulas for the area of a parallelogram, triangle, and trapezoid.

REMEMBER...
Use a straightedge to draw your figures.

1 Draw each figure and then label a base and height. Next, write the formula to calculate the area of each. Use *A* for the area, *b* for the length of the base, and *h* for the height.

ⓐ Parallelogram

ⓑ Triangle

ⓒ Trapezoid

❯ Consider △*RGM* and △*PGM*.

2 Without performing any calculations, determine which triangle has the greater area. Write a sentence to explain your reasoning.

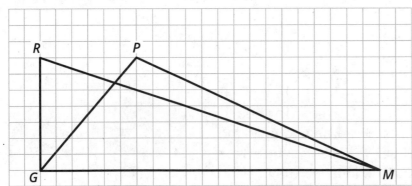

Parallelogram Cutouts

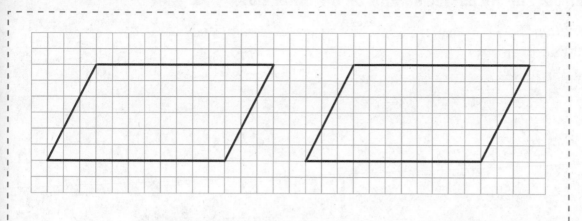

Why is this page blank?

So you can cut out the parallelograms on the other side.

> ❯ Use a separate piece of paper for your Journal entry.

JOURNAL ❯

Define each term in your own words.

1 height of a parallelogram

2 height of a triangle

REMEMBER

To determine the area of a parallelogram, triangle, or trapezoid, compose or decompose it into one or more figures.

Area of a parallelogram $= bh$

Area of a triangle $= \frac{1}{2}bh$

Area of a trapezoid $= \frac{1}{2}(b_1 + b_2)h$

PRACTICE ❯

1 Identify a base and corresponding height for the given parallelogram. Then determine its area.

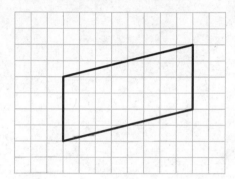

2 Calculate the area of the parallelogram.

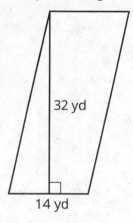

32 yd

14 yd

3 Identify a base and corresponding height for the given triangle. Then determine its area.

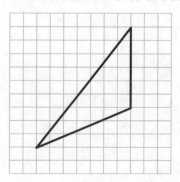

4 Calculate the area of the triangle.

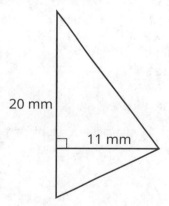

20 mm

11 mm

5 Yvonne cut pictures in the shapes shown to place into her scrapbook. What is the area of each picture?

ⓐ

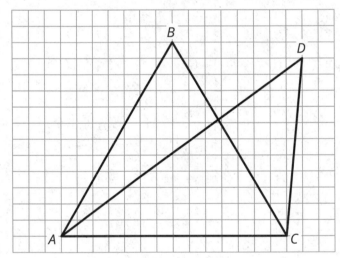

5 in.

4 in.

7 in.

ⓑ

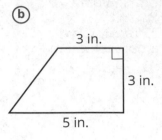

3 in.

3 in.

5 in.

6 Without performing any calculations, determine which triangle has the greater area. Write a sentence to explain your reasoning.

STRETCH Optional

1 What is the area of a parallelogram that has a base of $4\frac{3}{4}$ ft and a height of $1\frac{1}{3}$ ft?

2 Calculate the area of the triangle.

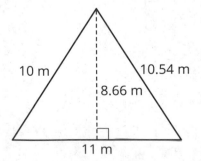

10 m

10.54 m

8.66 m

11 m

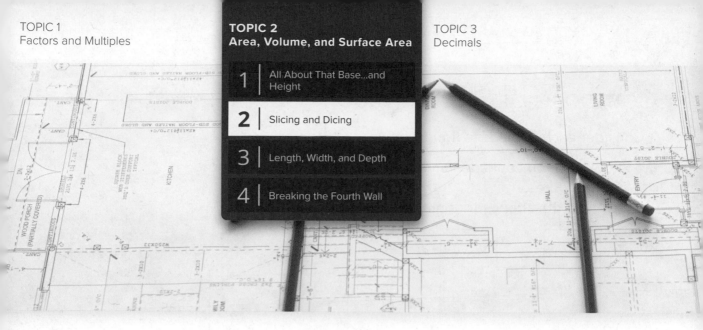

TOPIC 1
Factors and Multiples

TOPIC 2
Area, Volume, and Surface Area

1 | All About That Base...and Height

2 | Slicing and Dicing

3 | Length, Width, and Depth

4 | Breaking the Fourth Wall

TOPIC 3
Decimals

LESSON 2

Slicing and Dicing

Composite Figures

KEY TERM

composite figure

LEARNING GOALS

- Decompose composite geometric figures into rectangles, parallelograms, and/or triangles to determine their areas.

- Solve real-world problems by composing and decomposing shapes into triangles and rectangles.

REVIEW (1–2 minutes)

> Use a formula to determine the area of each figure.

1

$10\frac{1}{2}$ m

22 m

2

7 cm

11 cm

3

35 yd

30 yd

65 yd

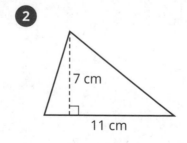

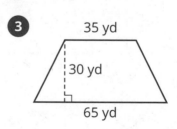

You know how to calculate the area of triangles, rectangles, parallelograms, and trapezoids.

How can you use what you know about the areas of these shapes to determine areas of more complex shapes?

Lesson 2 > Slicing and Dicing   **77**

GETTING STARTED

Area, Volume,
and Surface Area

TOPIC 2 ─ **LESSON 2**

Getting
Started

Activity
1   2

Talk
the Talk

Compose or Decompose?

❯ Consider each composite figure shown.

1 Show how you could decompose each figure into two or more familiar figures.

Describe the shapes that make up the composite figure.

ⓐ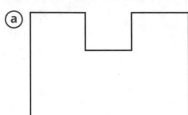

ⓑ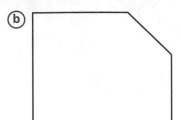

2 Show how you could compose each figure into a larger familiar figure.
Describe the shapes that make up the composite figure.

ⓐ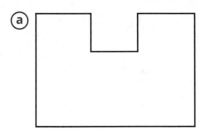

ⓑ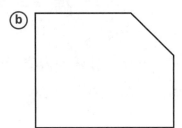

❯ Consider the blueprint of a floor plan for a kitchen, dining room, and living room combination.

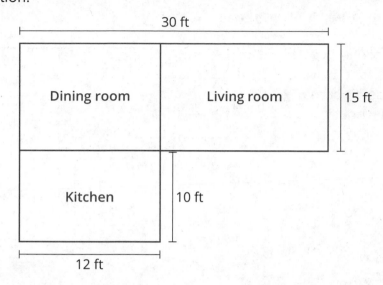

3 Suppose the homeowner wants to replace the floors in all the rooms.

ⓐ Wanda says she can determine the total area of flooring needed by decomposing the blueprint into two rectangles. Naveed says he can determine the total area of flooring needed by composing the blueprint into one large rectangle and subtracting the unused area. Who is correct?

ⓑ Show how to calculate the amount of flooring needed using Wanda's method.

ⓒ Show how to calculate the amount of flooring needed using Naveed's method.

ACTIVITY 1
MATHia CONNECTION
• Solving Area Problems

Area of Composite Figures

HABITS OF MIND
• Attend to precision.

❯ Solve each problem. **Show your work.**

1 Suppose that carpeting costs $1.20 per square foot. How much would it cost to carpet every room in this house except the kitchen?

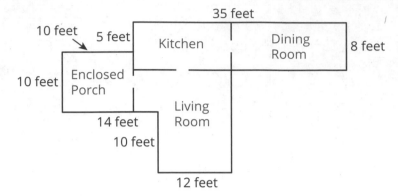

10 feet

5 feet

Kitchen

35 feet

Dining Room

8 feet

10 feet

Enclosed Porch

Living Room

14 feet

10 feet

12 feet

2 Suppose a gallon of paint covers about 400 square feet. How much paint would you need to paint the entire back of this house?

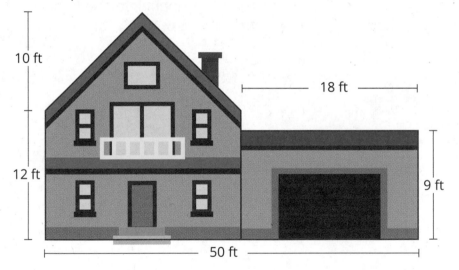

10 ft

12 ft

18 ft

9 ft

50 ft

THINK ABOUT...
Be sure that the simpler figures you draw do not have overlapping areas.

3 Tanner is spray painting an arrow to point to the entrance of his store. The can of paint he wants to use covers up to 12 square feet. Does Tanner have enough paint for his arrow?

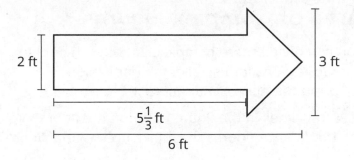

> Determine the area of the shaded region in each figure. **Show your work.**

4

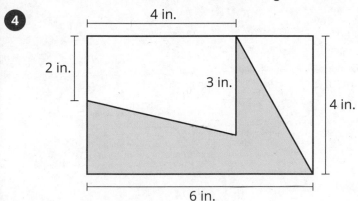

5

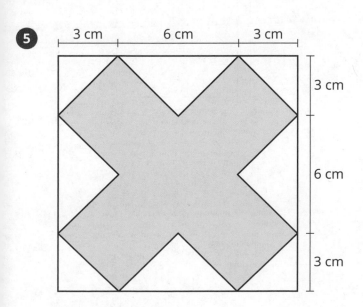

Area, Volume,
and Surface Area

TOPIC 2 — LESSON 2

Getting
Started
Activity
1   2
Talk
the Talk

ACTIVITY 2
MATHia CONNECTION
• Calculating Area of Composite Figures

Area of Complex Figures

You can divide more complex figures with oddly-figured regions into smaller familiar regions to calculate the approximate area.

1 Draw lines in the figure to divide the figure into smaller familiar figures. Then name the familiar figures that make up the total figure.

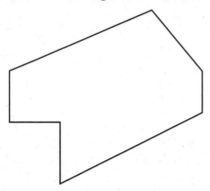

2 Determine the area of each complex figure.

ⓐ

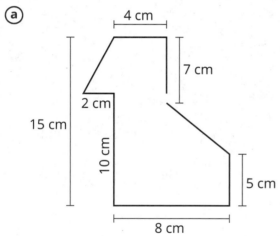

ⓑ

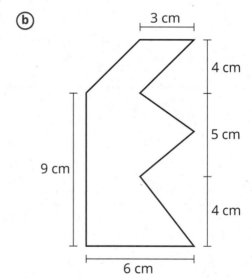

3 Estimate the area of France.

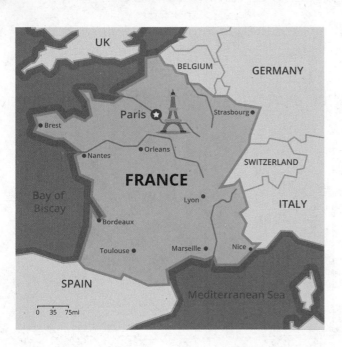

4 Estimate the area of Namibia.

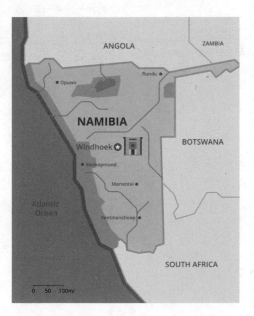

TALK THE TALK

Area, Volume,
and Surface Area

TOPIC 2   LESSON 2

Getting
Started

Activity
1   2

Talk
the Talk

Use Your Powers of Mathematical Reasoning

Sometimes a figure you are already familiar with is divided into smaller figures. You can use what you know about the areas of these figures to determine the area of a specific region.

1 Determine the area of the shaded triangle inside the square. **Explain your strategy.**

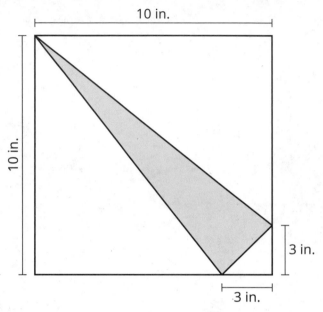

> Create a presentation of your solution strategy for the class.

> Use a separate piece of paper for your Journal entry.

JOURNAL

Define *composite figure* and draw a picture of an example.

REMEMBER

You can determine the area of a composite figure by decomposing it into familiar shapes and then adding together the areas of those shapes.

PRACTICE

1 Calculate the area of each composite figure.

(a)

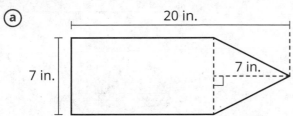

(b)

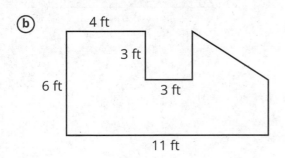

2 A city wants to create a garden according to the plan shown. Calculate the area of the garden.

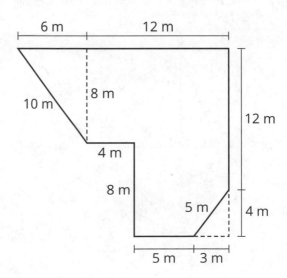

3 The figure shown is composed of a rectangle and a hexagon. The length of each side of the hexagon is 2 centimeters. Determine the area of the shaded region.

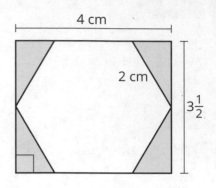

4 The figure shown is composed of a triangle within a trapezoid. Determine the area of the shaded region.

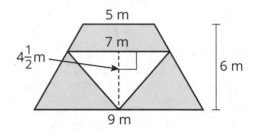

STRETCH Optional

> Calculate the area of each shaded region.

1 Given: $MR = RS$ = 5 feet, $ST = PT$ = 10 feet, and $NS = QS$ = 12 feet.

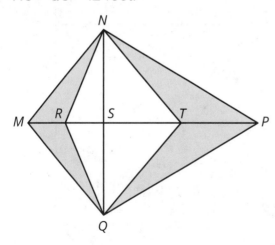

2 The figure is composed of 2 congrue[nt] triangles and a rhombus.

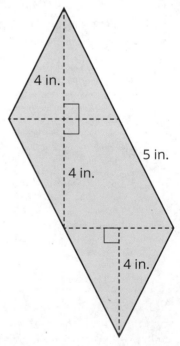

TOPIC 1
Factors and Multiples

TOPIC 2
Area, Volume, and Surface Area

TOPIC 3
Decimals

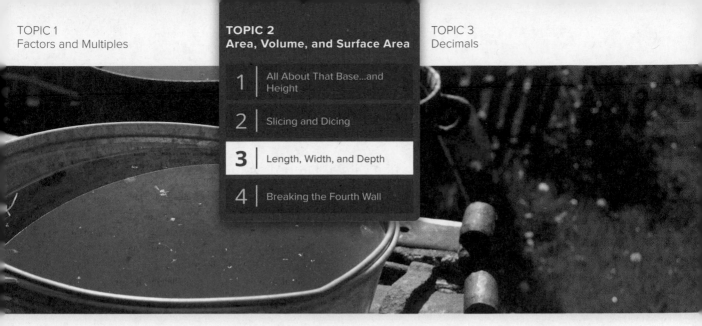

LESSON 3

Length, Width, and Depth

Deepening Understanding of Volume

Learning Goals

- Determine the volume of right rectangular prisms with fractional edge lengths using unit cubes with unit fractional dimensions.

- Determine the number of cubes with unit fractional dimensions that have the same volume as a unit cube.

- Determine the number of unit cubes with unit fractional dimensions that can pack a rectangular prism with fractional edge lengths.

- Connect the volume formulas $V = lwh$ and $V = Bh$.

KEY TERMS

volume
geometric solid
polyhedron
face
edge
vertex
unit cube
right rectangular prism
cube

REVIEW (1–2 minutes)

> Determine each least common multiple.

1 LCM(2, 10)

2 LCM(3, 8)

3 LCM(6, 14)

4 LCM(10, 15)

You know about three-dimensional figures such as cubes and other rectangular prisms. You also know how to operate with positive rational numbers.

How can you calculate the measurements of any rectangular prism, even one with fractional edge lengths?

Measuring Water

You have two empty containers, each with a different volume, as shown. You also have a source of water.

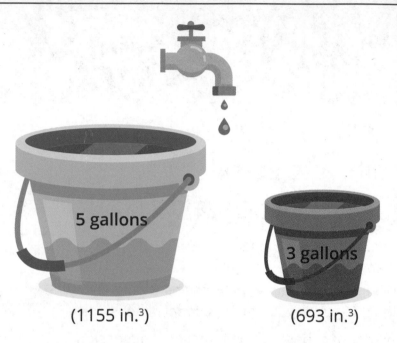

5 gallons

3 gallons

(1155 in.³)   (693 in.³)

1 Using just these containers, how can you measure out a volume of exactly 4 gallons (924 in.³)?

REMEMBER...

Volume is the amount of space occupied by an object. You measure the volume of an object in cubic units.

Volume of Prisms

Recall that a polygon is a closed figure formed by three or more line segments.
A **geometric solid** is a bounded three-dimensional geometric figure. A **polyhedron** is a three-dimensional solid figure made up of polygons. A **face** is one of the polygons that makes up a polyhedron. An **edge** is the intersection of two faces of a three-dimensional figure. The point where multiple edges meet is known as a **vertex** of a three-dimensional figure.

Figure A

Face
Face
Face

Figure A is a *right rectangular prism*. A **right rectangular prism** is a polyhedron with three pairs of congruent and parallel rectangular faces.

Figure B

Face
Face
Face

DID YOU KNOW?
A **unit cube** is a cube whose sides are all 1 unit long.

Figure B is an example of a *cube*, which is a special kind of right rectangular prism. A **cube** is a polyhedron that has congruent squares as faces.

TOPIC 2

1. Consider the fish tank shown.

   a. How can you determine the volume of the tank?

   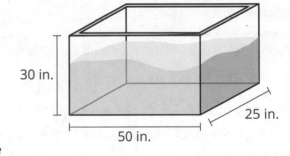

   30 in.
   25 in.
   50 in.

   b. How many cubic inches of water can the tank hold?

2. A planter box in the shape of a rectangular prism has a length of 3 feet, a width of 1 foot, and a height of $1\frac{1}{2}$ feet. How much potting soil can the planter box hold?

Recall that you can calculate the volume of a rectangular prism by packing it with unit cubes.

WORKED EXAMPLE

You can pack the prism shown with 7 unit cubes along its length, 3 unit cubes along its width, and 5 unit cubes along its height.

There are 7 × 3, or 21, unit cubes in each layer and there are 5 layers of cubes.

So you can pack the prism with a total of 21 × 5, or 105, unit cubes. It has a volume of 105 cubic inches.

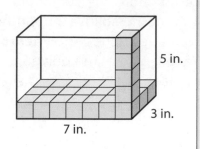

Consider the formulas for volume of a prism and area of a rectangle:

$$V = l \cdot w \cdot h$$
$$A = l \cdot w$$

If you use B to represent the area of the base of a rectangular prism, then you can rewrite the formula for area: $B = l \cdot w$.

3 How does the formula $V = Bh$ relate to the worked example?

Using both of these formulas, you can rewrite the formula for the volume of a rectangular prism as $V = B \cdot h$, where V represents the volume, B represents the area of the base, and h represents the height.

❯ Consider a cube that has side lengths that are each $\frac{1}{2}$ inch.

Each side of the $\frac{1}{2}$-inch cube is half the length of a unit cube, so it takes two of these cubes to measure the same length as a 1-inch cube.

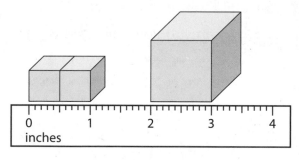

How many $\frac{1}{2}$-inch cubes does it take to fill the prism from the worked example?

4 Phillip says it will take twice as many cubes to fill the prism. Mara says it will take four times as many cubes to fill the prism. Daniel says it will take eight times as many cubes to fill the prism. Who's correct? **Explain your reasoning.**

5 Det...   ...nal cube it takes to fill a unit cube. Draw the
  fr...   ... Then determine the volume of each

ⓒ $\frac{1}{3}$-unit cube

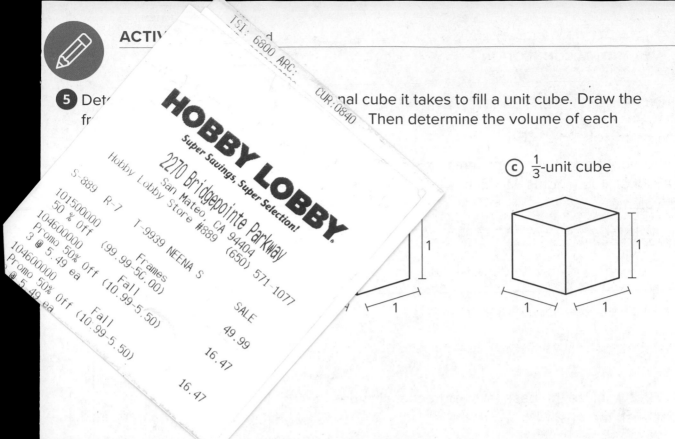

6 How did you determine the number of fractional cubes that filled each unit cube?

7 Describe any patterns you noticed between the size of the fractional cube and the number of those cubes that fill the unit cube.

ACTIVITY 2

MATHia CONNECTION
• Determining Volume Using Unit Fraction Cubes

Area, Volume, and Surface Area

TOPIC 2   LESSON 3

Getting Started 1   **Activity 2** 3   Talk the Talk

Packing a Prism with Fractional Cubes

> Think about packing a rectangular prism with fractional side lengths with cubes to determine its volume.

HABITS OF MIND
• Reason abstractly and quantitatively.
• Construct viable arguments and critique the reasoning of others.

WORKED EXAMPLE

Consider the prism with dimensions $1\frac{1}{2}$ in. × 2 in. × 3 in.

STEP 1 Pack the base of the prism with $\frac{1}{2}$-inch cubes.

STEP 2 Analyze the base layer of fractional cubes that pack the prism.

There are 3 × 4, or 12, cubes that each have a volume of $\frac{1}{8}$ cubic inch in the base.

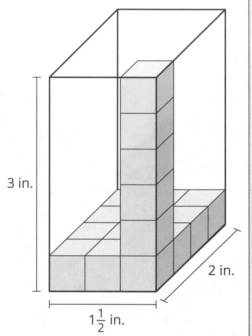
3 in.
2 in.
$1\frac{1}{2}$ in.

STEP 3 Determine the number of fractional cubes that pack the prism.

There are 6 layers of cubes that make up the height of the prism, so there are 6 × 12, or 72, cubes that each have a volume of $\frac{1}{8}$ cubic inch in the prism.

STEP 4 Determine the volume of the prism. $72 \times \frac{1}{8}$ cubic inch = 9 cubic inches

STEP 5 Use the volume formula to check your answer. $V = 1\frac{1}{2} \cdot 2 \cdot 3$
$$= \frac{3}{2} \cdot 2 \cdot 3$$
$$= 9 \text{ cubic inches}$$

1 Does it matter which size fractional cube you use to pack the right rectangular prism in the worked example? **Give examples to explain your reasoning.**

❯ Consider packing the rectangular prism shown
with fractional cubes to determine its volume.
How can you determine which size cube to use?

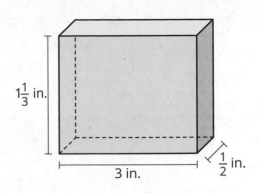

$1\frac{1}{3}$ in.

3 in.

$\frac{1}{2}$ in.

WORKED EXAMPLE

STEP 1 First, decide which
fractional cube to use. Identify the
least common multiple (LCM) of the
fraction denominators to determine
the dimensions of each cube.

$$LCM(2, 3) = 6$$
So, each cube will measure
$\frac{1}{6}$ in. $\times \frac{1}{6}$ in. $\times \frac{1}{6}$ in.
The volume of each fractional cube is
$\frac{1}{216}$ cubic inch.

STEP 2 Determine the number of
fractional cubes needed to pack
the prism in each dimension.

length	width	height
$3 \div \frac{1}{6} = 18$	$\frac{1}{2} \div \frac{1}{6} = 3$	$1\frac{1}{3} \div \frac{1}{6} = 8$

STEP 3 Determine the total number
of fractional cubes that make up the
right rectangular prism.

$$(18)(3)(8) = 432$$

STEP 4 Multiply the total number of
fractional cubes by the volume
of each fractional cube to
determine the volume of the
right rectangular prism.

$$432\left(\frac{1}{216}\right) = 2$$

The volume of the right rectangular prism is 2 cubic inches.

2 Interpret the worked example.

ⓐ How was the number of fractional cubes needed to pack the prism in each
dimension determined?

(b) Instead of $\frac{1}{6}$-inch cubes, suppose you used $\frac{1}{12}$-inch cubes. How does this change the volume of the rectangular prism?

(c) What is another way to determine the volume of the prism without packing it with cubes?

3 Use the method from the worked example to determine the volume of each rectangular prism. Then use the volume formula to check your answer.

(a)

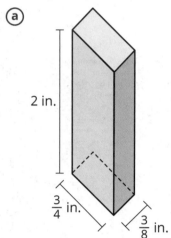

2 in.

$\frac{3}{4}$ in.

$\frac{3}{8}$ in.

(b)

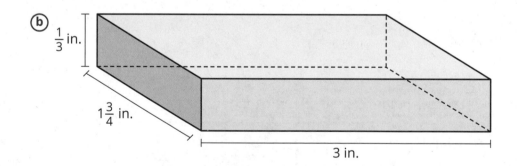

$\frac{1}{3}$ in.

$1\frac{3}{4}$ in.

3 in.

ACTIVITY 3
MATHia CONNECTION
• Calculating Volume of Right Prisms

Area, Volume,
and Surface Area

TOPIC 2   LESSON 3

Getting
Started

Activity
1   2   3

Talk
the Talk

Solving Volume Problems

❯ Solve each volume problem by packing the right rectangular prism with the appropriate fractional cube.

1 Calculate the volume of the right rectangular prism.

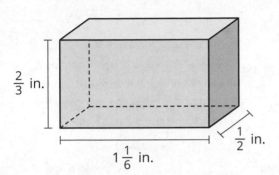

$\frac{2}{3}$ in.

$\frac{1}{2}$ in.

$1\frac{1}{6}$ in.

2 Arlene packs a moving truck with cube-shaped boxes that have side lengths of $1\frac{1}{2}$ feet. The back of the truck is a rectangular prism with the dimensions $7\frac{1}{2}$ feet by 15 feet by $7\frac{1}{2}$ feet.

ⓐ What is the volume of each box?

ⓑ Determine the number of boxes that will completely fill the back of the truck.

ⓒ Calculate the volume of the back of the moving truck.

TOPIC 2

Fractionally Full

❯ Solve each problem. Show your work.

1 Determine the volume of a right rectangular prism with dimensions $1\frac{1}{4}$ feet × 1 foot × $\frac{1}{2}$ foot by packing it with fractional cubes..

2 Haley makes earrings and packages them into cubic boxes that measure $\frac{1}{6}$-foot wide. How many $\frac{1}{6}$-foot cubic boxes can she fit into a shipping box that is $1\frac{1}{6}$ feet by $\frac{1}{3}$ foot by $\frac{1}{3}$ foot?

3 The school athletic director has a storage closet that is $4\frac{1}{2}$ feet long, $2\frac{2}{3}$ feet deep, and 6 feet tall.

  ⓐ She wants to put carpet in the closet. How much carpeting will she need?

  ⓑ The athletic director wants to store cube boxes that are $\frac{1}{2}$ foot wide. How many boxes will the storage closet hold?

LESSON 3 ASSIGNMENT

❯ Use a separate piece of paper for your Journal entry.

JOURNAL ▶

Suppose a rectangular prism has fractional edge lengths. Describe how you can determine the dimensions of cubes that will fill the rectangular prism completely with no overlaps or gaps.

REMEMBER

The volume of a rectangular prism is a product of its length, width, and height. You can also determine the volume by multiplying the area of the base times the height.

PRACTICE ▶

1 Determine the number of $\frac{1}{2}$-inch cubes that can pack the prism shown.

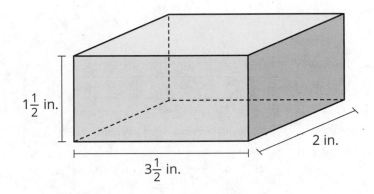

$1\frac{1}{2}$ in.

$3\frac{1}{2}$ in.

2 in.

2 What is the volume of a right rectangular prism that is packed with 300 $\frac{1}{5}$-foot cubes?

3 Calculate the volume of each right rectangular prism.

ⓐ

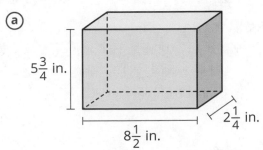

$5\frac{3}{4}$ in.

$8\frac{1}{2}$ in.

$2\frac{1}{4}$ in.

(b)

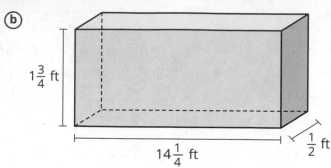

$1\frac{3}{4}$ ft

$14\frac{1}{4}$ ft

$\frac{1}{2}$ ft

(c)

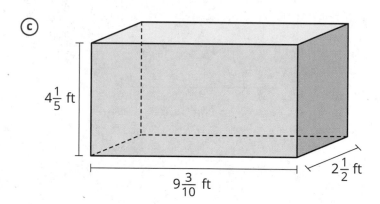

$4\frac{1}{5}$ ft

$9\frac{3}{10}$ ft

$2\frac{1}{2}$ ft

STRETCH Optional

> Calculate the volume for the triangular prism.

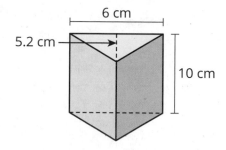

6 cm

5.2 cm

10 cm

TOPIC 1
Factors and Multiples

TOPIC 2
Area, Volume, and Surface Area

1	All About That Base...and Height
2	Slicing and Dicing
3	Length, Width, and Depth
4	Breaking the Fourth Wall

TOPIC 3
Decimals

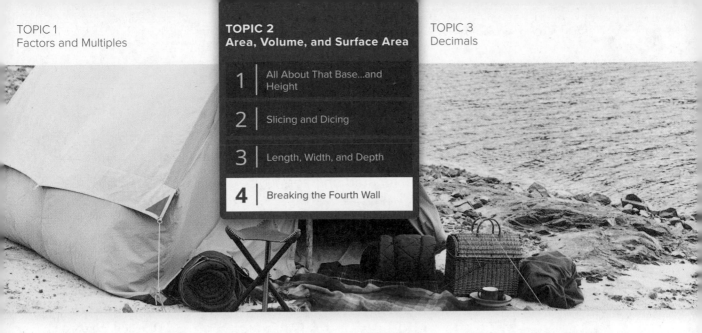

LESSON 4

Breaking the Fourth Wall

Surface Area of Prisms and Pyramids

Learning Goals

- Represent solid figures using two-dimensional nets made up of rectangles and triangles.

- Use nets of solid figures to determine the surface areas of the figures.

- Solve problems involving surface area.

REVIEW (1–2 minutes)

❯ Calculate the area of the composite figure.

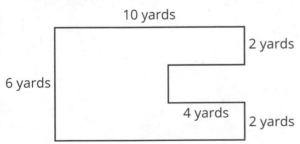

10 yards
2 yards
6 yards
4 yards
2 yards

You know how to determine how many cubic units fill a rectangular prism.

How can you calculate the number of square units it takes to cover the outside of a prism?

Breaking Down a Cube

A **net** is a two-dimensional representation of a three-dimensional geometric figure. A net is cut out, folded, and taped to create a model of a geometric solid.

1 Cut, fold, and tape the Cube Net located on page 109.

2 Are there other nets that form a cube? Circle the other 11 cutouts that can form a cube.

TAKE NOTE...
There are flaps included with the cutout to help connect the faces of the solid, but don't include them in the surface area of the solid.

3 How did you determine which are nets of cubes?

4 What do all of the nets for a cube have in common? Consider the number of faces, edges, and vertices in your explanation.

Nets of Rectangular Prisms

The **surface area** of a polyhedron is the total area of all its two-dimensional faces. You can think about surface area as the total area covered by the net of the solid.

> **HABITS OF MIND**
> • Model with mathematics.
> • Use appropriate tools strategically.

❯ Consider the cube you created in the Getting Started.

1 How is the area of a face of a cube measured? Analyze the two responses and explain why Leticia is incorrect in her reasoning.

Leticia
This is a 3D figure, which means that its measurements are cubic units.

Isaiah
Surface area is still measuring area, which is always measured in square units.

2 Describe a strategy that you can use to determine the surface area of a cube.

3 Consider the cube net shown. Calculate the surface area.

2 in.

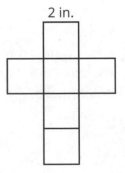

4 What is the surface area of a unit cube?

> Consider a different rectangular prism.

5 Describe the dimensions of the faces of the net that are on opposite sides of the rectangular prism.

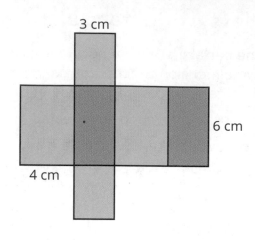

3 cm

6 cm

4 cm

6 Calculate the surface area of the right rectangular prism. **Explain your calculation.**

7 Calculate the surface area of the solid figure represented by the net.

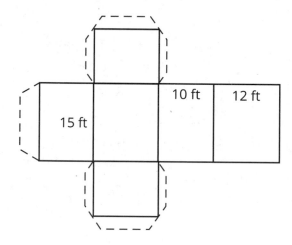

10 ft   12 ft

15 ft

THINK ABOUT...
How you can use the fact that opposite faces of a rectangular prism have the same size to calculate its surface area more efficiently?

8 Draw a net to represent the solid figure. Label the net with measurements and then calculate the surface area of the solid figure.

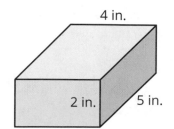

4 in.

2 in.   5 in.

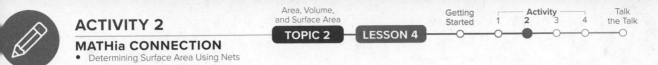

ACTIVITY 2
MATHia CONNECTION
• Determining Surface Area Using Nets

Area, Volume, and Surface Area
TOPIC 2   **LESSON 4**

Getting Started   Activity 1 **2** 3 4   Talk the Talk

Prisms and Pyramids

The base of a prism is not always rectangular. It can be a triangle, pentagon, hexagon, and so on.

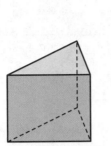
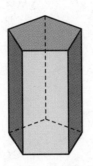
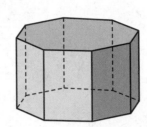

A **pyramid** is a polyhedron with one base and the same number of triangular faces as there are sides of the base. The vertex of a pyramid is the point at which all the triangular faces intersect. A **slant height** of a pyramid is the distance measured along a triangular face from the vertex of the pyramid to the midpoint of an edge of the base.

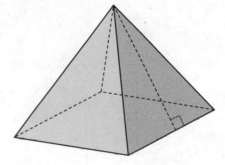

TOPIC 2

1 Locate the nets for the triangular prism located on page 111 and the triangular pyramid located on page 113.

  (a) Cut out, fold, and tape each net.

  (b) Identify the number of bases in each solid. Describe the shape of each base.

  (c) Identify the number of faces in each solid. Describe the shape of each face.

  (d) What is the difference between the number of bases of each solid?

  (e) What is the difference between the number of faces of each solid?

2 Label each net with the name of the solid it forms.

(a)
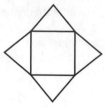

(b)
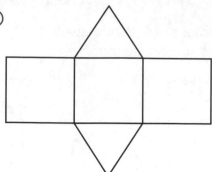

3 Draw a net to represent each solid figure.

(a)
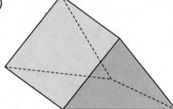

(b)

ACTIVITY 4

Area, Volume, and Surface Area

TOPIC 2   LESSON 4

Getting Started

Activity
1   2   3   4

Talk the Talk

Surface Area Problems

> Read the situation and answer each question.

Scents-R-Us produces candles in a variety of shapes. To produce each candle, the company first creates a mold, and then pours hot wax into the mold. When the hot wax cools and solidifies, the mold is removed.

Candle Mold A

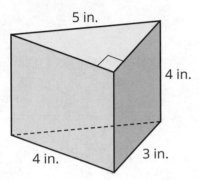

Candle Mold B

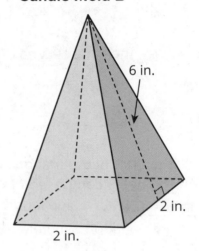

TOPIC 2

1 Draw the net needed to create each mold.

2 Calculate the surface area of each candle.

3 If Scents-R-Us charges $0.05 per square inch, what is the price of each candle?

TALK THE TALK

Area, Volume,
and Surface Area

TOPIC 2 — LESSON 4

Getting
Started   Activity
1   2   3   4

Talk
the Talk

Covering All the Faces

1 A rectangular prism has a height of 6 feet, a length of $7\frac{1}{2}$ feet, and a width of 5 feet.

(a) Draw a net of the rectangular prism and label its measurements.

(b) Calculate the surface area of the prism.

2 Consider the net of the triangular pyramid shown. The net is composed of 4 equilateral triangles, each with a side length of 4 meters and a height of approximately $3\frac{1}{2}$ meters.

(a) Label the pyramid with its measurements.

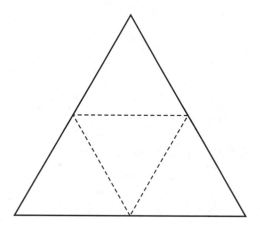

(b) Calculate the surface area of the pyramid.

3 Explain in your own words how to determine the surface area of a pyramid.

Cube Net

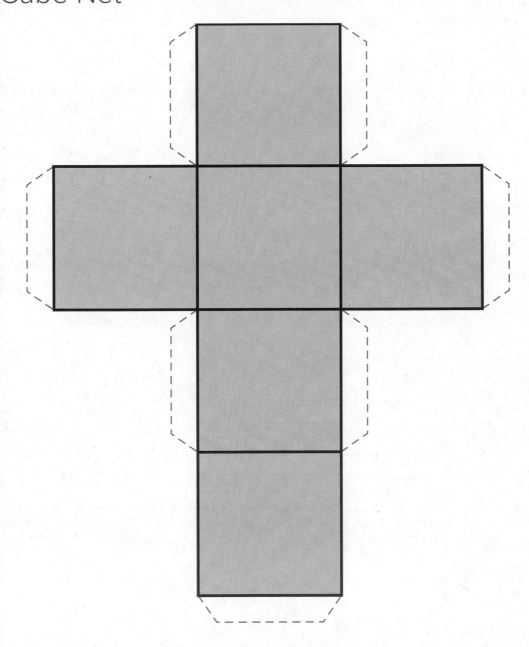

Why is this page blank?

So you can cut out the net on the other side.

MIXED PRACTICE

> This Mixed Practice worksheet includes two sections: Spaced Review and End-of-Topic Review. **Use a separate piece of paper to show your work.**

Spaced Review

> Practice concepts from previous topics.

1 Decompose the rectangle into two or three smaller rectangles to demonstrate the Distributive Property. Then write the area of the rectangle in the form $a(b + c) = ab + ac$.

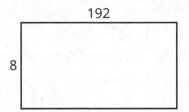

2 Use the Distributive Property to write an equivalent addition expression for each.

   (a) $6(9 + 1)$ (b) $(14 + 3)7$

   (c) $\frac{1}{2}(7 + 10)$

3 Determine the GCF of each set of numbers.

   (a) 72 and 30   (b) 30 and 54

4 Determine the LCM of each set of numbers.

   (a) 10 and 12   (b) 8 and 9

5 Write the prime factorization of each number.

   (a) 36   (b) 60

6 Calculate each product.

   (a) $\frac{2}{3} \times \frac{4}{9}$ (b) $\frac{1}{6} \times \frac{12}{13}$

7 Elena wants to store 60 minutes worth of music on her computer. She looks online and finds a source that says the average song length is $3\frac{1}{2}$ minutes. If this is true, about how many songs will Elena be able to store?
Show your work.

8 Yaz plans to make handkerchiefs that each require $\frac{1}{6}$ of a yard of fabric. The table shows how much of each fabric she has. How many plaid handerkerchiefs can Yaz make? Show your work.

Fabric	Plaid	Tie-dyed	Striped	Polka-dotted
Amount (yards)	$\frac{11}{12}$	$1\frac{7}{9}$	$2\frac{2}{9}$	$1\frac{3}{4}$

End-of-Topic Review

AVAILABLE ONLINE
1. A **Topic Summary** reviews the main concepts for the topic.
2. A video of the **Worked Example** is provided.

> Practice concepts you learned in **Area, Volume, and Surface Area**.

9 Determine the area of a square picture that has a side length of 14 cm.

10 Calculate the surface area of a cube that has a width of 57 millimeters.

11 Determine the area of the shaded region of the figure.

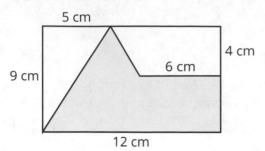

5 cm

4 cm

6 cm

9 cm

12 cm

12 Consider the right rectangular prism.

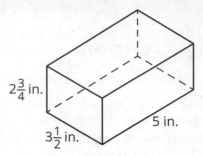

$2\frac{3}{4}$ in.

5 in.

$3\frac{1}{2}$ in.

(a) Determine the number of $\frac{1}{4}$-inch cubes that will pack the prism.

(b) Calculate the volume of the prism using $\frac{1}{4}$-inch cubes.

> Calculate the area of each figure.

13

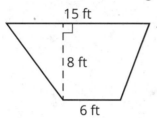

15 ft

8 ft

6 ft

14

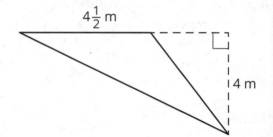

$4\frac{1}{2}$ m

4 m

15

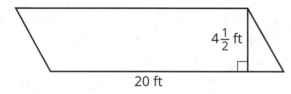

$4\frac{1}{2}$ ft

20 ft

16

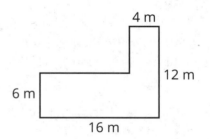

4 m

12 m

6 m

16 m

17 Consider the solid figure.

(a) Draw the net of the solid figure.

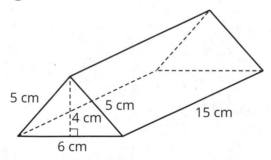

5 cm

5 cm

4 cm

15 cm

6 cm

(b) Calculate the surface area of the solid.

LESSON 1

You Have a Point

Plotting, Ordering, and Comparing Rational Numbers

Learning Goals

- Plot decimals on a number line.

- Compare and order decimal values.

- Compare fractions and decimals using a number line.

> **REVIEW** (1–2 minutes)

❯ Write each decimal in expanded form.

1 240.12

2 5.06

You know how to represent a number in more than one way by decomposing it.

How can you compare numbers represented in different ways?

GETTING STARTED

Decimals

TOPIC 3 — LESSON 1

Getting Started

Activity 1

Talk the Talk

Representations and Misrepresentations

Recall that you can write decimals to represent fractions with a denominator of 10 or a power of 10 (such as 100, 1000, 10,000, and so on). You can use decimals to write amounts of money.

1 Steve saw this advertisement outside a convenience store. He went in and handed the cashier a penny to pay for his bottle of water. The cashier told him that it wasn't enough money. Who's correct? **Explain your reasoning.**

16 oz. Bottle of water

.99¢

2 Consider the representations shown for the cost of each item. Circle the correct representations. If a representation is not correct, state why not.

ⓐ Item A costs one dollar and fifty cents.

- $1\frac{1}{2}$ dollars

- $1\frac{1}{2}$ cents

- $1.50

- 1.50¢

ⓑ Item B costs one dollar.

- $1

- 100 cents

- $1.00

- 1.00¢

Using a Number Line to Compare Decimals

Decimals are valuable when you need more precision for measurements between whole numbers.

The decimal point in a number separates the whole part of the number from the fractional part. The digits following the decimal point represent a value less than 1.

❯ Let's use a number line to represent decimals.

Your teacher will assign students to participate in the activity. Be sure to record what happens on the number line.

REMEMBER...
You can write a rational number in the form $\frac{a}{b}$ where b is not equal to 0. If you can write a decimal as a fraction, then it is a rational number.

1 Plot and label the point where each student stands on the number line.

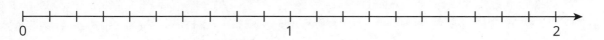

2 Plot a point on the number line to represent each decimal.

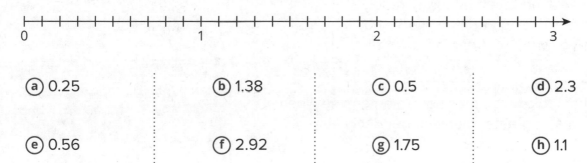

(a) 0.25   (b) 1.38   (c) 0.5   (d) 2.3

(e) 0.56   (f) 2.92   (g) 1.75   (h) 1.1

3 Which number has the greatest value? The least value?

4 How can you use a number line to compare numbers?

TOPIC 3

5 Analyze the number line.

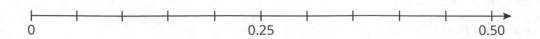

0   0.25   0.50

ⓐ Label each tick mark on the number line with the decimal value it represents. Then plot points to represent 0.3 and 0.4.

ⓑ Plot and label four points that represent decimals between 0.3 and 0.4.

6 Write four decimals between 0.45 and 0.46.

You are babysitting your neighbor Remlee, who is in the fourth grade. Remlee is doing her homework and asks you whether her work is correct.

Circle the greater decimal in each pair shown.

1.	0.32	(0.45)
2.	(0.35)	0.4
3.	0.6	(0.09)
4.	(0.999)	1.00

7 Write a rule that states how to determine when a decimal is greater than another decimal.

8 Explain to Remlee whether or not her homework is correct and instruct her on how to correct any incorrect answers.

9 Explain to Sarah why she is incorrect.

> ## Sarah
> I can tell how large each decimal is by looking at its last digit. If the last digit of one decimal is greater than the last digit of a second decimal, then the first decimal is greater.

You can compare fractions and decimals using a number line.

WORKED EXAMPLE

Consider $\frac{1}{2}$ and 0.35. Which value is greater?

Plot each value on a number line.

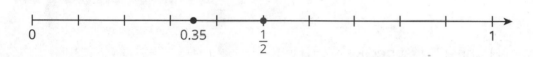

Because $\frac{1}{2}$ is to the right of 0.35 on the number line, you can say that $\frac{1}{2}$ is greater than 0.35, or $\frac{1}{2} > 0.35$. You can also say that 0.35 is less than $\frac{1}{2}$, or $0.35 < \frac{1}{2}$.

---

10 Plot each pair of values on a number line. Then, use > , < , or = to compare each pair of numbers.

(a) $\frac{9}{10}$ ___ 0.71

(b) 0.15 ___ $\frac{1}{4}$

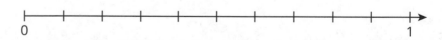

(c) $\frac{3}{4}$ ___ 0.67

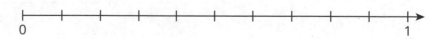

(d) $\frac{1}{5}$ ___ 0.2

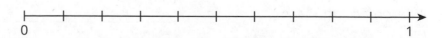

TALK THE TALK

Decimals
TOPIC 3   LESSON 1

Getting
Started

Activity
1

Talk
the Talk

Be Fast on Your Feet

You can compare decimals to solve
real-world problems.

Yvonne and Regina are judges at
the sixth-grade track meet. They
recorded these results for the
200-meter dash. The runners' names
and their times are shown.

Runner	Time (seconds)
Felicia	26.98
Nia	25.23
Vonetta	25.16
Ronnie	25.3
Danielle	27.78

1 Yvonne claims Ronnie is first because 25.3 is
the fastest time. Regina insists Vonetta is
the winner because 25.16 is the fastest time.
Who's correct? **Explain your reasoning.**

2 Identify which runner won each medal or ribbon.

Gold Medal/First Place _____

Silver Medal/Second Place _____

Bronze Medal/Third Place _____

Ribbon/Fourth Place _____

Ribbon/Fifth Place _____

> Use a separate piece of paper for your Journal entry.

JOURNAL

Use your own words to define *rational number*.

REMEMBER

To determine whether one decimal is greater than another, compare digits of each place value from left to right.

PRACTICE

1 Plot each decimal on the number line shown.

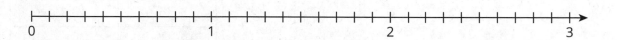

0   1   2   3

ⓐ 1.8   ⓑ 0.62   ⓒ 2.25

ⓓ 0.05   ⓔ 1.37   ⓕ 2.9

2 Write four decimals between 0.82 and 0.83.

3 Order the decimals from greatest to least.

516.84	512.78	516.24
512.79	512.04	513.64
513.98	516.09	513.99

4 Compare the values in each pair using > , < , or = .

  ⓐ $\frac{7}{10}$ ___ 0.48
                       ⓑ $\frac{2}{5}$ ___ 0.25

  ⓒ 0.04 ___ $\frac{1}{25}$
                    ⓓ 0.56 ___ $\frac{3}{5}$

5 Janet's dog had eight puppies. She recorded the weight of each puppy at birth. List the weights of the puppies in ounces from least to greatest.

Puppy weights	
13.6 oz	13.09 oz
12.88 oz	12.96 oz
13.75 oz	14.1 oz
12.47 oz	13.32 oz

STRETCH Optional

❯ Order the values listed from least to greatest.

3.61 $4\frac{2}{3}$ $\frac{27}{8}$ 470%   385% $\frac{18}{5}$ 4.05 $\frac{29}{6}$

TOPIC 1
Factors and Multiples

TOPIC 2
Area, Volume, and Surface Area

TOPIC 3
Decimals

1 | You Have a Point

2 | **Get in Line**

3 | Product Placement

4 | Dividend in the House

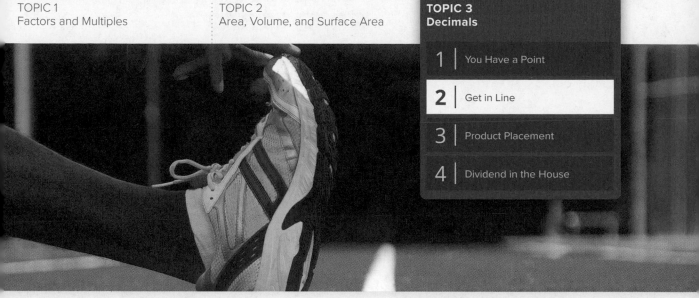

LESSON 2

Get in Line

Adding and Subtracting Decimals

Learning Goals

- Estimate decimal sums and differences.
- Use the standard algorithm to add and subtract decimals.

REVIEW (1–2 minutes)

❯ Rewrite one number in each pair so that each has the same number of digits after the decimal point.

1 4.6 and 5.08

2 17.602 and 9.2

3 25.077 and 12.09

4 2.5467 and 62.1

You have compared decimals by looking at the place values of the digits to the right of the decimal point.

How can you use place value to add and subtract decimals?

A Bit Fitter

Estimation is a helpful strategy when computing with decimals and can give you a sense of the reasonableness of a solution.

Jennie has a goal to run at least 25 kilometers each week.

Her fitness app tracks the distances she runs each day and gives her a summary at the end of the week.

The table shows the summary for this week.

Day	Kilometers
Monday	4.75
Tuesday	5.5
Wednesday	6.25
Thursday	2.15
Friday	1.6

1 Round each decimal value to the nearest whole number and then estimate the total distance Jennie ran this week.

Samuel added the distances Jennie ran and said she ran about 14 kilometers this week.

Samuel

```
  1 2
  4.75
  5.5
  6.25
  2.15
+ 1.6
─────
 13.86
```

2 Jennie knew she ran more than 14 kilometers. What did Samuel do incorrectly when calculating the kilometers Jennie ran?

Adding and Subtracting Decimals

When you add or subtract decimals, it is important to align the digits in like place values. Let's consider adding decimals.

> **HABITS OF MIND**
> • Attend to precision.

WORKED EXAMPLE

$3.421 + 9.5 + 12.85 = ?$

Before calculating the sum, estimate the answer so you know the approximate sum.

$3 + 10 + 13 = 26$

To calculate the exact sum, line up the decimals so that like place values are in the same column.

$$\begin{array}{r} 3.421 \\ 9.500 \\ + 12.850 \\ \hline 25.771 \end{array}$$

You can insert trailing zeros to help you align numbers in the correct place-value column.

The estimate of 26 and the actual sum of 25.771 are reasonably close, so the sum appears to be correct.

TAKE NOTE...
In a decimal, a trailing zero is any zero that appears to the right of both the decimal point and every digit other than zero.

---

1 Recall the situation in the Getting Started. How many total kilometers did Jennie actually run?

2 Calculate each sum.

ⓐ $15.85 + 3.2 + 7.03$

ⓑ $4.347 + 18 + 130.6 + 51.1$

ⓒ $5.804 + 126.19 + 7.236 + 38.3$

You can use a similar algorithm for subtracting decimals. Let's consider two different subtraction problems.

WORKED EXAMPLE

	18.205 − 3.91	22.4 − 8.936
First, estimate the answer so you know the approximate difference.	18 − 4 = 14	22 − 9 = 13
Then, line up the decimals so that like place values are in the same column and subtract.	$\begin{array}{r} \overset{7\ 11\ 10}{1\,8.2\,0\,5} \\ -\ 3.9\,1\,0 \\ \hline 1\,4.2\,9\,5 \end{array}$	$\begin{array}{r} \overset{1\ 11\ 13\ 9\,10}{2\,2.4\,0\,0} \\ -\ 8.9\,3\,6 \\ \hline 1\,3.4\,6\,4 \end{array}$
Compare the answer to your estimate to check your work.	The estimate of 14 and the difference of 14.295 are reasonably close, so the difference appears to be correct.	The estimate of 13 and the difference of 13.464 are reasonably close, so the difference appears to be correct.

3 Recall the situation in the Getting Started. If Jennie ran 20.25 kilometers, how many more kilometers does she need to run to reach her goal of 25 kilometers this week?

4 Calculate each difference.

(a) 459.6 − 12.43

(b) 68.998 − 9.9

(c) 17.4 − 3.256

ACTIVITY 2

MATHia CONNECTION
• Decimal Sums and Differences

Decimals
TOPIC 3 — **LESSON 2**

Getting Started | ┌ Activity ┐ | Talk the Talk
               | 1   2 |

Solving Decimal Addition and Subtraction Problems

❯ Use the algorithms you have learned for adding and subtracting decimals to solve each problem without the use of a calculator.

1 Amy finished the first leg of her race in 87.924 seconds and the second half in 79.06 seconds. How long did it take her to complete the entire race?

2 Chris completed a 100-meter breaststroke swimming race in 92.542 seconds. Michael completed the 100-meter breaststroke swimming race in 95.6 seconds. How much faster was Chris's time than Michael's?

3 It is 639.18 miles from Atlanta to Washington, D.C., and 881.4 miles from Atlanta to New York City.

ⓐ How much farther is it from Atlanta to New York City than it is from Atlanta to Washington, D.C.?

ⓑ If a bus goes from Atlanta to Washington, D.C., and then travels on to New York City, and finally returns to Atlanta, how many miles has it traveled?

4 Kara is flying to Hawaii. If her packed suitcase weighs more than 50 pounds when she checks in at the airport, she will have to pay a fee. Her empty suitcase weighs 11.3 pounds, and she has to pack all her camera equipment, which weighs 14.25 pounds. To stay under the weight limit, what is the maximum possible weight of her other packed items?

Wipe Out the Sevens

In this lesson, you learned to add and subtract decimals precisely without the use of calculator. You will now use a calculator and number sense to complete this activity.

❯ Use your calculator to wipe out the sevens from each number. Write the number you can subtract to wipe out the seven(s), changing them to a zero without changing the other digits. Then, write the difference.

1 5.927   – _____ = _____

2 769.333   – _____ = _____

3 27.328   – _____ = _____

4 476.0574   – _____ = _____

5 3.407682   – _____ = _____

6 79.7856   – _____ = _____

7 124.27744   – _____ = _____

8 4870.7672   – _____ = _____

9 79.767676   – _____ = _____

10 9.857777   – _____ = _____

LESSON 2 ASSIGNMENT

❯ Use a separate piece of paper for your Journal entry.

REMEMBER

When you add or subtract decimals, it is important to align the digits in like place values.

PRACTICE

1 Calculate each sum or difference.

   ⓐ $43.78 + 21.05 + 52.29$ ⓑ $18.867 + 7.3 + 8.92$

   ⓒ $74.51 - 13.02$ ⓓ $97.268 - 75.21$

   ⓔ $15.79 + 4.54 - 2.006$ ⓕ $86.25 - 19.807 + 2.057$

2 Ginger completed a race 6.8 seconds behind Will, who completed the race in 53.786 seconds. What was Ginger's time?

3 A newborn elephant at the zoo weighed 92.8 kilograms at birth. Its mother weighs 2024.25 kilograms. What is the difference in weight between the mother and baby elephant?

4 Cristina wants to purchase four items at the sporting goods store. The items she wants to buy are soccer cleats for $24.99, shin guards for $12.99, soccer socks for $4.49, and a soccer ball for $19.95. If she pays for the items with a $100 bill, how much change will she get?

STRETCH Optional

> Write the numbers 0.3, 0.4, 0.5, 0.6, 0.7, and 0.8 in the squares so that all the numbers in the column and all the numbers in the row have a sum of 2.

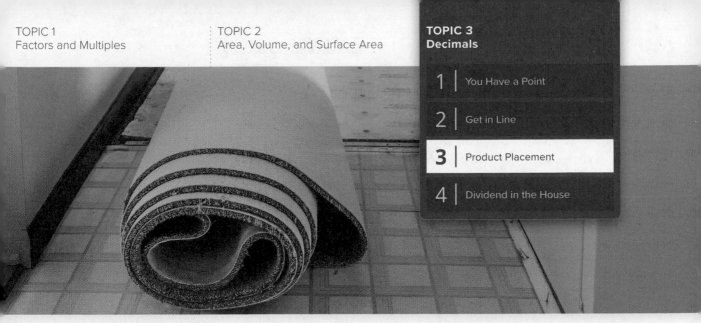

TOPIC 1
Factors and Multiples

TOPIC 2
Area, Volume, and Surface Area

TOPIC 3
Decimals

1 | You Have a Point

2 | Get in Line

3 | Product Placement

4 | Dividend in the House

LESSON 3

Product Placement

Multiplying Decimals

🔑 **KEY TERMS**

kite

composite solid

Learning Goals

- Estimate the product of decimals.

- Analyze patterns of products of decimals.

- Multiply decimals by whole numbers.

- Use the standard algorithm to multiply two decimals.

- Solve real-world and mathematical problems involving area and volume.

REVIEW (1–2 minutes)

❯ Round each decimal to the nearest ten and then to nearest tenth.

1 19.54

2 11.96

3 124.35

4 245.339

5 10.888

6 1258.445

You know how to multiply multi-digit whole numbers.

How can you use place value to determine the position of a decimal point in the product of decimals?

GETTING STARTED

Decimals

TOPIC 3   LESSON 3

Getting
Started

Activity
1   2

Talk
the Talk

Doing Some Re-Modeling

You previously used an area model to show the product of two fractions. An area model can also represent the product of two decimals.

1 Write the multiplication problem represented by the area model.

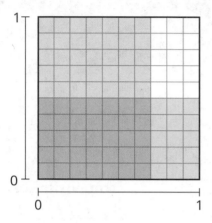

2 Use the hundredths grid to model the expression 0.2 × 0.8 and determine the product.

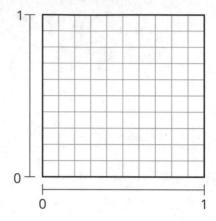

3 Benny says that the product of any two decimals that are less than one will always be less than one. Angel says that the product can be greater than one. Who's correct? **Use the area model to explain your reasoning.**

ACTIVITY 1
MATHia CONNECTION
- Exploring Decimal Facts
- Patterns with Products and Quotients

Decimals
TOPIC 3 — **LESSON 3**

Getting Started | Activity 1 — 2 | Talk the Talk

Decimal Products

In this activity, you will investigate strategies for multiplying decimals.

> Kenji needs to calculate the area of the floor in a hallway of his house so he can buy new carpeting. The floor is 32.75 feet long and 7.5 feet wide.

HABITS OF MIND
- Look for and make use of structure.
- Look for and express regularity in repeated reasoning.

Kenji said, "I use estimation to help place the decimal point correctly in the product."

WORKED EXAMPLE

The area of the floor is 32.75 feet × 7.5 feet.

He estimates the product.

- 32.75 is close to 30
- 7.5 is close to 7
- $30 \times 7 = 210$

So, he knows the product is close to 210, but larger since he rounded down.

Kenji then calculates the product of 32.75 × 7.5.

He knows the product is close to but greater than 210, so he must place the decimal point after the 8.

$$
\begin{array}{r}
32.64 \\
\times \quad 7.3 \\
\hline
9792 \\
+ \quad 228480 \\
\hline
238.272
\end{array}
$$

The area of the floor is 238.272 square feet.

TAKE NOTE...
Multiply decimals as you would with whole numbers. Then place the decimal point in the product.

TOPIC 3

1 Use Kenji's estimation strategy to insert a decimal point into each multiplication sentence to make the sentence true.

(a) $52.6 \times 0.83 = 43658$

(b) $7.9 \times 0.6 = 474$

(c) $0.94 \times 24.9 = 23406$

2 Casey thought that using a pattern would help her understand how to calculate the product in a decimal multiplication problem.

(a) Complete the table.

Problem	Product	Problem	Product	Problem	Product
32 × 100		3.2 × 100		0.32 × 100	
32 × 10		3.2 × 10		0.32 × 10	
32 × 1		3.2 × 1		0.32 × 1	
32 × 0.1		3.2 × 0.1		0.32 × 0.1	
32 × 0.01		3.2 × 0.01		0.32 × 0.01	
32 × 0.001		3.2 × 0.001		0.32 × 0.001	

(b) Describe any patterns that you notice.

3 Use the fact that 26 × 31 = 806 to determine each product. Do not use your calculator.

(a) 2.6 × 31   (b) 2.6 × 3.1   (c) 0.26 × 3.1   (d) 2.6 × 0.31

(e) 0.26 × 31   (f) 2.6 × 0.031   (g) 0.026 × 0.31   (h) 0.26 × 0.31

4 Look at the pattern in Question 3. How can you tell without multiplying which expressions will have the same product?

5 Consider Selena's statement.

> **Selena**
>
> Write a zero at the end of a number to multiply it by 10, and two zeros at the end to multiply it by 100. So, 3.2 × 10 = 3.20 and 3.2 × 100 = 3.200

(a) Explain to Selena why her reasoning is incorrect.

(b) Explain to Selena the similarities and differences between these number sentences.

$$32 \times 10 = 320 \qquad 3.2 \times 10 = 32 \qquad 32 \times 100 = 3200 \qquad 3.2 \times 100 = 320$$

When multiplying decimals, the number of decimal places in the product is equal to the sum of the decimal places in the factors.

6 Consider Camila's statement.

> **Camila**
>
> I multiplied 3.65 × 4.22 on my calculator and got 15.403. There should be four decimal places in the product, so it must actually be 1.5403

(a) Explain to Camila why the calculator is correct.

(b) How could the estimate of 3.65 × 4.22 have helped Camila understand?

TOPIC 3

ACTIVITY 2

MATHia CONNECTION
• Multiplying Decimals
• Decimal Products

Decimals
TOPIC 3 · LESSON 3

Getting Started

Activity 1 · Activity 2

Talk the Talk

Solving Problems with Decimals

> Use the algorithms for operating with decimals to solve each problem.

1 A water bottle holds 16.9 fluid ounces of water. Jonah drinks 8 bottles of water each day. How many fluid ounces of water does Jonah drink each day?

2 Holly is buying 2.5 pounds of sliced turkey from the deli. The sliced turkey sells for $6.72 a pound. How much will Holly pay for the sliced turkey?

3 One inch is approximately 2.54 centimeters. About how many centimeters is a rope that is 7.625 feet long?

4 A poster is rolled up and mailed in a cardboard box in the shape of a triangular prism. The rolled-up poster takes up 113.04 cubic inches of space. Calculate the amount of space left in the cardboard box after the poster is placed inside it.

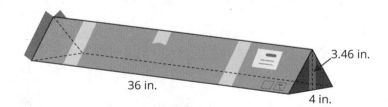

36 in.

3.46 in.

4 in.

5 Reene is designing her own kite. She uses two wooden sticks as a frame to hold the material. The longer stick measures 39.9 inches and divides the shorter stick into equal lengths of 12.7 inches where they cross. Determine the area of the material on Reene's kites.

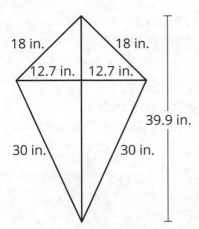

TAKE NOTE...
In mathematics, a **kite** is a quadrilateral with two pairs of consecutive congruent sides.

6 The garden club is installing a concrete chair in the community garden. A drawing of the chair design is shown. Calculate the amount of concrete needed to build the chair.

TAKE NOTE...
The chair is a *composite solid*. A **composite solid** is made up of more than one geometric solid.

TOPIC 3

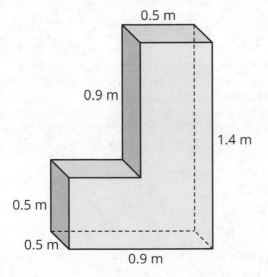

TALK THE TALK

Decimals

TOPIC 3 — LESSON 3

Getting Started

Activity 1 2

Talk the Talk

Disappearing Decimals

> Use the patterns of decimal products learned in this lesson to complete this activity.

You did your homework on multiplying decimals, but when you were walking to school, it started raining and some of the decimal points got washed away.

1 Insert decimal points to make each multiplication sentence correct.

ⓐ 368 × 526 = 19.3568

ⓑ 8962 × 9121 = 81.742402

ⓒ 75.6 × 98.75 = 7465500

ⓓ 152 × 152 = 231.04

ⓔ 5875 × 2569 = 0.15092875

ⓕ 94.05 × 6.27 = 5896935

LESSON 3 ASSIGNMENT

> Use a separate piece of paper for your Journal entry.

JOURNAL

Describe a way to use estimation to help place the decimal point correctly in the product of two decimals.

REMEMBER

When multiplying decimals, the number of decimal places in the product is equal to the sum of the decimal places in the factors.

PRACTICE

1 Insert decimal points into each multiplication sentence to make the sentence true.

(a) $25.7 \times 3.4 = 8738$

(b) $4157 \times 321 = 13.34397$

(c) $135.4 \times 15.04 = 2036416$

(d) $256 \times 1111 = 284.416$

2 Estimate each product to the nearest whole number. Then calculate each product.

(a) 3.9×1.4

(b) 6.18×9.4

(c) 4.07×7.25

(d) 5.216×2.87

3 Determine the volume of each figure.

(a)

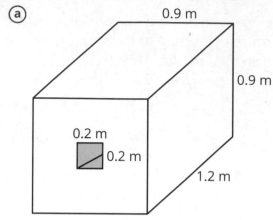

0.9 m

0.9 m

0.2 m

0.2 m

1.2 m

(b)

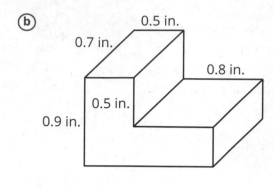

0.5 in.

0.7 in.

0.8 in.

0.5 in.

0.9 in.

STRETCH Optional

Regina is building a hot tub next to her swimming pool. The interior dimensions are 6 feet by 7.5 feet. It includes solid bench seating on all four sides. The bench has a width of 1.5 feet. The bench is positioned 1.75 feet from the ground and 2.25 feet from the top as shown.

1 When the hot tub is filled, the water level will be 0.25 feet from the top. How much water will it take to fill the hot tub?

2 How many cubic feet of concrete is needed to build the hot tub?

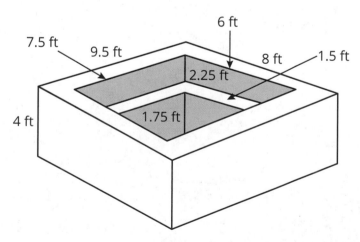

6 ft

7.5 ft

9.5 ft

8 ft

1.5 ft

2.25 ft

4 ft

1.75 ft

TOPIC 3
Decimals

1 | You Have a Point

2 | Get in Line

3 | Product Placement

4 | Dividend in the House

LESSON 4

Dividend in the House

Dividing Whole Numbers and Decimals

KEY TERMS

terminating decimal

repeating decimal

Learning Goals

- Estimate quotients.
- Develop an algorithm for dividing whole numbers and decimals.
- Use the standard algorithm to solve problems.
- Write fractions as decimals.

REVIEW (1–2 minutes)

> Write a fact family for each division expression.

1 $72 \div 8 = 9$

2 $84 \div 6 = 14$

3 $2464 \div 308 = 8$

You know how to use place value to multiply a number by a power of 10.

How can you use this knowledge to determine the quotients of decimals?

Just the Facts

You previously learned that division helps you determine how many times one number contains another number. In other words, division is determining the quotient given a dividend and a divisor.

$$\text{divisor)}\overline{\text{dividend}}^{\text{quotient}}$$

or

$$(\text{quotient})(\text{divisor}) = (\text{dividend})$$

> Consider the expression $48 \div 6$.

1 John evaluated the expression using the following strategy.

> **John**
>
> I know that $6 \times 8 = 48$, so $48 \div 6 = 8$.

ⓐ Describe the strategy John used to evaluate the expression.

ⓑ Identify the dividend, divisor, and quotient in the statement $48 \div 6 = 8$.

ⓒ Which values in the statement $48 \div 6 = 8$ can you switch and the statement is still true? **Explain your reasoning.**

2 Is John's strategy reasonable for evaluating any division expression? **Explain your reasoning.**

TAKE NOTE...
Quotients can be whole numbers, decimals, or fractions.

REMEMBER...
Multiplication and division are inverse operations.

ACTIVITY 1

Decimals

TOPIC 3   LESSON 4

Getting Started

Activity
1 2 3 4 5

Talk the Talk

Whole Number Division

If you don't know a fact family for a division problem, you can use other strategies to determine the quotient.

> HABITS OF MIND
> • Reason abstractly and quantitatively.
> • Construct viable arguments and critique the reasoning of others.

❯ Consider the expression 34,098 ÷ 6. Analyze Lori's strategy to determine the quotient.

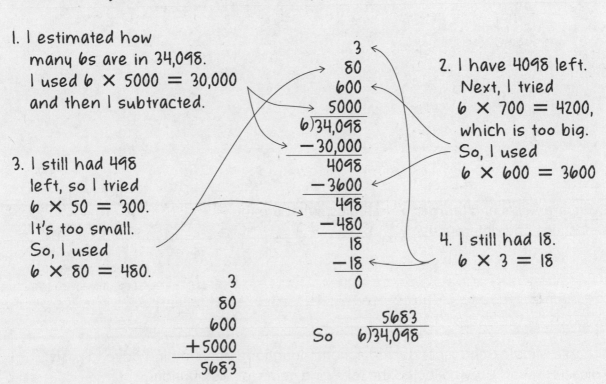

Lori

I used an organized estimation strategy.

1. I estimated how many 6s are in 34,098. I used 6 × 5000 = 30,000 and then I subtracted.

3. I still had 498 left, so I tried 6 × 50 = 300. It's too small. So, I used 6 × 80 = 480.

$$
\begin{array}{r}
3 \\
80 \\
600 \\
5000 \\
6\overline{)34,098} \\
-30,000 \\
\hline
4098 \\
-3600 \\
\hline
498 \\
-480 \\
\hline
18 \\
-18 \\
\hline
0
\end{array}
$$

2. I have 4098 left. Next, I tried 6 × 700 = 4200, which is too big. So, I used 6 × 600 = 3600

4. I still had 18. 6 × 3 = 18

$$
\begin{array}{r}
3 \\
80 \\
600 \\
+5000 \\
\hline
5683
\end{array}
$$

So
$$
6\overline{)34,098}^{\,5683}
$$

1 In each step, why did Lori subtract after she determined each estimate?

TOPIC 3

Rob and Morgan agreed with Lori's logic, but shortened the process.

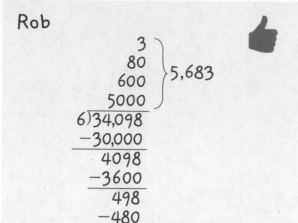

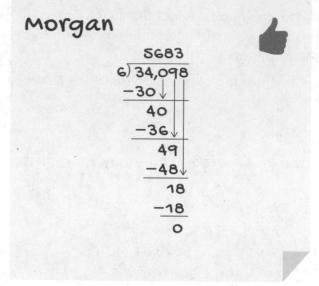

2 Compare Rob's and Morgan's strategies. What are the similarities and differences?

TAKE NOTE...
You can use double lines at the end of a long division problem when the last difference is 0.

Carnegie Middle School conducted a month-long food and clothing drive to assist in disaster relief. They collected the following items for distribution.

- 13,312 cans of food
- 9472 blankets
- 19,456 batteries
- 26,112 bottles of water

If the students want to make 256 disaster-relief shipping crates, how many bottles of water will they put in each shipping crate?

3 Analyze each solution.

Morgan

I used my strategy
from earlier.

$$
\begin{array}{r}
102 \\
256\overline{)26{,}112} \\
-256 \\
\hline
512 \\
-512 \\
\hline
\end{array}
$$

They must load 102 bottles of
water into each crate.

Dustin

I think there are
12 bottles of water in
each crate.

$$
\begin{array}{r}
1\ 2 \\
256\overline{)26{,}112} \\
-256 \\
\hline
512 \\
-512 \\
\hline
\end{array}
$$

(a) What did Dustin do incorrectly?

(b) How could Dustin have checked his work to know that his answer was incorrect?

(c) Dustin should have 3 digits in his quotient. How could he have determined that
before he started dividing?

TOPIC 3

4 Use Morgan's method of long division to determine how many of each item the students must load into each of the 256 shipping crates.

(a) Cans of food

(b) Blankets

(c) Batteries

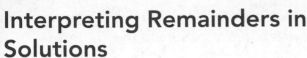
Interpreting Remainders in Solutions

HABITS OF MIND
- Reason abstractly and quantitatively.
- Construct viable arguments and critique the reasoning of others.

In division problems, the remainder can mean different things in different situations. Sometimes you can ignore the remainder, and sometimes the remainder is the answer to the problem. Sometimes the answer is the number without the remainder, and sometimes you need to use the next whole number up from the correct answer.

1 The Red Cross disaster relief fund collected 3551 winter coats to distribute to flood victims. If there are 23 distribution centers, how many coats can be sent to each center? Marla's calculations are shown.

Marla said, "The Red Cross can send $154\frac{9}{23}$ coats to each center." Madison replied, "You cannot have a fraction of a coat. So, each center will receive 154 coats and there will be 9 coats left over." Who's correct? **Explain your reasoning.**

$$
\begin{array}{r}
154\frac{9}{23} \\
23\overline{)3551} \\
-23 \\
\hline
125 \\
-115 \\
\hline
101 \\
-92 \\
\hline
9
\end{array}
$$

2 The Carnegie Middle School is hosting a picnic for any fifth grader who will be attending school next year as a sixth grader. The hospitality committee is planning the picnic for 125 students. Each fifth grader will get a sandwich, a drink, and a dessert.

   (a) The hospitality committee is ordering large sandwiches that each serve 8 people. If 125 fifth graders are coming to the picnic, how many sandwiches should the committee buy?

THINK ABOUT...

You can round down when you don't need to use the remainder, and you can round up when you need the next whole number larger than your answer.

TOPIC 3

ⓑ The committee is planning to have frozen fruit bars for dessert. If frozen fruit bars come in boxes of 12, how many boxes of frozen fruit bars should they order?

ⓒ They plan to serve bottles of water. Bottled water comes in cases of 24. How many cases of water will they need? Will they have any extra bottles of water? If so, how many?

ⓓ The fifth graders will take a bus from the elementary school to the middle school on the afternoon of the picnic. If each bus seats 32 passengers, how many buses will they need to transport the students? How many seats will be empty?

3 Throughout the year, local businesses collected 28,654 pairs of eyeglasses for disaster victims. If they have requests from 236 relief organizations, how many pairs of eyeglasses can each organization receive? How many pairs, if any, will be left over?

ACTIVITY 3
MATHia CONNECTION
- Dividing Decimals
- Whole Number and Decimal Quotients

Decimal Division

You can use hundredths grids to model dividing decimals.

> Consider the quotient 3.57 ÷ 3.

WORKED EXAMPLE

The combined shading on the hundredths grids represents 3.57.

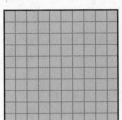  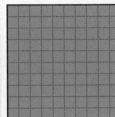 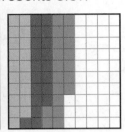

You can divide the shaded model into three equal groups.

One whole grid and 19 small squares are in each group. So, 3.57 ÷ 3 = 1.19.

You can also use a standard algorithm to divide 3.57 ÷ 3.

WORKED EXAMPLE

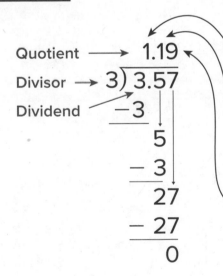

Quotient → 1.19

Divisor → 3) 3.57

Dividend
−3
5
−3
27
−27
0

STEP 1
3 ones divided into 3 equal groups is 1 one in each group with 0 ones left over.

STEP 2
5 tenths divided into 3 equal groups is 1 tenth in each group with 2 tenths left over.

STEP 3
2 tenths and 7 hundredths is 27 hundredths. 27 hundredths divided into 3 equal groups is 9 hundredths in each group with 0 hundredths left over.

TOPIC 3

1 Compare the two worked examples.

   (a) Describe how the hundredths grid model represents different parts of the standard algorithm.

   (b) Why does the standard algorithm show subtracting 3 from the 3 ones in the dividend?

   (c) What does the 05 represent in the standard algorithm?

   (d) What does 27 − 27 represent in the standard algorithm? **Use the hundredths grid model to help you explain.**

If you multiply both the dividend and the divisor by the same number, the quotient remains unchanged.

$12 \div 3 = 4$

$(12 \times 10) \div (3 \times 10) = 4$

$(12 \times 100) \div (3 \times 100) = 4$

You can use this information to change any divisor into a whole number to make the division of a decimal easier to solve.

TAKE NOTE...
The quotient remains the same because you are dividing by a form of 1.

WORKED EXAMPLE

Consider 7.56 ÷ 3.6.

Multiply both numbers by the **least power of 10** that makes the divisor into a whole number.

$(7.56 \times \mathbf{10}) \div (3.6 \times \mathbf{10}) = 7.56 \div 36$

Then, divide with whole numbers.

$$
\begin{array}{r}
2.1 \\
36\overline{)75.6} \\
-72\downarrow \\
\overline{36} \\
-36 \\
\overline{0}
\end{array}
$$

---

2 Rewrite each division problem so the divisor is a whole number. **Explain how you determined your answer.**

ⓐ 48 ÷ 8.6

ⓑ 59.5 ÷ 0.17

ⓒ 6.2 ÷ 0.02

You have seen how to divide decimals by whole numbers. Let's think about how to divide decimals by decimals.

3 Look at each division problem.

7)56   70)560   700)5600   7,000)56,000

ⓐ How are the divisors and dividends in the last three problems related to the first problem?

ⓑ Calculate all four quotients. What do you notice about them?

ⓒ What happens to the quotient when you multiply the dividend and divisor by the same number?

4 Which of the division expressions shown have the same quotient as 475 ÷ 25? **How do you know?**

(a) 4.75 ÷ 0.25

(b) 47.5 ÷ 0.025

(c) 0.475 ÷ 0.25

(d) 0.0475 ÷ 0.0025

REMEMBER...
The definition of division is $a \div b = \frac{a}{b}$. Therefore, you can use what you already know about equivalent fractions to determine which expressions have the same quotient as 475 ÷ 25.

5 Calculate each quotient.

(a) 74.4 ÷ 0.12

(b) 66.22 ÷ 2.2

Fraction and Decimal Equivalents

You can use fraction strips to determine equivalent decimals.

1 Use a straightedge and the chart to determine the decimal that is equal to or approximately equal to the fractions given. Write the decimal to the nearest hundredth.

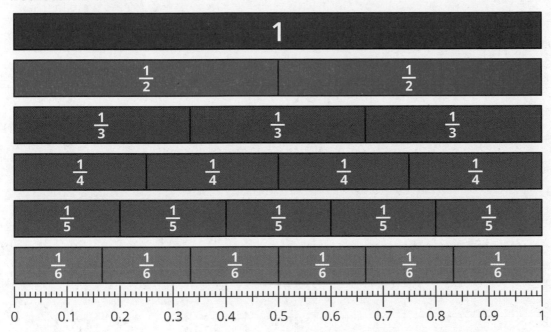

(a) $\frac{1}{3} =$ _____

(b) $\frac{3}{5} =$ _____

(c) $\frac{1}{4} =$ _____

(d) $\frac{1}{5} =$ _____

(e) $\frac{4}{6} =$ _____

(f) $\frac{1}{6} =$ _____

You can also change a fraction to a decimal using the meaning of the fraction bar.

WORKED EXAMPLE

$\frac{3}{8}$ means 3 divided by 8.

$$\begin{array}{r} 0.375 \\ 8\overline{)3.000} \\ -\underline{24}\downarrow \\ 60 \\ -\underline{56}\downarrow \\ 40 \\ -\underline{40} \\ 0 \end{array}$$

So, $\frac{3}{8} = 0.375$

WORKED EXAMPLE

$\frac{2}{3}$ means 2 divided by 3.

$$\begin{array}{r} 0.666 \\ 3\overline{)2.000} \\ -\underline{18}\downarrow \\ 20 \\ -\underline{18}\downarrow \\ 20 \\ -\underline{18} \\ 2 \end{array}$$

So, $\frac{2}{3} = 0.6\overline{6}$

You call the decimal 0.375 a **terminating decimal** because there is a remainder of 0. So, the denominator divides evenly into the numerator.

The decimal $0.6\overline{6}$ is called a *repeating decimal*. A **repeating decimal** is a decimal in which a digit or a group of digits repeats without end. So, the denominator does not divide evenly into the numerator.

TAKE NOTE...
The bar over the 6 means that the 6 repeats without ending.

2 Convert each fraction to a decimal written to the nearest thousandths place. Identify whether the decimal is terminating or repeating.

(a) $\frac{1}{8}$

(b) $\frac{5}{8}$

(c) $\frac{2}{3}$

(d) $\frac{13}{25}$

(e) $\frac{1}{6}$

(f) $\frac{7}{20}$

3 Use a calculator to write the first 10 digits of the decimal for each fraction. Do not round the answers.

(a) $\frac{1}{7}$

(b) $\frac{2}{7}$

(c) $\frac{3}{7}$

(d) $\frac{4}{7}$

4 Consider the decimals you wrote in Question 3.

(a) What pattern do you notice in the decimals values?

(b) Use the pattern to write the first ten digits of the decimal equivalent of $\frac{5}{7}$.
Explain your reasoning.

5 Write the first 4 digits of the decimal for each fraction. Do not round the answers.

(a) $\frac{1}{9}$

(b) $\frac{2}{9}$

(c) $\frac{3}{9}$

(d) $\frac{4}{9}$

(e) $\frac{5}{9}$

(e) $\frac{6}{9}$

6 Consider the decimals you wrote in Question 5.

(a) What pattern do you notice in the decimal values?

(b) Use the pattern to write the first 4 digits of the decimal equivalents of $\frac{7}{9}$ and $\frac{8}{9}$.

ACTIVITY 5

MATHia CONNECTION
• Solving Real-World Problems Using Decimal Operations

Decimals
TOPIC 3 **LESSON 4**

Solving Problems Using Decimal Division

> Solve each problem without the use of a calculator.

HABITS OF MIND
• Reason abstractly and quantitatively.
• Construct viable arguments and critique the reasoning of others.

1 A portable self-storage container is in the shape of a rectangular prism. Nia is packing it with cube-shaped boxes that each have a side length of 2.5 feet.

What is the greatest number of boxes that Nia can fit into the storage container?

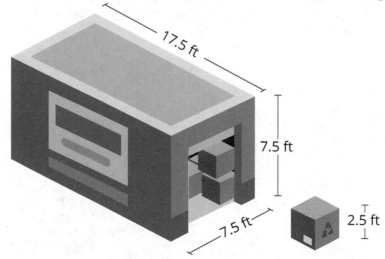

17.5 ft

7.5 ft

7.5 ft

2.5 ft

2 Calculate the area of each face of a cube with the given surface area.

Ⓒ 36.45 square inches

Ⓓ 768 square feet

Ⓔ 59.94 square centimeters

3 The triangle shown on the grid represents a sailboat racecourse. Each square on the grid represents 0.1 mile by 0.1 mile.

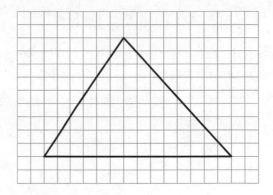

The race organizers want any boats anchored within the perimeter of the course to have at least 0.002 square mile of space to prevent overcrowding. What is the maximum number of boats that can anchor within the perimeter of the racecourse?

4 Marjorie uses a loaf pan to make cornbread. The pan is 8.5 inches long, 4.5 inches wide, and 2.5 inches deep.

(a) The pan has a volume of approximately 6.6 cups. What is the approximate volume of each cup in cubic inches? Estimate and then calculate your answer. **Show your work.**

(b) The cornbread Marjorie makes fills only half the depth of the loaf pan. How much cornbread does Marjorie make? **Give your answer in cups and cubic inches.**

It's Great to Estimate!

Recall that estimation is a helpful strategy when operating with decimals to make sense of your solutions.

1 Estimate the quotients for each expression shown. **Make sure to show your work.**

(a) $7.5 \div 0.8$ (b) $98.3 \div 23$ (c) $99.2 \div 1.6$

(d) $10.35 \div 0.45$ (e) $24.6 \div 0.6$ (f) $7.4 \div 25$

2 Divide each problem in Question 1 using your calculator. Round your answers to the nearest thousandth. **Compare your estimates to the actual calculations.**

3 Place the decimal point in each quotient to make the division sentence true. Use estimation with powers of 10.

(a) $23.4 \div 0.9 = 260$ (b) $5.51 \div 0.16 = 344375$

(c) $10.25 \div 8.2 = 125$

4 Jared started his homework and did the first two problems

$1.3 \div 0.25 = \underline{\text{ 0.52 }}$

$39.6 \div 0.11 = \underline{\text{ 36 }}$

Adam said immediately that his answers were wrong.
How did Adam know there was a mistake just by looking at the two problems and not doing any calculations?

LESSON 4 ASSIGNMENT

> Use a separate piece of paper for your Journal entry.

JOURNAL

Describe what is meant by the operation of division using the terms *dividend, divisor,* and *quotient.*

REMEMBER

In a division sentence, if you multiply the dividend and the divisor by the same number, the quotient remains the same.

PRACTICE

1. A local superstore had a surplus of 10,000 pencil packs and decided to donate them to area schools. If there are 27 schools and the store wants to donate the same number of packs to each school, how many pencil packs will each school receive?

2. Write a different division expression that has the same quotient as the division expression given.

   (a) $36.5 \div 0.005$

   (b) $63.196 \div 14.8$

   (c) $0.3 \div 9$

   (d) $440.618 \div 3.02$

   (e) $8 \div 0.75$

   (f) $51.38 \div 1.27$

3. Estimate each quotient. Then calculate the quotient using long division. Round to the nearest hundredth.

   (a) $51.68 \div 8$

   (b) $93.45 \div 6.23$

(c) 29.988 ÷ 2.04

(d) 38 ÷ 7

(e) 49.7 ÷ 25.3

(f) 118 ÷ 26

(g) 24.4 ÷ 8.3

(h) 603 ÷ 98

STRETCH Optional

❯ The volume of the trapezoidal prism is 1279.152 cubic feet. Determine the height of the trapezoid base.

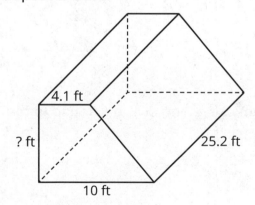

MIXED PRACTICE

❯ This Mixed Practice worksheet includes two sections: Spaced Review and End-of-Topic Review. **Use a separate piece of paper to show your work.**

Spaced Review

❯ Practice concepts from previous topics.

1 Determine the LCM of each pair of numbers.

    ⓐ 8 and 12   ⓑ 9 and 15

2 Determine the area of a triangle that has a height of 4 feet and a base of $6\frac{1}{2}$ feet.

3 Write a fact family relating each set of numbers.

    ⓐ $\frac{3}{4}, \frac{1}{2}, \frac{3}{8}$ ⓑ $\frac{1}{3}$, 6, 2

4 Calculate the surface area of a cube that has a width of 25 centimeters.

5 Determine each quotient.

    ⓐ $\frac{3}{4} \div \frac{1}{8}$ ⓑ $\frac{4}{5} \div \frac{1}{3}$ ⓒ $12\frac{3}{4} \div 1\frac{1}{5}$

6 Calculate the area of each shape.

    ⓐ

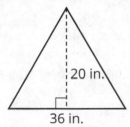

20 in.

36 in.

    ⓑ

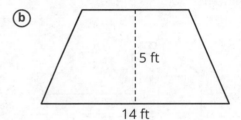

5 ft

14 ft

7 Consider the triangular prism.

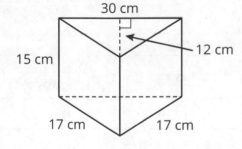

30 cm

12 cm

15 cm

17 cm   17 cm

    ⓐ Draw a net of the solid and label its dimensions.

    ⓑ Calculate the surface area of the solid.

8 Consider the rectangular prism shown.

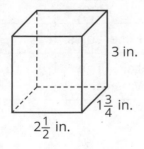

3 in.

$1\frac{3}{4}$ in.

$2\frac{1}{2}$ in.

    ⓐ Determine the number of $\frac{1}{4}$-inch cubes that can pack the prism.

    ⓑ Calculate the volume of the rectangular prism.

End-of-Topic Review

> Practice concepts you learned in **Decimals.**

9 Write 4 decimals that are between 0.25 and 0.26.

10 Order the decimals from least to greatest.
208.07   218.2   207.65   208.4   218.12

11 Determine each sum or difference.

   (a) 1.009 + 6.965

   (b) 14.08 − 6.4

12 Determine the product of each.

   (a) 3.01 × 5.8

   (b) 1.2 × 1.2

13 Write a different division expression that has the same quotient as each division expression.

   (a) 7.16 ÷ 1.3

   (b) 505.308 ÷ 9

14 Calculate each quotient using long division.

   (a) 138 ÷ 24

   (b) 56.8 ÷ 1.6

15 Determine the volume of the composite solid.

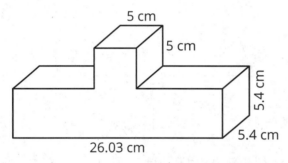

5 cm
5 cm
5.4 cm
5.4 cm
26.03 cm

16 One hundred twenty-five sixth-graders take a bus to the science museum for a field trip. If each bus seats 32 passengers, how many buses will they need to transport the students? How many seats will be empty?

17 Kendra wants to record some of her favorite Broadway shows. The table shows the musicals she has chosen and how much space they each take up in megabytes.

   (a) Calculate the total amount of memory the musicals will take up.

   (b) How much out of 700 megabytes will Kendra have left after she records her musicals? First estimate, then calculate the answer. Show your work.

Musical	Disc Space (megabytes)
Annie	109.785
Beauty and the Beast	131.642
Into the Woods	79.4
Les Miserables	192.27
Shrek – The Musical	117.005

Relating Quantities

MATHia

Introduction to Ratios
- Differentiating Additive and
  Multiplicative Relationships
- Understanding Ratio Relationships

Determining Equivalent Ratios
- Introduction to Double Number Lines
- Using Double Number Lines to
  Determine Equivalent Ratios
- Problem Solving with Equivalent Ratios
  and Rates Using Double Number Lines

**Using Tables to Represent
Equivalent Ratios**
- Introduction to Ratio Tables
- Using Tables to Determine Equivalent
  Ratios
- Problem Solving with Equivalent Ratios
  and Rates using Tables

Graphs of Ratios
- Using Graphs to Determine Equivalent
  Ratios
- Problem Solving with Equivalent Ratios
  and Rates Using Graphs

**Using and Comparing Ratio
Representations**
- Multiple Representations of Ratios

**Percent, Fraction, and Decimal
Equivalence**
- Percent Models
- Fraction, Decimal, Percent Conversions

**Determining the Part and the Whole
in Percent Problems**
- Determining a Part Given a Percent
  and a Whole
- Determining a Whole Given a Percent
  and a Part

**Using Ratio Reasoning to Convert
Units**
- Converting Within Systems
- Converting Between Systems

Introduction to Unit Rates
- Understanding Unit Rates
- Determining and Comparing Unit Rates

Getting Ready for Module 2
Relating Quantities

You will investigate different ways quantities are related to each other. Building on your work with fractions and part-to-whole relationships, you will explore and reason about ratio relationships using double number lines, ratio tables, and graphs. You will apply your knowledge of ratios to work with percents, unit rates, and unit conversions.

The lessons in this module build on your prior experiences with equivalent fractions, ordered pairs, and measurements.

Review these key terms and how to generate a conversion table to get ready to relate quantities.

KEY TERMS

equivalent fractions

Fractions that represent the same part-to-whole relationship are equivalent fractions.

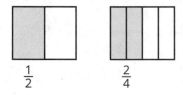

$\frac{1}{2}$ $\frac{2}{4}$

ordered pair

A pair of real numbers of the form (x, y) used to locate a point on a coordinate plane is an ordered pair.

The first number is the x-coordinate, and the second number is the y-coordinate.

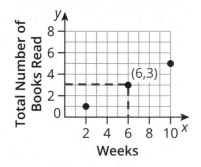

SKILLS YOU WILL NEED

Unit Conversions

Converting units starts with knowing the relationship between the units.

For example, knowing 1 pound equals 16 ounces will help convert between pounds and ounces.

Pounds (lb)	1	3	**5**
Ounces (oz)	16	**48**	80

To complete the table, you multiply to convert 3 pounds to ounces.

$$3 \text{ lb} \times \frac{16 \text{ oz}}{\text{lb}} = 48 \text{ oz}$$

$$3 \text{ lb} = 48 \text{ oz}$$

To convert 80 ounces to pounds, you divide.

$$80 \text{ oz} \div \frac{16 \text{ oz}}{\text{lb}} = 5 \text{ lb}$$

$$80 \text{ oz} = 5 \text{ lb}$$

> REVIEW

> Convert between hours and minutes to complete the table.
> (1 hour = 60 minutes)

Hours	2			15
Minutes		300	480	

See the Appendix on page 719 for answers.

 **MATHia**

Brush up on your skills.
If you need more practice with these skills, ask your teacher for access to corresponding workspaces in MATHia.

LESSON 1

It's All Relative

Introduction to Ratios

🔑 **KEY TERMS**

additive reasoning

multiplicative reasoning

ratio

percent

Learning Goals

- Distinguish between additive and multiplicative relationships between two quantities.
- Understand the concept of a ratio.
- Write ratios in different forms and use ratio language to represent relationships between two quantities.
- Distinguish between part-to-part and part-to-whole ratios.
- Understand that percents are part-to-whole ratios between a quantity and 100.

REVIEW (1–2 minutes)

❯ Answer each question.

1 Laquan put $15 in savings this week. This was $3 more than the amount he put in savings last week. How much did Laquan put in savings last week?

2 Joanne bought three times as many books as Mitchell at the book fair. If Mitchell bought 5 books, how many books did Joanne buy?

You know how to make additive and multiplicative comparisons. You can answer questions like, "If Johnny has 6 apples and Suzie has 12 apples, who has more apples?"

Are there other ways to compare values?

GETTING STARTED

Ratios

TOPIC 1   LESSON 1

Getting Started

Activity
1   2   3   4   5

Talk the Talk

Predict the Score

The Crusaders and the Blue Jays just finished the first half of their basketball game.

	Halftime Score	Final Score
	0:00	
Crusaders	30	?
Blue Jays	20	?

1 Predict the final score. **Explain your reasoning.**

ACTIVITY 1
MATHia CONNECTION
• Differentiating Additive and Multiplicative Relationships

Ratios
TOPIC 1   LESSON 1

Getting
Started   Activity   Talk
                 1   2   3   4   5   the Talk

Additive and Multiplicative Reasoning

HABITS OF MIND
• Attend to precision.

Robena and Eryn each predicted the final score of a basketball game between the Crusaders and the Blue Jays.

1 Analyze each prediction.

Robena

	Halftime Score	Final Score
Crusaders	30	60
Blue Jays	20	40

I think the final score will be double the score at halftime.

Eryn

	Halftime Score	Final Score
Crusaders	30	50
Blue Jays	20	40

I think the Crusaders will play hard enough to stay 10 points ahead of the Blue Jays.

a Describe the reasoning that Robena and Eryn used to make each statement.

b Based on the two predictions, which team scored more points in the second half?

TOPIC 1

One of the students used *additive reasoning* to make her comparison and the other used *multiplicative reasoning*. **Additive reasoning** focuses on the use of addition and subtraction for comparisons. **Multiplicative reasoning** focuses on the use of multiplication and division.

2 Which student used additive reasoning and which used multiplicative reasoning?

❯ Read the age scenario and answer each question.

Vicki and her nephew Benjamin share the same birthday. They were both born on March 4.

Vicki: "Today I'm 40 years old, and you're 10. I'm 4 times as old as you are!"

Benjamin: "Wow, you're old!"

Vicki: "Yeah, but in 5 years, I'll be 45, and you'll be 15. Then I will only be three times as old as you."

Benjamin: "I'm catching up to you!"

Vicki: "And 15 years after that, I'll be 60 and you'll be 30. Then I'll only be twice as old as you!"

Benjamin: "In enough time, I'll be older than you, Aunt Vicki!"

3 Is Vicki correct about how their ages change? Is Benjamin correct in thinking that he will eventually be older than his aunt?

4 The table shown represents the different statements between Vicki and Benjamin. Let V represent Vicki's age and B represent Benjamin's age.

Verbal Statement	Numeric Value	Relationship	
		Equation	**Comparison**
Today I'm 40 years old, and you're 10.	$V = 40, B = 10$	$V = B + 30$	
I'm 4 times as old as you are!	$V = 40, B = 10$	$V = 4B$	
Yeah, but in 5 years, I'll be 45, and you'll be 15.	$V = 45, B = 15$	$V = B + 30$	
Then I will only be three times as old as you.	$V = 45, B = 15$	$V = 3B$	
And 15 years after that, I'll be 60 and you'll be 30.	$V = 60, B = 30$	$V = B + 30$	
Then I'll only be twice as old as you!	$V = 60, B = 30$	$V = 2B$	

a Complete the last column by identifying each relationship as either additive or multiplicative.

b At any point in this age scenario, which relationship does not change?

Comparing Quantities

❯ Let's think about a different comparison of two quantities.

> The school colors at Riverview Middle School are a shade of green and white. The art teacher, Mr. Raith, knows to get the correct color of green it takes 3 parts blue paint to every 2 parts yellow paint.

There are different ways to think about this relationship and make comparisons. One way is to draw a picture or model.

From the model, you can make comparisons of the different quantities.

- blue parts to yellow parts

- blue parts to total parts

- yellow parts to blue parts

- yellow parts to total parts

Each comparison is called a *ratio*. A **ratio** is a comparison of two quantities that uses division. The comparisons in the first column are part-to-part ratios because you are comparing the individual quantities. The comparisons in the second column are part-to-whole ratios because you are comparing one of the parts to the total number of parts.

> Suppose Mr. Raith needs 2 parts blue paint and 5 parts yellow paint to make green paint.

1 Compare the quantities of blue and yellow paint in Mr. Raith's mixture by writing all possible ratios for each type.

ⓐ Part-to-part ratios

ⓑ Part-to-whole ratios

What is the difference between the part-to-part ratios that you wrote?

What is the difference between the part-to-whole ratios that you wrote?

Ratio Hunt

You can find ratios all around you, even in your classroom! Just consider two different quantities.

For example, how many students in your class wear glasses? How many students don't wear glasses?

> **HABITS OF MIND**
> • Reason abstractly and quantitatively.
> • Construct viable arguments and critique the reasoning of others.

1 Write a ratio to describe each given relationship.

Part-to-Part Ratio

(a) The number of students wearing glasses to the number of students not wearing glasses

(c) The number of students not wearing glasses to the number of students wearing glasses

Part-to-Whole Ratio

(b) The number of students wearing glasses to total number of students

(d) The number of students not wearing glasses to total number of students

> Let's go on a Ratio Hunt!

2 Search around your classroom for at least 2 pairs of quantities to compare. For each pair:

- Identify the two quantities that you are comparing.
- Write all possible part-to-part and/or part-to-whole comparisons of the quantities.
- Identify each ratio as part-to-part or as part-to-whole.
- Be prepared to share your treasures from the Ratio Hunt with the class.

(a) Quantities being compared:

(b) Quantities being compared

Ratio(s):

Ratio(s):

Making Sense of Ratios

In this activity, you will represent ratios in different ways.

> **HABITS OF MIND**
> • Look for and make use of structure.
> • Look for and express regularity in repeated reasoning.

> The Lanterton Middle School is adopting a new nickname. They have narrowed their search to the following two names: **Tigers** or **Lions**. To choose a nickname, they conducted a school-wide survey and tallied all the votes.

Each homeroom analyzed the results of the school-wide survey and reported the results in a different way.

School-Wide Survey Results

Homeroom 6A	Homeroom 6B
The votes for Tigers outnumbered the votes for Lions by a ratio of 240 to 160.	There were 80 more votes for Tigers than Lions.
Homeroom 7A	**Homeroom 7B**
The votes for Tigers outnumbered votes for Lions by a ratio of 3 to 2.	3 out of 5 votes were for Tigers.

1 Describe the meaning of each statement. Then identify which describe ratios, and if so, whether the ratios are part-to-part or part-to-whole ratios.

WORKED EXAMPLE

Let's consider the results reported by Homeroom 7A: "The votes for Tigers outnumbered votes for Lions by a ratio of 3 to 2."

This comparison is an example of a part-to-part ratio expressed in words. There are two other ways you can express this part-to-part ratio.

With a Colon

3 votes for Tigers: 2 votes for Lions

In Fractional Form

$$\frac{3 \text{ votes for Tigers}}{2 \text{ votes for Lions}}$$

TAKE NOTE...

Fractional form simply means writing the relationship in the form $\frac{a}{b}$. Just because a ratio looks like a fraction does not mean it represents a part-to-whole comparison.

TOPIC 1

Next, let's consider the results of the student vote as reported by Homeroom 7B: "3 out of 5 votes were for Tigers."

2 Complete the part-to-part and part-to-whole ratios written in words. Then write each ratio with a colon and in fractional form. **Label all quantities.**

Part-to-Part Ratio

In Words	With a Colon	In Fractional Form
_____ votes for Tigers for every 2 votes for Lions.		
2 votes for Lions for every _____ votes for Tigers.		

Part-to-Whole Ratio

In Words	With a Colon	In Fractional Form
3 out of 5 votes were for Tigers.		
_____ out of 5 votes were for Lions.		

Finally, let's consider the results of the survey as reported by Homeroom 6A: "The votes for Tigers outnumbered the votes for Lions by a ratio of 240 to 160.

3 Complete the part-to-part and part-to-whole ratios written in words. Then write each ratio with a colon and in fractional form. **Label all quantities.**

Part-to-Part Ratio

In Words	With a Colon	In Fractional Form
_____ votes for Tigers _____ votes for Lions.		
_____ votes for Lions _____ votes for Tigers.		

Part-to-Whole Ratio

In Words	With a Colon	In Fractional Form
_____ votes out of _____ votes were for Tigers.		
_____ votes out of _____ votes were for Lions.		

4 Based on the survey, which mascot name did the students prefer?

Special Types of Ratios

> Consider each statement.

HABITS OF MIND
• Attend to precision.

• There is an 80 percent chance of rain tomorrow.
• Diego always gives 110%.
• Your battery is 50% charged.
• Joe received a 90% on a 10-question quiz.

Each situation describes a special type of ratio called a *percent*. A **percent** is a part-to-whole ratio where the whole is equal to 100.

• Percent is another name for hundredths.
• The percent symbol "%" means "per 100," or "out of 100."

WORKED EXAMPLE

35% means 35 out of 100.

You can shade 35 of the 100 squares on the hundredths grid to represent 35%.

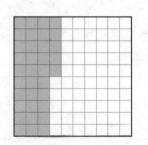

> Write a fraction and a percent to represent the shaded part of each grid. Each hundredths grid represents a whole.

1

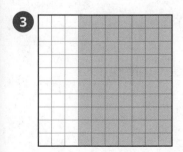

2

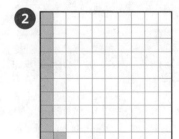

3

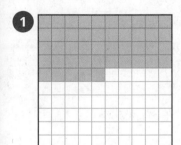

4

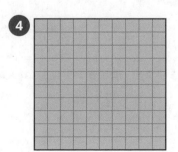

TOPIC 1

Writing and Classifying Ratios

There are several ways to compare two quantities and write ratios.

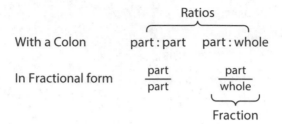

1 Consider the statement: There are n sixth grade band members and t total sixth graders.

   ⓐ Write a part-to-whole ratio using colon notation.

   ⓑ Write a part-to-part ratio using colon notation.

2 A survey of sixth graders with pets revealed that c students prefer cats and d students prefer dogs.

   ⓐ How would you compare these two statements using part-to-part ratios?

   ⓑ How would you compare these two statements using part-to-whole ratios?

LESSON 1 ASSIGNMENT

> Use a separate piece of paper for your Journal entry.

REMEMBER

A ratio is a comparison of two quantities using division.

A part-to-whole ratio compares a part of a whole to the total number of parts.

A part-to-part ratio compares parts.

A percent is a part-to-whole ratio where the whole is 100.

PRACTICE >

The Lewis brothers joined a club that provides them with free movies based on a list that they pre-select. The boys pick the first 10 movies for their list by choosing their favorite type of movie. John David puts 5 sports movies on the list; Parker chooses 3 sci-fi movies; and Stephen adds 2 comedies.

1 Write the ratio in colon and in fractional form to express each relationship.

(a) Sports movies to sci-fi movies

(b) Comedies to total movies

(c) Sci-fi movies to comedies

(d) Sports movies to total movies

(e) Comedies to sports movies

(f) Sci-fi movies to total movies

2 Identify which of the ratios in Question 1 are part-to-part ratios and which are part-to-whole ratios.

3 Write the percent that represents the shaded part of each grid. Each hundredth grid represents a whole.

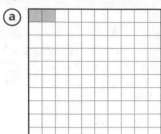

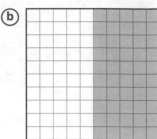

STRETCH ▶ Optional

During the 2018 regular season, the Pittsburgh Pirates won 82 baseball games, and they won 44 of those games in their home stadium. The regular season included 161 games.

❯ Write a ratio for each and identify it as part-to-whole or part-to-part.

1 Number of games won to number of games lost

2 Number of games won to number of games played

3 Number of games lost to number of games played

4 Number of games won at home to number of games won away

5 Number of games won at home to number of games won

LESSON 2

Going Strong

Comparing Ratios to Solve Problems

🔑

KEY TERMS

qualitative reasoning

quantitative reasoning

Learning Goals

- Apply qualitative ratio reasoning to compare ratios in real-world and mathematical problems.

- Apply quantitative ratio reasoning to compare ratios in real-world and mathematical problems.

- Compare and order part-to-part and part-to-whole ratios represented verbally, pictorially, and numerically.

REVIEW (1–2 minutes)

> Use reasoning to compare the fractions in each pair.

1 $\frac{6}{7}$ and $\frac{8}{9}$

2 $\frac{7}{13}$ and $\frac{5}{11}$

3 $\frac{4}{5}$ and $\frac{4}{3}$

You know how to write a ratio as a comparison of two quantities.

What strategies can you use to compare two ratios to make decisions in real-world situations?

Lemony-er Lemonade

❯ The shaded portion in each glass represents an amount of lemonade. Read each situation and answer the question. **Explain your reasoning.**

1 Tammy's glass of lemonade has a weaker tasting lemon flavor than Jen's glass of lemonade. If you add one teaspoon of lemon mix to both Jen's and Tammy's glasses, which glass will contain the lemonade with the stronger lemon flavor?

Tammy's Glass   Jen's Glass

2 Beth's glass of lemonade has a weaker tasting lemon flavor than John's glass of lemonade. If you add two ounces of water to Beth's glass and one teaspoon of lemon mix to John's glass, which glass will contain the lemonade with the stronger lemon flavor?

Beth's Glass   John's Glass

3 Jimmy and Jake have glasses of lemonade that taste the same. If you add one teaspoon of lemon mix to each glass, which glass will contain the lemonade with the stronger lemon flavor?

Jimmy's Glass   Jake's Glass

Qualitative Comparisons

In this activity, you will compare ratios without measuring or counting quantities. When you reason like this, it is called **qualitative reasoning**.

TOPIC 1

❯ Choose the correct statement to complete each sentence and explain your reasoning. **If you cannot determine the answer, explain why not.**

1 If Luke plans to use four more tablespoons of orange mix today than what he used yesterday to make the same amount of orange drink, his orange drink today would have:

• a stronger tasting orange flavor.

• a weaker tasting orange flavor.

• a mix that has the same strength of orange taste as yesterday.

2 Dave and Sandy each made a pitcher of orange drink. Sandy's pitcher is larger than Dave's pitcher. Sandy used more orange mix than Dave. Dave's orange drink has:

• a stronger tasting orange flavor.

• a weaker tasting orange flavor.

• a mix that has the same strength of orange taste as Sandy's drink.

3 If a race car travels more laps in less time than it did yesterday, its speed would be:

• slower.

• exactly the same.

• faster.

ACTIVITY 2

Ratios

TOPIC 1   LESSON 2

Getting
Started   1   **Activity**
                    2   3   Talk
the Talk

Comparing Comparisons

In this activity, you will compare ratios by measuring or counting quantities. When you reason like this, it is called **quantitative reasoning**.

HABITS OF MIND
- Reason abstractly and quantitatively.
- Construct viable arguments and critique the reasoning of others.

The 6th-grade students are making hot chocolate to sell at the Winter Carnival. Each homeroom suggested a different recipe.

TAKE NOTE...
The "T" in each recipe stands for Tablespoon!

HR 6A
2 cups milk
3T cocoa powder

HR 6B
5 cups milk
8T cocoa powder

HR 6C
3 cups milk
4T cocoa powder

HR 6D
4 cups milk
7T cocoa powder

1 Consider the given recipes to answer each question.

   (a) Use reasoning to determine which recipe has the strongest chocolate taste and which recipe has the weakest chocolate taste.

   (b) Show how you used ratio reasoning to order the recipes. Identify the ratios that you used as part-to-part or part-to-whole.

   (c) Create a poster to explain your answer and strategies to the class. Prepare to share.

ACTIVITY 3

Ratios
TOPIC 1 LESSON 2

Getting
Started

Activity
1 2 3

Talk
the Talk

Ordering Part-to-Part and Part-to-Whole Ratios

The Parent-Teacher Association bought lemon-lime soda and pineapple juice to combine for the punch, but they did not say how much of each to use. Several students submitted suggestions for how to make the tastiest punch.

❯ Cut out the punch ratio cards on page 189.

1 Order the cards from the least lemon-lime concentration to the most lemon-lime concentration. If you think more than one card describes the same ratio of lemon-lime soda and pineapple juice, group those cards together.

lemon-lime soda   pineapple juice

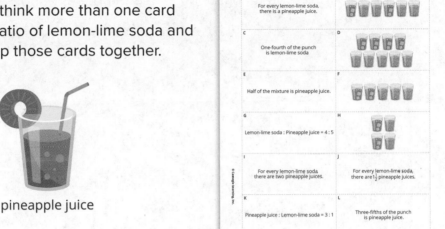

ACTIVITY 3 CUTOUTS

Punch Ratio Cards

A
For every lemon-lime soda, there is a pineapple juice.

B

C
One-fourth of the punch is lemon-lime soda

D

E
Half of the mixture is pineapple juice.

F

G
Lemon-lime soda : Pineapple juice = 4 : 5

H

I
For every lemon-lime soda there are two pineapple juices.

J
For every lemon-lime soda, there are 1½ pineapple juices.

K
Pineapple juice : Lemon-lime soda = 3 : 1

L
Three-fifths of the punch is pineapple juice.

Lesson 2 ❯ Going Strong   189

Describe the strategies you used to sort and order the cards.

Put Me In, Coach

A soccer team was awarded a penalty shot at the end of a tie game. If the team makes the penalty shot, it will win the league championship. The coach is considering three players to take the penalty.

- Amber has taken 4 penalty shots this season and has made 3 of them.
- Lindsay has taken 6 penalty shots and made 4.
- Li has taken 3 penalty shots and made 2.

1 Which player would you recommend taking the penalty shot? **Explain your choice.**

2 How could you change just the number of shots taken for each player so that they all have the same ratio of shots made to shots taken?

Punch Ratio Cards

A

For every lemon-lime soda,
there is a pineapple juice.

B

C

One-fourth of the punch
is lemon-lime soda.

D

E

Half of the mixture is pineapple juice.

F

G

Lemon-lime soda : Pineapple juice = 4 : 5

H

I

For every lemon-lime soda,
there are two pineapple juices.

J

For every lemon-lime soda,
there are $1\frac{1}{2}$ pineapple juices.

K

Pineapple juice : Lemon-lime soda = 3 : 1

L

Three-fifths of the punch
is pineapple juice.

Why is this page blank?

So you can cut out the cards on the other side.

LESSON 2 ASSIGNMENT

> ❯ Use a separate piece of paper for your Journal entry.

JOURNAL ▶

Describe in your own words what it means to compare ratios using qualitative vs. quantitative reasoning.

REMEMBER

You can compare ratios using qualitative or quantitative reasoning.

PRACTICE ▶

Megan is making fruit punch using fruit juice and ginger ale. She tries different combinations to get the mixture just right. If the ratio of fruit juice to ginger ale is too high, the punch is too fruity; if the ratio is too low, the punch is too gingery.

1 For each attempt, write a ratio Megan can try next time.

(a) She tried 16 cups of fruit juice and 4 cups of ginger ale. That was too fruity.

(b) She tried 10 cups of fruit juice and 8 cups of ginger ale. That was too gingery.

(c) She tried 10 cups of fruit juice and 1 cup of ginger ale. That was too fruity.

(d) She tried 8 cups of fruit juice and 4 cups of ginger ale. That was a little too gingery.

2 Based on Megan's attempts in parts (a) through (d), what might be a good ratio of fruit punch to ginger ale? Explain your thinking.

3 Order the five ratios from least to greatest.

$\frac{1}{5}$ 2 : 12   1 : 1 $\frac{5}{3}$ $\frac{25}{100}$

STRETCH Optional

> Order the recipes from the least chocolate chips per cookie to the most chocolate chips per cookies. Explain your answer.

Recipe 1

$1\frac{3}{4}$ cups of chips for a batch of 2 dozen cookies

Recipe 2

1 cup of chips for a batch of 18 cookies

Recipe 3

$\frac{3}{4}$ cups of chips for a batch of 12 cookies

LESSON 4 ASSIGNMENT

> Use a separate piece of paper for your Journal entry.

REMEMBER

You can use a table to represent, organize, and determine equivalent ratios. You can use addition and multiplication strategies to create other equivalent ratios.

PRACTICE

Each table represents the ratio of yellow daffodils to white daffodils for different garden displays. Complete each ratio table. Explain your calculations.

1

Yellow daffodils	9	36	45	
White daffodils	15			90

2

Yellow daffodils		14		49
White daffodils	6	12		42

3

Yellow daffodils	32			16
White daffodils		48	6	12

4

Yellow daffodils	5	1		9
White daffodils		3	30	

5

Yellow daffodils		105	84	21
White daffodils	20	60		

Go to LiveHint.com for help on the **PRACTICE** questions.

6

Yellow daffodils	55		77	
White daffodils	25	10		5

7 Look at the ratio table in Question 1. How could you use addition to determine the number of white daffodils that go with 99 yellow daffodils?

8 Look at the ratio table in Question 5. How could you use subtraction to determine the number of yellow daffodils that go with 40 white daffodils?

STRETCH Optional

❯ Complete each double number line.

1

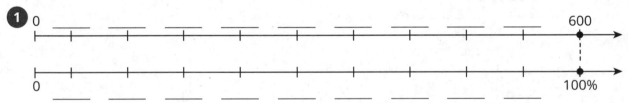

0 _____ _____ _____ _____ _____ _____ _____ _____ _____ _____ 600

0   100%
_____ _____ _____ _____ _____ _____ _____ _____ _____ _____

2

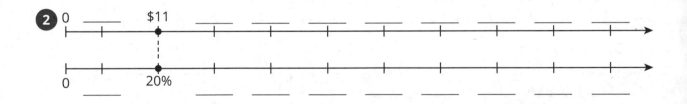

0 _____ $11 _____ _____ _____ _____ _____ _____ _____

0   20%
_____ _____ _____ _____ _____ _____ _____ _____

3

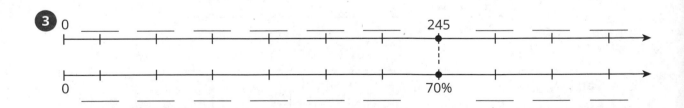

0 _____ _____ _____ _____ _____ _____ 245 _____ _____ _____

0   70%
_____ _____ _____ _____ _____ _____ _____ _____ _____ _____

LESSON 5

They're Growing!

Graphs of Ratios

KEY TERM

linear
relationship

Learning Goals

- Plot ratios and equivalent ratios on a coordinate plane.

- Read equivalent ratios from graphs.

- Use ratio reasoning to determine equivalent ratios from graphs.

- Recognize the graphical representation of equivalent ratios.

REVIEW (1–2 minutes)

A tree grows at a constant rate of 3 feet per year.

1 Write a ratio to represent the amount of growth in feet : the number of months.

2 Create a double number line that describes the growth of the tree every 12 months over a 48-month period.

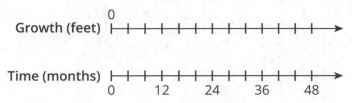

So far, you have used pictures, tape diagrams, scaling up or scaling down, double number lines, and tables to determine equivalent ratios.

How can you use a coordinate plane to determine equivalent ratios?

GETTING STARTED

Ratios

TOPIC 1   LESSON 5

Getting Started

Activity
1   2   3   4   5

Talk the Talk

Growing Rectangles

❯ Cut out and analyze the rectangles located on page 239. Note that you have 2 copies of Rectangle A. You need both for the next activity.

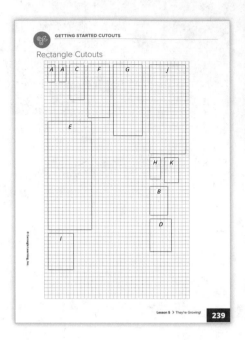

1 Determine the side lengths of each rectangle. Label each rectangle with the length of its short side and the length of its long side.

2 Ava and Gabriel each grouped the rectangles in different ways. Use your cutouts to make sense of their reasoning.

ⓐ Ava grouped Rectangles A, C, E, F, G, and J. **What do you think was her reasoning?**

ⓑ Gabriel's sort was similar to Ava's, but he included Rectangle A with Rectangles B, D, H, I, and K. **What do you think was his reasoning?**

3 Complete each table. Write the ratios in fractional form, comparing the length of the short side to the length of the long side.

Ava's Group			
	Short	**Long**	**Ratio**
A	2	5	
C	4	10	
E	12	30	
F	6	15	
G	8	20	
J	10	25	

Gabriel's Group			
	Short	**Long**	**Ratio**
A	2	5	
B	5	8	
D	6	9	
H	3	6	
I	7	10	
K	4	7	

4 Compare the ratios in each table. **What do you notice?**

ACTIVITY 1

Ratios

TOPIC 1 ▸ **LESSON 5**

Getting Started

Activity

1 2 3 4 5

Talk the Talk

Analyzing Rectangle Ratios

❯ Stack Ava's and Gabriel's groups of rectangles from the Getting Started with the smallest rectangle on top so that their longer sides are horizontal and their lower left corners align.

HABITS OF MIND
- Look for and make use of structure.
- Look for and express regularity in repeated reasoning.

TOPIC 1

1 What do you notice about the rectangles in each group?

   ⓐ Ava's Group

   ⓑ Gabriel's Group

2 Attach each set of stacked rectangles to the appropriate coordinate grid aligning each rectangle's lower-left corner at the origin.

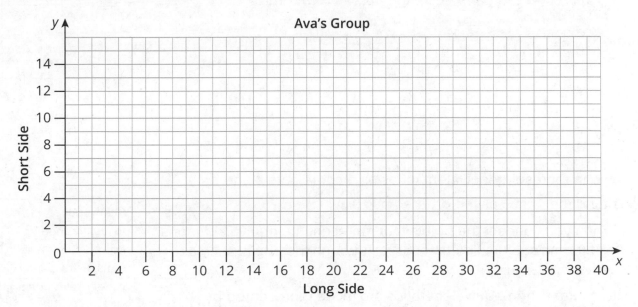

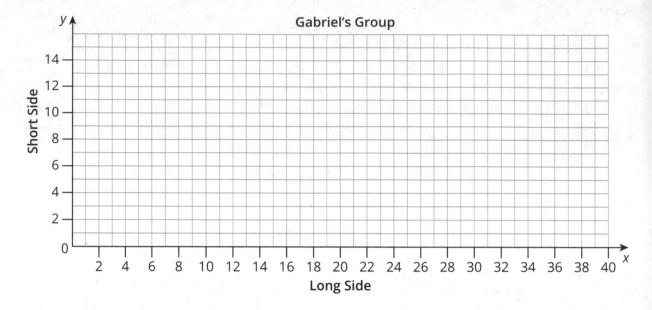

3 Label the coordinates of the upper right corner of each rectangle. **What do you notice about the coordinates of each rectangle?**

4 Draw a line through the labeled points on each graph. **What do you notice about which ordered pairs each line passes through?**

You can represent equivalent ratios on a coordinate plane by plotting the ratio $\frac{y}{x}$ as the ordered pair (x, y).

- When you connect the points that represent the equivalent ratios, you form a straight line that passes through the origin, such as with Ava's Group.

- In contrast, non-equivalent ratios are those represented by points that do not create a straight line through the origin, like Gabriel's Group.

TAKE NOTE...
When a set of points graphed on a coordinate plane forms a straight line, a **linear relationship** exists.

ACTIVITY 2
MATHia CONNECTION
• Using Graphs to Determine Equivalent Ratios

Ratios
TOPIC 1   LESSON 5

Getting Started   Activity   Talk the Talk
1   2   3   4   5

TOPIC 1

Graphing Equivalent Ratios

You have used tables and double number lines to represent equivalent ratios. Let's investigate how you can use a graph to determine other equivalent ratios and understand the connections between the representations.

HABITS OF MIND
• Model with mathematics.
• Use appropriate tools strategically.

Ava wants to create more rectangles that maintain the same ratio of side lengths. The table shows the lengths of the sides of the rectangles she grouped.

Short side (units)	2	4	6	8	10	14
Long side (units)	5	10	15	20	25	35

The double number line shown represents the same data.

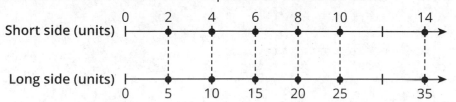

ASK YOURSELF...

Compare the labels on the double number line and the labels on the x- and y-axis. What do you notice?

You can also represent equivalent ratios on a coordinate plane.

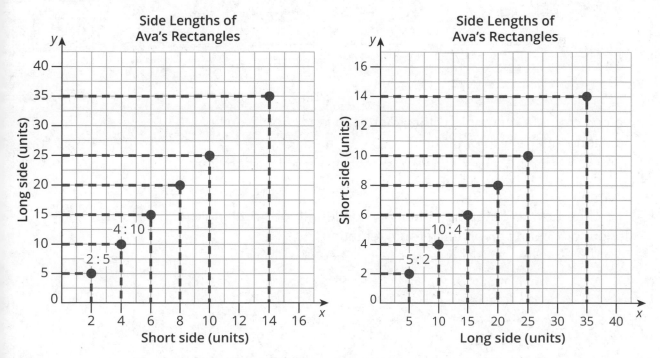

1 Label the remaining ratios on each graph.

❯ Consider the question: What rectangle can Ava create that has a short side length of 12 units?

WORKED EXAMPLE

You know 6 different equivalent ratios from the original graph. The graph shows how to use the ratios 2 : 5 and 10 : 25, or 2 : 5 and 14 : 35, to determine the equivalent ratio 12 : 30.

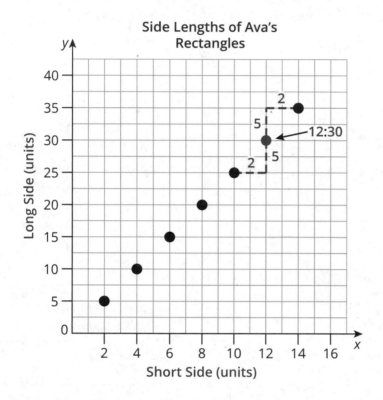

Ava can create a rectangle with a short side length of 12 units and a long side length of 30 units.

---

2 Describe how to determine the long side length of a rectangle with a short side length of 16 units given each representation.

ⓐ Graph

ⓑ Table

ⓒ Double number lines

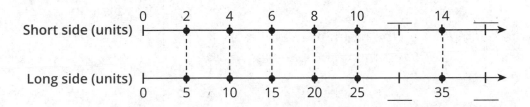

One way to analyze the relationship between equivalent ratios displayed on a graph is to draw a line to connect the points. You can also extend the line to make predictions of other equivalent ratios.

Sometimes, all of the points on the line make sense. Other times when you draw a line, not all the points on the line make sense.

3 Draw a line through all the points you plotted on your graph. Do all the points on the line you drew make sense in this problem situation? **Why or why not?**

ASK YOURSELF...
You are comparing side lengths of rectangles. Do fractional values make sense?

4 How do all the representations—tables, double number lines and graphs—show equivalent ratios? How are they similar? **Describe some of the advantages of each representation.**

ACTIVITY 3

Ratios

TOPIC 1 **LESSON 5**

Getting
Started

Activity

1 2 **3** 4 5

Talk
the Talk

MATHia CONNECTION
• Problem Solving with Equivalent Ratios and Rates Using Graphs

Using Ratio Graphs to Solve Problems

You know different ways to think about ratios. So, you can use different strategies to solve problems.

1 The graph shown represents the number of gallons of water used for the number of times a toilet is flushed.

(a) Write each point on the graph as the ratio of *gallons of water used : number of flushes.*

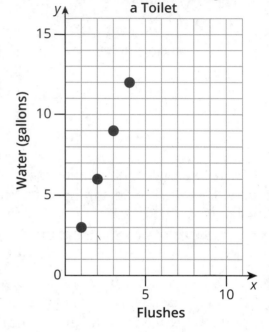

Water Used Flushing a Toilet

(b) What do you notice about each ratio?

(c) How many gallons of water would you use if you flushed the toilet 8 times? **Explain the method you used.**

ASK YOURSELF...

How do you know this graph represents equivalent ratios?

(d) How many times would you flush the toilet to use 18 gallons of water? **Explain the method you used.**

(e) Did you use the same method to answer each question? **If not, why?**

ACTIVITY 3 Continued

2 The graph shown represents the number of gallons of water used for the number of loads of laundry washed.

(a) Write each point on the graph as the ratio of gallons of water used : number of loads of laundry.

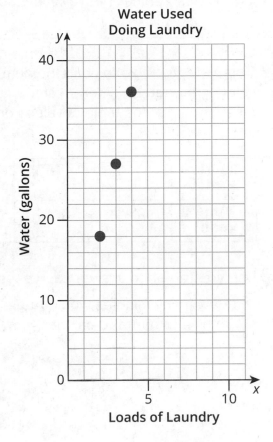

Water Used Doing Laundry

(b) What do you notice about each ratio?

(c) How many gallons of water would you use for 7 loads of laundry? **Explain the method you used.**

(d) How many loads of laundry can you do if you use 45 gallons of water? **Explain the method you used.**

(e) Did you use the same method to answer each question? **If not, why?**

Augie burns 225 calories for every 30 minutes he rides his bike.

3 Complete the table to chart the number of calories burned for different amounts of time. Then plot the table of values on the graph.

Calories Burned				
Time (min)	30	10	60	50

4 Use your graph to answer each question.

(a) How many minutes would Augie have to bike to burn 150 calories?

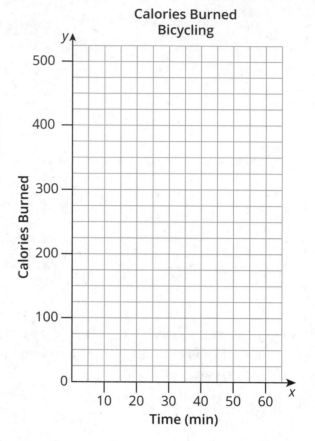

Calories Burned Bicycling

(b) About how many calories can he burn if he bikes for 25 minutes?

TAKE NOTE...

Drawing a line may help you see the relationships.

5 How was the graph helpful? Were there any limitations when using the graph to determine values?

Analyzing Graphs of Linear Relationships

TOPIC 1

❯ Consider the relationship modeled by each graph.

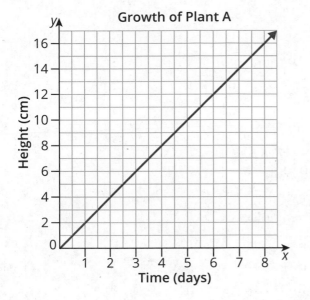

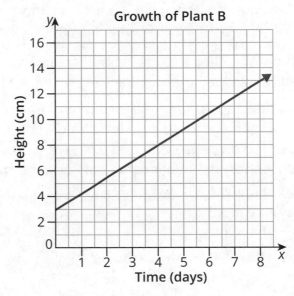

1 Determine whether each graph represents a set of equivalent ratios. **Explain your reasoning.**

  (a) Plant A   (b) Plant B

2 Consider the graph for plant A.

  (a) What does the point (0, 0) on the graph of plant A represent?

  (b) How many centimeters did plant A grow each day?

3 Consider the graph for plant B.

  (a) What does the point (0, 3) on the graph of plant B represent?

  (b) How many centimeters did plant B grow each day?

Additive and Multiplicative Representations

Two different jogging situations are given on the next two pages, along with a diagram showing the current relationship between the joggers.

❯ Cut out the diagrams, equations, graphs, and verbal statements located on page 241.

1 Identify the appropriate location for each representation and glue it to the graphic orginzers located on pages 235 and 236. Then explain why it describes that relationship between the two joggers.

(a) Choose and affix the diagram that shows the relationship between the joggers after 5 minutes.

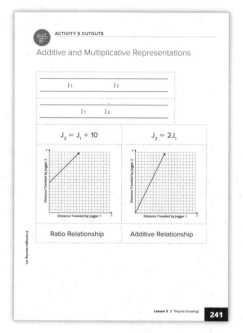

(b) Choose and affix the equation that represents the relationship between the two joggers.

(c) Choose the graph that models the relationship between the two joggers.

(d) Identify the type of relationship (additive or multiplicative) between the position of the two joggers.

TAKE NOTE...

In a proportion, the quantities composing each part of the ratio have the same multiplicative relationship between them. A multiplicative relationship is also known as a proportional relationship.

> **Two joggers are running at the same speed.**

Diagram of the current position of the two joggers.

J_1 J_2

Diagram of the two joggers after 5 minutes.

Explanation:

Equation

Explanation:

Graph

Explanation:

Verbal Statement

Explanation:

Jogger 2 runs twice as fast as Jogger 1.

Diagram of the current position of the two joggers.

J₁   J₂

Diagram of the two joggers after 5 minutes.

Explanation:

Equation   Explanation:

Graph   Explanation:

Verbal Statement   Explanation:

TALK THE TALK

Ratios
TOPIC 1   **LESSON 5**

Getting
Started   Activity
1 2 3 4 5   Talk
the Talk

TOPIC 1

To Graph or Not to Graph

> Go back and examine the graphs that represent equivalent ratios in this lesson.

1 What is similar about the graphs?

2 What is different about all the graphs?

3 Describe how you can use a line to analyze equivalent ratios. What are the benefits and limitations of using a graph to display and interpret ratios?

4 Complete the graphic organizer to demonstrate your understanding of ratios.

Ratio

Definition

Characteristics

Example

Non-example

Rectangle Cutouts

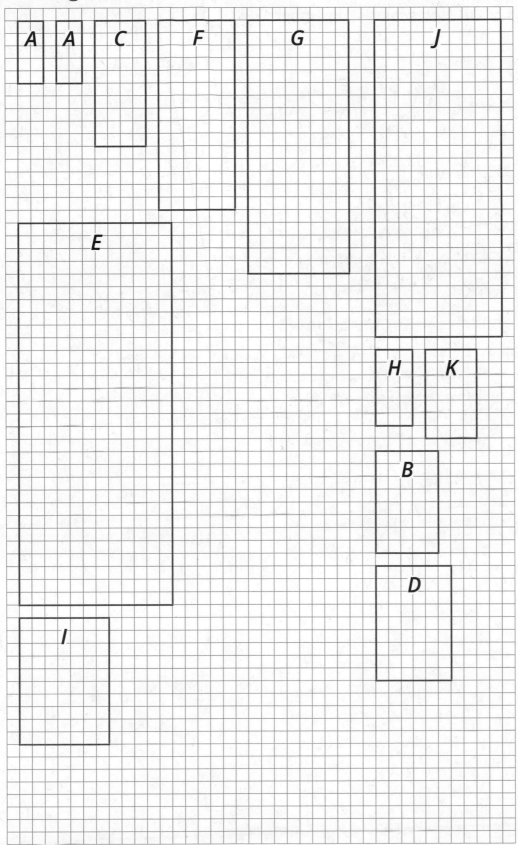

Why is this page blank?

So you can cut out the rectangles on the other side.

Additive and Multiplicative Representations

J_1 J_2

J_1 J_2

$$J_2 = J_1 + 10$$

$$J_2 = 2J_1$$

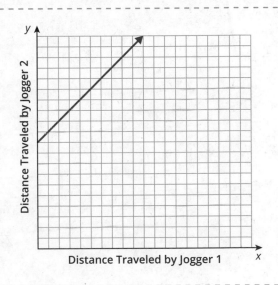

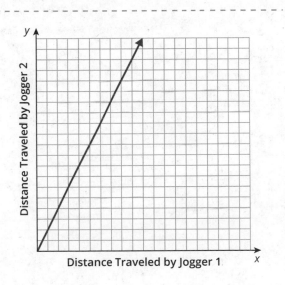

Ratio Relationship

Additive Relationship

Why is this page blank?

So you can cut out the representations on the other side.

LESSON 5 ASSIGNMENT

❯ Use a separate piece of paper for your Journal entry.

JOURNAL

Compare the graph of a ratio relationship with the graph of a relationship that is not represented by a ratio. How are they similar and different? Use an example to explain.

REMEMBER

You can represent equivalent ratios on a coordinate plane. The ratio $\frac{y}{x}$ is plotted as the ordered pair (x, y).

The points that represent the equivalent ratios form a straight line that passes through the origin.

PRACTICE

❯ Create a graph to represent the values shown in each ratio table.

1

Weight (pounds)	1	2	4	5
Cost (dollars)	3	6	12	15

(a) What is the cost for a weight of 3 pounds?

(b) What is the weight for a cost of $9?

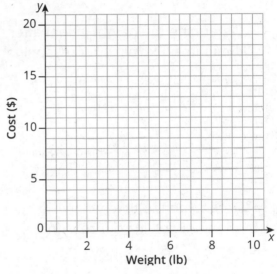

2

Time (hours)	1	3	5	7
Distance (miles)	25	75	125	175

(a) What is the distance at 6 hours?

(b) What is the time at 275 miles?

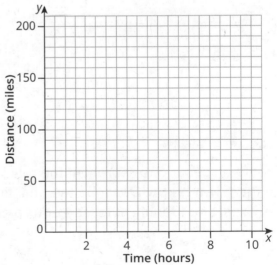

3

Time (minutes)	15	30	45	60
Calories	80	160	240	320

(a) What is the number of calories at 24 minutes?

(b) What is the time at 280 calories?

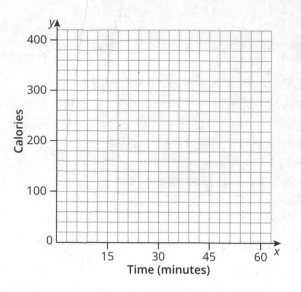

4 Consider the graph of the set of equivalent ratios shown.

(a) Determine the height in feet after 4 minutes. Explain your reasoning.

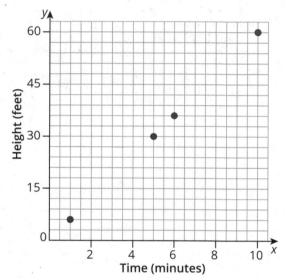

(b) Determine the time when the height is 48 feet. Explain your reasoning.

STRETCH Optional

> Create a scenario to represent the relationship on the given graph. Describe the quantities, label the axes, and identify at least 4 equivalent ratios.

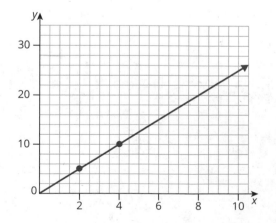

LESSON 6 ASSIGNMENT

> Use a separate piece of paper for your Journal entry.

JOURNAL

Describe the advantages and disadvantages of using double number lines, tape diagrams, equations, tables, and graphs to write, represent, and compare ratios.

REMEMBER

You can use many different representations, like graphs, tables, double number lines, and tape diagrams to analyze ratios and solve problems.

PRACTICE

1 Use a graph to answer each question.

(a) Serena is driving to the mountains for a summer camping trip. The graph shows the ratio time : distance. How far has Serena traveled after 4 hours?

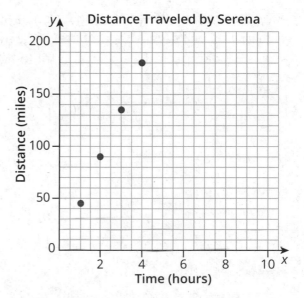

(b) Cisco is exercising. The graph shows the ratio calories burned : time for Cisco. How many calories did Cisco burn in 30 minutes?

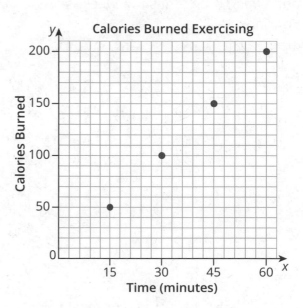

Go to LiveHint.com for help on the **PRACTICE** questions.

2 A recipe calls for 2 eggs for every 5 cups of milk. How many eggs do you use if you use 20 cups of milk? Draw a double number line to answer the question.

3 Alberto is in charge of making lunch at a summer camp. He knows that 3 tuna casseroles will serve 15 campers. How many tuna casseroles should Alberto make to serve 35 campers? Use the ratio table to explain your reasoning.

Casseroles	1	3		
Campers		15	30	35

STRETCH Optional

❯ Use the graphs to determine which recipe has the strongest taste of lemon-lime and which recipe has the weakest taste of lemon-lime. Use the graph to explain your answer.

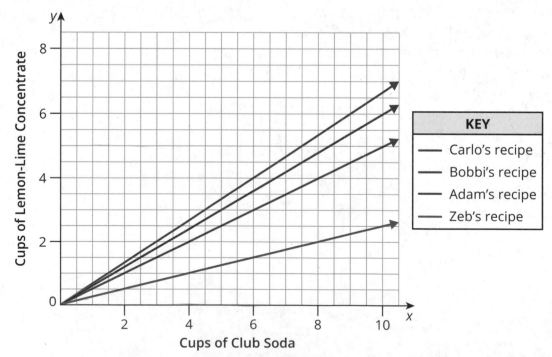

❯ This Mixed Practice worksheet includes two sections: Spaced Review and End-of-Topic Review. **Use a separate piece of paper to show your work.**

Spaced Review

❯ Practice concepts from previous topics.

1 The winning time for the middle school 4-person 100-meter relay was 62.59 seconds. Suppose that each runner ran exactly the same amount of time. What would the time be for each runner?

2 Use estimation to place the decimal point in the correct position in each quotient.

ⓐ $2.1\overline{)48.72} = 232$

ⓑ $8\overline{)204.8} = 256$

3 Determine each quotient.

ⓐ $\frac{1}{6} \div \frac{2}{3}$ ⓑ $\frac{5}{8} \div \frac{1}{2}$

4 Spring Hill Park is on a rectangular piece of land that measures 0.75 mile by 1.25 miles. Determine the area of the park.

5 Determine the surface area of each figure based on the measurements of its net.

ⓐ

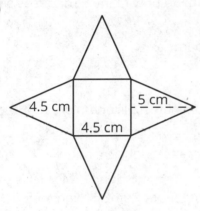

4.5 cm

5 cm

4.5 cm

ⓑ

3.7 cm

4.5 cm

4.5 cm

4.5 cm 3.7 cm

7.3 cm

4.5 cm

6 Estimate each sum or difference to the nearest whole number. Then, calculate each sum or difference.

ⓐ Cristina wants to purchase soccer cleats for $24.99, shin guards for $12.99, soccer socks for $4.49, and a soccer ball for $19.95. How much will the four items cost?

ⓑ Jada and Tonya ran a 400-meter race. Jada ran the race in 75.2 seconds. Tonya ran the race in 69.07 seconds. How much faster did Tonya run the race?

End-of-Topic Review

> Practice concepts you learned in **Ratios.**

7 A sports drink mix calls for 7 scoops for every gallon of water. Describe how you can change either the number of scoops or the amount of water to give the drink a stronger flavor.

8 Of the 75 students at Hillbrook who play a spring sport, 30 run track, 25 play baseball, and 20 play lacrosse. Write the ratios and determine whether a part-to-part or part-to-whole relationship exists.

(a) track runners to baseball players

(b) track runners to total number of athletes

9 Ellen can make 5 dresses with 45 yards of cloth.

(a) If Ellen has 72 yards of cloth, how many dresses can she make?

(b) If Ellen makes a dress for herself, how many yards of cloth does she need?

10 Last week, Cecelia built 7 birdhouses with 2 boards. Determine how many birdhouses she can build for each number of boards.

(a) 6 boards

(b) 10 boards

11 During an online typing test, Morgan typed 144 words in 2 minutes, Elizabeth typed 150 words in 3 minutes, and Ruth typed 65 words in 1 minute.

(a) Create a ratio table to show each girl's typing speed for 1 through 6 minutes.

(b) Plot each set of equivalent ratios on a coordinate plane. Use × to denote Morgan's typing speed, □ to denote Elizabeth's typing speed, and ★ to denote Ruth's typing speed.

(c) Draw three separate lines through the points that represent each ratio. What do you notice?

(d) Who is the fastest typist? Who is the slowest typist? Explain how you can tell by looking at the three lines on your graph.

ACTIVITY 4
MATHia CONNECTION
• Fraction, Decimal, and Percent Conversions

Percents
TOPIC 2 — **LESSON 1**

Getting
Started   Activity   Talk
1   2   3   4   the Talk

Matching Percents, Fractions, and Decimals

HABITS OF MIND
• Attend to precision.

It's time to play The Percentage Match Game. In this game, you will use your knowledge of percents, fractions, and decimals.

❯ Either you or your partner needs to cut out the cards located on page 267.

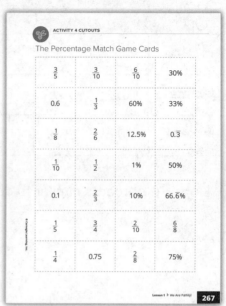

ACTIVITY 4 CUTOUTS

The Percentage Match Game Cards

$\frac{3}{5}$	$\frac{3}{10}$	$\frac{6}{10}$	30%
0.6	$\frac{1}{3}$	60%	33%
$\frac{1}{8}$	$\frac{2}{6}$	12.5%	$0.\overline{3}$
$\frac{1}{10}$	$\frac{1}{2}$	1%	50%
0.1	$\frac{2}{3}$	10%	$66.\overline{6}\%$
$\frac{1}{5}$	$\frac{3}{4}$	$\frac{2}{10}$	$\frac{6}{8}$
$\frac{1}{4}$	0.75	$\frac{2}{8}$	75%

Lesson 1 ❯ We Are Family!   267

Rules of the Game:

• Lay out all the cards facedown.

• The first player chooses any card. That player then turns over another card to see if it is an equivalent match.

   • When the values on the two cards are equivalent, then the player keeps the match and repeats the process.

• When the first player does not have an equivalent match, turn the cards back over.

   • The second player now follows the same process for picking and matching cards.

• Continue taking turns until the players have made all possible matches.

• The player with the most equivalent matches wins the game.

Family Resemblances

You can interchange percents, fractions, and decimals. The chart shows some common equivalent fractions, decimals, and percents.

Common Equivalent Fractions, Decimals, and Percents									
Fraction	$\frac{1}{5}$	$\frac{1}{4}$	$\frac{1}{3}$	$\frac{2}{5}$	$\frac{1}{2}$	$\frac{3}{5}$	$\frac{2}{3}$	$\frac{3}{4}$	$\frac{4}{5}$
Decimal	0.2	0.25	$0.\overline{3}$	0.4	0.5	0.6	$0.\overline{6}$	0.75	0.8
Percent	20%	25%	$33\frac{1}{3}\%$	40%	50%	60%	$66\frac{2}{3}\%$	75%	80%

1 How are percents similar to decimals? How are percents and decimals different?

2 How are percents similar to fractions? How are percents and fractions different?

3 How are percents similar to ratios? How are percents and ratios different?

The Percentage Match Game Cards

$\frac{3}{5}$	$\frac{3}{10}$	$\frac{6}{10}$	30%
0.6	$\frac{1}{3}$	60%	33%
$\frac{1}{8}$	$\frac{2}{6}$	12.5%	$0.\overline{3}$
$\frac{1}{10}$	$\frac{1}{2}$	1%	50%
0.1	$\frac{2}{3}$	10%	$66.\overline{6}\%$
$\frac{1}{5}$	$\frac{3}{4}$	$\frac{2}{10}$	$\frac{6}{8}$
$\frac{1}{4}$	0.75	$\frac{2}{8}$	75%

Why is this page blank?

So you can cut out the cards on the other side.

❯ Use a separate piece of paper for your Journal entry.

JOURNAL

Define *percent* in your own words. Then describe how to write fractions and decimals as percents.

REMEMBER

A percent is a part-to-whole relationship with a whole of 100. To convert a decimal to a percent, multiply the decimal by 100. To convert a percent to a decimal, divide the percent by 100.

PRACTICE

1 Label each mark on the number line with a fraction, decimal, and percent.

	0			1

Fraction	0	$\frac{1}{5}$	____	$\frac{3}{5}$	____	1
Decimal	0.0	____	0.4	____	____	1.0
Percent	0%	____	____	____	80%	100%

2 The table shows the portion of sixth graders at a school who have a particular number of siblings. Complete the table by representing each portion as a part-to-whole ratio, a fraction, a decimal, and a percent.

Number of Siblings	Ratio	Fraction	Decimal	Percent
0		$\frac{3}{20}$		
1		$\frac{1}{5}$		20%
2	3 : 8	$\frac{3}{8}$		
		$\frac{6}{25}$	0.24	
4 or more		$\frac{7}{200}$		

STRETCH Optional

Write each percent as a fraction and as a decimal. Explain your strategy.

1 117%

2 1048%

3 0.15%

4 0.0593%

❯ This Mixed Practice worksheet includes two sections: Spaced Review and End-of-Topic Review. **Use a separate piece of paper to show your work.**

Spaced Review

❯ Practice concepts from previous topics.

1 Bill is painting his room a certain shade of green. The paint is a mixture of 3 parts blue paint to 2 parts yellow paint. To get the correct shade of green, how much yellow paint should he add to 6 quarts of blue paint?

2 LaShaya answered 9 out of 10 questions correctly on her math quiz. Her twin sister LaTeisha answered 22 out of 25 questions correctly on her math test. Did they have the same ratio of correct problems to total problems?

3 Determine each product.

  (a) 0.6×95

  (b) 210×0.75

4 Determine the area of each face of a cube with the given surface area.

  (a) 306.6 square meters

  (b) 450 square inches

5 Use the standard algorithm to determine each quotient.

  (a) $885 \div 6$ (b) $9218 \div 330$

  (c) $8302 \div 28$ (d) $39.13 \div 4.3$

6 The preschool teacher at Kids Unlimited Daycare must split the children's time between playing and learning. For every 30 minutes, the children will spend 18 minutes playing and 12 minutes learning. Complete the table of equivalent ratios.

Total amount of time	30	90		
Playing time	18			144
Learning time	12		48	

7 Consider the right rectangular prism.

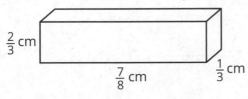

$\frac{2}{3}$ cm $\frac{7}{8}$ cm $\frac{1}{3}$ cm

  (a) Determine the volume of the prism.

  (b) Determine the surface area of the prism.

8 Calculate each quotient or product.

  (a) $\frac{3}{8} \div \frac{4}{5}$ (b) $2\frac{9}{10} \times \frac{2}{5}$

  (c) $\frac{2}{5} \times \frac{7}{3}$ (d) $4\frac{1}{6} \times 3\frac{4}{5}$

  (e) 25×0.31 (f) 7.05×3.72

End-of-Topic Review

AVAILABLE ONLINE
1. A **Topic Summary** reviews the main concepts for the topic.
2. A video of the **Worked Example** is provided.

> Practice concepts you learned in **Percents.**

9 At Union Middle School, 99 girls, or 33% of the girls, play basketball. How many girls attend Union Middle School?

10 Kasey gets a 35% employee discount on anything she buys at The Foot Parade. If Kasey got a $5.25 discount on her new flip-flops, how much did they cost originally?

11 In Tampa, Florida, the sun shines about 66% of the year. About how many days does the sun shine in Tampa?

12 Jai has a 28% free throw rate in basketball. That means when he shoots a free throw he makes a basket 28% of the time. Jai shoots 120 free throws in a season. How many baskets is he likely to make? Use benchmark percents of 1% and 10% to help you determine the answer.

(a) What is 1% of 120?

(b) What is 10% of 120?

(c) What is 20% of 120?

(d) What is 8% of 120?

13 Complete the table. Write each as a fraction, decimal, and percent.

Fraction	Decimal	Percent
		3%
	1.5	
$\frac{13}{20}$		
$\frac{2}{3}$		

TOPIC 1	TOPIC 2
Ratios	Percents

TOPIC 3
Unit Rates and Conversions

1	Many Ways to Measure
2	What Is the Best Buy?
3	Seeing Things Differently

LESSON 1

Many Ways to Measure

Using Ratio Reasoning to Convert Units

KEY TERM

convert

Learning Goals

- Use ratio reasoning with double number lines and ratio tables to convert measurement units.

- Use scaling up or scaling down and unit analysis to convert and transform measurement units appropriately.

REVIEW (1–2 minutes)

> Complete each common measurement conversion.

1 1 foot = _____ inches

2 1 yard = _____ feet

3 1 kilogram = _____ grams

4 1 meter = _____ centimeters

5 1 gallon = _____ quarts

In previous grades, you have worked with the U.S. customary system and the metric system of measurement. In this course, you have also learned about ratios.

How can you use ratio reasoning to convert from one measurement unit to another?

GETTING STARTED

Unit Rates and
Conversions

TOPIC 3   LESSON 1

Getting
Started

Activity
1 2 3 4

Talk
the Talk

Customary to Whom?

You've learned about the relationships between inches and feet, feet and yards, quarts and gallons, meters and millimeters—to name a few.

1 Name a U.S. customary system unit and a metric system unit that is an appropriate size to measure each quantity.

Quantity	U.S. Customary System	Metric System
Your height		
Length of your pencil		
School-to-beach distance		
Weight of your math book		
Amount of water in a bottle		
Amount of water in a pool		

2 Circle the most appropriate measurement for each item.

(a) The weight of a dog

- 15 pounds
- 18 ounces
- 1 ton
- 25 fluid ounces

(b) The amount of gas in a car's tank

- 50 milliliters
- 2 kiloliters
- 55 liters
- 12 kiloliters

(c) The height of your classroom

- 90 inches
- 1 mile
- 2 yards
- 12 feet

(d) The height of a basketball hoop

- 3 meters
- 70 centimeters
- 500 millimeters
- 1 kilometer

DID YOU KNOW?
In the U.S., people use customary units for business, personal, and social purposes. Sciences, including the medical field, use the metric system.

Reasoning About Unit Conversions

HABITS OF MIND
- Reason abstractly and quantitatively.
- Construct viable arguments and critique the reasoning of others.

You can use more than one measurement to describe the same length, weight, or capacity.
For example, you may say that a football field is 100 yards long or 300 feet long.
You could also say that the football field is about 90 meters long. In each case, the lengths are the same—you just say them in different ways.

There are many situations in which you need to *convert* measurements to different units. To **convert** a measurement means to change it to an equivalent measurement in different units.

1 Name a situation in which you need to convert from one measurement to another.

TAKE NOTE...
When you convert a measurement to a different unit, the size of the object does not change; only the units and the number of those units change.

TOPIC 3

Before you start converting units, it is useful to estimate the number of units to expect in a conversion. Here are a few estimates comparing common U.S. customary and metric measures.

- One yard is slightly longer than 1 meter.
- One inch is about 2.5 centimeters.
- One kilometer is a little more than half of a mile.
- One foot is about 30 centimeters.
- One liter is a little more than a quart.
- One kilogram is a little more than 2 pounds.

> Use the estimates given and your knowledge of U.S. customary and metric measures to answer each question.

2 Which measurement has a greater numeric value?

(a) The length of a table in inches or feet

(b) The length of a table in meters or centimeters

(c) The length of a table in meters or yards

(d) The distance from school to your house in miles or kilometers

(e) The weight of your math book in kilograms or pounds

3 How did you decide which value was greater in Question 2?

TAKE NOTE...
Although the numeric values of these measurements are different, the size of each object is the same no matter how you measure it.

4 Estimate each measurement conversion.

(a) The distance to Toronto is 548 km. About how many miles is that?

(b) You order 5 kilograms of food pellets for your guinea pig. About how many pounds are you ordering?

5 Describe the strategies you used to estimate each measurement conversion in Question 4.

Because most conversions compare two quantities using multiplicative strategies, you can write conversion estimates using ratio language. You can also write them symbolically in terms of equality.

Ratio Language	Symbolically
For every inch, there are approximately 2.5 centimeters.	1 in. ≈ 2.5 cm
For every meter, there are approximately 1.1 yards.	1 m ≈ 1.1 yd
For every foot, there are approximately 30 centimeters.	1 ft ≈ 30 cm
For every 12 inches, there is exactly 1 foot.	12 in. = 1 ft
For every 1 kilometer, there are exactly 1000 meters.	1 km = 1000 m

DID YOU KNOW?

The ≈ symbol means approximately equal.

TAKE NOTE...

Because conversions compare two quantities measured in different units, you can also call conversion ratios conversion rates.

When you use a conversion ratio to convert between units of measure, you often write it as an equation: 12 in. = 1 ft.

However, you can also write it as a ratio in fractional form: $\frac{12 \text{ in.}}{1 \text{ ft}}$.

6 Rewrite each common conversion using ratio language and as a ratio in fractional form.

    (a) 3 ft = 1 yd   (b) 5280 ft = 1 mi

    (c) 1 lb ≈ 0.45 kg   (d) 4 qt = 1 gal

    (e) 1 m = 100 cm   (f) $\frac{1}{1000}$ m = 1 mm

TOPIC 3

Using Double Number Lines to Convert Units

When you learned about ratios, you learned how to use double number lines to determine equivalent ratios. You can also use double number lines to convert from one unit to another.

Many rulers are set up as double number lines. You can use this type of ruler to convert between inches and centimeters.

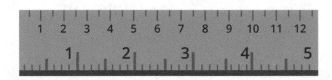

1 Label the scale that represents inches and the one that represents centimeters. **How did you decide?**

ASK YOURSELF...
Can you think of other real-world examples of double number lines?

2 Use the ruler as a double number line to determine each approximate conversion.

(a) 1 cm ≈ _____ in.   (b) 1 in. ≈ _____ cm   (c) 5 cm ≈ _____ in.

You are baking cookies at your friend's house. You cannot find the measuring cups, but you can find the tablespoon.

3 Use the double number line to determine how many tablespoons you need of each ingredient in the recipe.

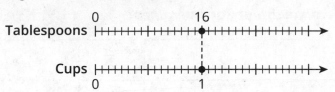

ASK YOURSELF...

How does the double number line represent the conversion rate?

ⓐ 2 cups of sugar

ⓑ $1\frac{3}{4}$ cups of flour

ⓒ $\frac{1}{2}$ cup of raisins

ⓓ Suppose you had found the cup but not the tablespoon. How many cups will you need if the recipe calls for 2 tablespoons of vanilla extract?

You need to measure your room for new carpeting, paint, and a border on the walls. But you have only a meter stick. You need to know the dimensions in feet to purchase the materials. You record these measurements:

- The length of the room is 5 meters.
- The width of the room is 4 meters.
- The height of the room is 2.5 meters.

4 Create a double number line and use it to convert each dimension to feet.

ⓐ length   ⓑ width   ⓒ height

REMEMBER...
1 meter ≈ 3.28 feet

TOPIC 3

ACTIVITY 3

Unit Rates and Conversions

TOPIC 3 — LESSON 1

Getting Started

Activity 1 2 3 4

Talk the Talk

Using Ratio Tables and Scaling to Convert Units

You can use ratio tables, as you did when determining equivalent ratios, as another strategy to convert units.

1 Complete the ratio table by converting between pounds and ounces. **Which strategies did you use to determine the unknown values?**

Pounds	1	2	$\frac{1}{4}$	$1\frac{1}{4}$	$\frac{1}{2}$	$\frac{3}{8}$	$2\frac{1}{2}$
Ounces	16		4			6	40

2 Complete the ratio table by converting between milliliters and liters. **Which strategies did you use to determine the unknown values?**

Milliliters	1000	100		50	1		575
Liters		0.1		0.05	0.001	0.01	

Ratio tables are helpful tools for converting within a given system of measurement. You can set up a proportion using the conversion rate based on the given measurement. Then scale up or down to convert one unit to another.

DID YOU KNOW?

Most conversions that require moving between the U.S. customary and metric systems are approximations. So, in general, you will use conversion rates rounded to the nearest hundredth in your calculations.

You can scale up or down a ratio to convert between units.

WORKED EXAMPLE

You can scale up to determine how many kilograms are in 2.5 pounds. Because you want to determine the number of kilograms for a specific number of pounds, use the conversion rate 1 lb ≈ 0.45 kg or $\frac{1\ lb}{0.45\ kg}$.

$\frac{1\ lb}{0.45\ kg} = \frac{2.5\ lb}{?\ kg}$ ⟶ $\overset{\times 2.5}{\frac{1\ lb}{0.45\ kg} = \frac{2.5\ lb}{1.125\ kg}}\underset{\times 2.5}{}$

TAKE NOTE...

1 oz ≈ 28.35 g
1 g ≈ 0.035 oz
1 lb ≈ 0.45 kg
1 m ≈ 3.28 ft
1 kg ≈ 2.2 lb
1 gal ≈ 3.79 L
1 L ≈ 0.26 gal
1 m ≈ 1.09 yd
1 mi ≈ 1.61 km

---

3 Why does the worked example use the conversion rate $\frac{1\ lb}{0.45\ kg}$ rather than the rate $\frac{2.2\ lb}{1\ kg}$?

❯ Set up a proportion and scale up or down to answer each question.

4 The school cafeteria has eight huge cans of tomato sauce for making pizza. Each can contains 2 gallons of sauce. Is there more or less than 50 L of sauce in these 8 cans?

5 Tyrone, the quarterback for the Tigers Football team, can throw a football 40 meters. Jason, the quarterback for the Spartans, can throw a football 45 yards. Who can throw farther? **How do you know?**

6 Molly says that she is 1.5 meters tall. Shawna is 5 feet tall. Molly says that she is taller, but Shawna disagrees. Who is correct? **Explain your reasoning.**

7 Larry weighs 110 pounds, Casey weighs 98 pounds, Shaun weighs 42 kg, and Jamal weighs 52 kg. Place the boys in order from the least weight to the greatest weight using pounds and kilograms.

8 Karen has a gold bracelet that weighs 24 grams. She wants to sell the bracelet, but she needs a minimum of one ounce of gold to sell it. Can Karen sell her bracelet? **Why or why not?**

MATHia CONNECTION
- Converting Within Systems
- Converting Between Systems

Using Unit Analysis to Convert Units

You can use different methods to convert units of measure. You can set up a proportion and scale up or down to convert one unit to another.

You can also use a method called unit analysis. To use this method you multiply the given measurement by a form of 1 to rewrite it with different units.

WORKED EXAMPLE

If 1 kg ≈ 2.2 lb, determine the quantity in pounds that is equivalent to 4.5 kilograms.

Scaling Up	Unit Analysis

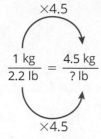

$$\times 4.5$$

$$\frac{1 \text{ kg}}{2.2 \text{ lb}} = \frac{4.5 \text{ kg}}{? \text{ lb}}$$

$$\times 4.5$$

Unit Analysis

$$4.5 \text{ kg} \left(\frac{2.2 \text{ lb}}{1 \text{ kg}} \right)$$

$$\frac{4.5 \cancel{\text{ kg}}}{1} \left(\frac{2.2 \text{ lb}}{1 \cancel{\text{ kg}}} \right) = 9.9 \text{ lb}$$

4.5 kilograms is about 9.9 pounds.

TAKE NOTE...

Notice that in the unit analysis method, the units carry through all calculations. Units divide out in the same way that factors divide out.

$$\cancel{\text{given unit}} \times \frac{\text{desired unit}}{\cancel{\text{given unit}}}$$

$$= \text{desired unit}$$

HABITS OF MIND
- Look for and make use of structure.
- Look for and express regularity in repeated reasoning.

1 Analyze the worked examples.

(a) Both strategies used a form of 1 to determine the equivalent number of pounds in 4.5 kilograms. How is the form of 1 used in scaling up different from the form of 1 used in unit analysis?

(b) Why do you cross out the labels for kilograms in the unit analysis strategy?

TOPIC 3

ACTIVITY 4 Continued

> A marathon is a long-distance foot race with an official distance of 42.195 kilometers (26 miles and 385 yards).

Christopher and Max want to determine the number of miles in 5 kilometers using unit analysis.

Christopher

$5 \text{ km} \left(\dfrac{1.61 \text{ km}}{1 \text{ mi}} \right) \approx 8.05 \text{ mi}$

Max

$5 \text{ km} \left(\dfrac{1 \text{ mi}}{1.61 \text{ km}} \right) \approx 3.11 \text{ mi}$

2 Explain why Christopher's answer is not reasonable.

3 Explain what is different in how Christopher and Max set up their multiplication problem. What is important about how they arranged the units in the conversion rates?

4 There are many other distances in which runners can train to race. Complete the table shown by writing the unknown measurements.

Race	Kilometers	Miles
Short Distance	5	3.1
Medium Distance	10	
Medium Distance	20	
Half Marathon		13.1
Ultramarathon	100	
Ironman Triathlon Swim		2.4
Ironman Triathlon Bike		112

Conversion rates are also common in other contexts, like currency. During one summer, the currency exchange rate between the U.S. dollar and the Brazilian real (pronounced "ray-all") was $1 US for every 3.17 BRL.

5 Alejandra's family went on a trip that summer, and she budgeted $500 to spend while she was gone.

(a) Write the conversion rate:_____ US = _____ BRL

(b) Did Alejandra budget more or less than 500 BRL? **Explain your reasoning.**

(c) How many BRL could she spend in Rio de Janeiro?

(d) After Rio de Janeiro, Alejandra's family traveled to Mexico, where 1 BRL was equal to 5.92 pesos. If Alejandra had 295 BRL remaining, how many pesos did she have?

TOPIC 3

6 Emma is preparing to re-carpet her room. She measured the room to be 6 yards long and 8 yards wide. When she got to the carpet store, all of the measurements were in square feet.

(a) Determine how many square yards of carpet Emma needs to buy to re-carpet her room.

(b) Determine how many square feet of carpet Emma needs to buy to re-carpet her room. **How can you check your answer?**

REMEMBER...

Area is the space inside a two-dimensional figure and you label area measurements in square units.

Larger or Smaller?

❯ Compare the two conversions.

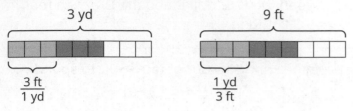

3 yd

$\dfrac{3\ \text{ft}}{1\ \text{yd}}$

9 ft

$\dfrac{1\ \text{yd}}{3\ \text{ft}}$

1 How are they similar? How are they different?

2 When you convert a measurement with smaller units to a measurement with larger units does the number of units increase or decrease?

3 When you convert a measurement with larger units to a measurement with smaller units, does the number of units increase or decrease?

❯ Complete each conversion. **Show your work.**

4 12 gal ≈ _____ L

5 240 oz = _____ lb

6 0.380 km = _____ m

7 324 in. = _____ yd

LESSON 1 ASSIGNMENT

> Use a separate piece of paper for your Journal entry.

REMEMBER

You can use more than one unit to describe the same length, weight, or capacity.

To convert a measurement means to change it to an equivalent measurement in different units. You can use conversion rates to convert units.

PRACTICE

> Use any strategy to convert between the specified units.

1 Janine is travelling to Botswana, where the unit of currency is the pula, which means "rain" in the local language. Suppose $1 is equivalent to 7 pula.

ⓐ If Janine has $500 to spend in Botswana, how many pula does she have to spend?

ⓑ The safari lodge where she stays in Chobe National Park costs 434 pula each night. What is the cost per night in dollars?

ⓒ When she goes to dinner at the safari lodge, the bill comes to 91 pula. How many dollars did Janine spend on dinner?

2 How many feet are in 4 yards?

3 How many gallons are in 14 quarts?

4 Jin Lee volunteers at a zoo and helps weigh a penguin's egg. The egg weighs 0.15 kilogram.

ⓐ Is this more or less than the average weight of 145 grams?
Explain your reasoning.

ⓑ If Jin Lee expands the penguin area to be 500 meters wider than it is now, how many more kilometers wide is the area?

5 Harold wants to buy a new car. Some of the cars he has researched provide measurements in the U.S. customary system, and some provide measurements in the metric system.

(a) One car manufacturer reports the mass of the car to be 3307 lb. About how many kilograms is this?

(b) Another manufacturer recommends that the owner change the oil every 12,075 kilometers. After about how many miles should the owner change the oil?

(c) Harold is a tall man and prefers cars with high ceilings. One car lists 43.3 inches of headroom, and another car lists 99.3 centimeters of headroom. Which car has more headroom?

(d) Harold is shopping for a new car and finds three cars that he likes. Because he commutes a long distance to work, he wants to compare fuel tank capacities.

- The Skyte has a fuel capacity of 19 gallons.
- The Madrid has a fuel capacity of 64.4 liters.
- The Cougar has a fuel capacity of 63.6 quarts.

  Compare the fuel tank capacities of the cars using both gallons and liters. Order the cars from least to greatest fuel tank capacity.

STRETCH ▸ Optional

Anthony measured the dimensions of a rectangular box and got 45 cm by 35 cm by 2 m.

1 Determine the volume of the box in cubic meters.

2 Convert the volume of the box to cubic centimeters.

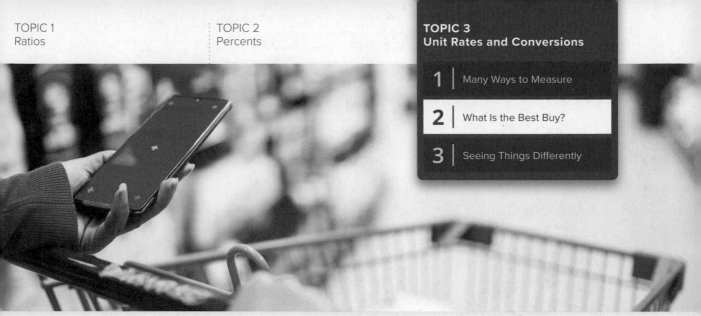

TOPIC 1
Ratios

TOPIC 2
Percents

TOPIC 3
Unit Rates and Conversions

1 | Many Ways to Measure

2 | What Is the Best Buy?

3 | Seeing Things Differently

LESSON 2

What Is the Best Buy?
Introduction to Unit Rates

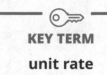

KEY TERM

unit rate

Learning Goals

• Write and calculate unit rates.

• Use unit rates to solve problems involving unit pricing, better buys, and constant speeds.

• Use unit rates and unit rate language to make comparisons.

REVIEW (1–2 minutes)

> Determine the unknown quantity in each proportion.

1 $\dfrac{18 \text{ arrows}}{3 \text{ bows}} = \dfrac{162 \text{ arrows}}{? \text{ bows}}$

2 $\dfrac{18 \text{ arrows}}{3 \text{ bows}} = \dfrac{? \text{ arrows}}{1 \text{ bow}}$

3 $\dfrac{8 \text{ shoes}}{80 \text{ socks}} = \dfrac{? \text{ shoes}}{1600 \text{ socks}}$

4 $\dfrac{8 \text{ shoes}}{80 \text{ socks}} = \dfrac{1 \text{ shoes}}{? \text{ socks}}$

Most of your previous work with ratios involved writing equivalent ratios, but you can also use ratios, specifically unit rates, to answer many different questions.

How can you use unit rates to make comparisons and solve real-world problems?

Which One Would You Buy?

Marta and Brad go to the store to buy some laundry detergent for a neighbor. They see that the brand she wants comes in two different sizes:

26 fl. oz.
$9.75

20.5 fl. oz.
$7.25

1 Which size should Marta and Brad buy? **Explain the reason for your decision.**

ACTIVITY 1

Unit Rates and
Conversions

TOPIC 3   LESSON 2

Getting
Started   1   2   Activity
                   3   4   5   Talk
the Talk

Using Models to Estimate Unit Rates

As you learned previously, a rate is a ratio comparing two quantities measured in different units.

A **unit rate** is a comparison of two measurements in which the numerator or denominator has a value of one unit. One way to compare the values of items is to calculate the unit rate for each item.

Marta and Brad both chose the smaller bottle of detergent as the better buy, but for different reasons.

Marta estimated unit rates for the two detergents this way:

Marta

The larger bottle of detergent is about 25 fluid ounces for about $10.

$$——— $10 ———$$

1 fl oz

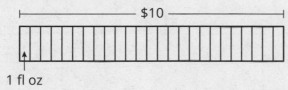

$$\frac{\$10}{25 \text{ fl oz}} = \frac{\$0.40}{1 \text{ fl oz}}$$

So, each fluid ounce costs about $0.40.

The smaller bottle of detergent is about 21 fluid ounces for about $7.

$$——— $7 ———$$

1 fl oz

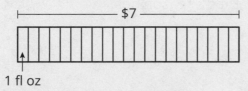

$$\frac{\$7}{21 \text{ fl oz}} = \frac{\$0.33}{1 \text{ fl oz}}$$

So, each fluid ounce costs about $0.33. This means that you pay less for each fluid ounce of the smaller bottle of detergent, so it is the better buy.

HABITS OF MIND

- Model with mathematics.
- Use appropriate tools strategically.

DID YOU KNOW?

You may have encountered unit rates at the grocery store. Unit rates can help you determine which of two or more items is the best buy.

TOPIC 3

Brad

For the larger bottle of detergent, you spend about $10 for about 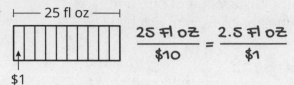 25 fluid ounces.

⊢―― 25 fl oz ――⊣

$$\frac{25 \; fl \; oz}{\$10} = \frac{2.5 \; fl \; oz}{\$1}$$

$1

So, for each dollar you spend on the larger bottle of detergent, you get about 2.5 fluid ounces.

For the smaller bottle of detergent, you spend about $7 for about 21 fluid ounces.

⊢― 21 fl oz ―⊣

$$\frac{21 \; fl \; oz}{\$7} = \frac{3 \; fl \; oz}{\$1}$$

$1

So, for each dollar you spend on the smaller one, you get about 3 fluid ounces.

Because you get more detergent in the smaller bottle for each dollar you spend, the smaller bottle is the better buy.

---

1 Explain the differences in Marta's and Brad's reasonings.

2 Calculate the actual unit rate for each of the two sizes of detergent using two different unit rates.

ACTIVITY 2
MATHia CONNECTION
• Understanding Unit Rates

Unit Rates and Conversions
TOPIC 3 → **LESSON 2**

Getting Started | Activity 1 2 3 4 5 | Talk the Talk

Writing Unit Rates

In this activity, you will write unit rates with either quantity as the unit rate.

> **HABITS OF MIND**
> • Reason abstractly and quantitatively.
> • Construct viable arguments and critique the reasoning of others.

1 Each situation relates a quantity and a price. Calculate the two different unit rates associated with each situation: price per item and number of items per dollar.

(a) A bottle of 250 vitamins costs $12.50.

(b) A pack of 40 AAA batteries costs $25.95.

(c) A package of 24 rolls of toilet paper costs $16.25.

(d) A box of 500 business cards costs $19.95.

2 Not all unit rates involve money. Write two different unit rates associated with each situation.

(a) The 5 goats eat 12 tomatillos.

(b) The exchange rate is 10 U.S. dollars for every 9 euros.

> **TAKE NOTE...**
> A *stalactite* is a formation that hangs from the ceilings of caves.

(c) The average stalactite grows 30 mm every 10 years.

(d) Sandy buys 500 coffee pods every year.

3 For each part of Question 2, identify which unit rates are useful in discussing the situation.

When solving a unit rate problem, the question often asks for which unit rate is needed.

4 For each situation, identify the unit rate that would answer the question. **Explain how you decided which unit rate to write.**

ⓐ How many tomatillos did each goat eat?

ⓑ About how many euros is each U.S. dollar worth?

ⓒ How much does each stalactite grow in a month?

ⓓ How many coffee pods does Sandy use each week?

ACTIVITY 3

Unit Rates and
Conversions

TOPIC 3   LESSON 2

Getting
Started   1   2   **Activity**
3   4   5   Talk
the Talk

Using Unit Rates to Determine the Better Buy

❯ Use the given rates to solve each problem.

1 Compare the prices for various sizes of popcorn sold at the local movie theater.

ⓐ What is the unit rate price per ounce for each bag of popcorn?

Mega Bag (32 oz)	Giant Bag (24 oz)	Medium Bag (16 oz)	Kid's Bag (8 oz)
$10.24	$6.00	$4.48	$2.40

ⓑ Which size popcorn is the best buy? **Explain your reasoning.**

2 Bottles of water are sold at various prices and in various sizes. Write the price of each bottle as a unit rate. Which bottle is the best buy? **Explain how you know.**

Bottle 1	**Bottle 2**	**Bottle 3**	**Bottle 4**
$0.39 per 12 oz	$0.57 per 24.3 oz	$0.70 per 33.8 oz	$1.39 per 128 oz

3 Use unit rates to determine which is the better buy. **Explain your reasoning.**

ⓐ 22 vitamins for $1.97 or 40 vitamins for $3.25

ⓑ 24.3 ounces for $8.76 or 32.6 ounces for $16.95

TOPIC 3

ACTIVITY 4

Unit Rates and
Conversions

TOPIC 3   LESSON 2

Getting
Started   1   2   Activity
3   4   5

Talk
the Talk

Using Unit Rates to Make Comparisons

HABITS OF MIND
• Attend to precision.

> The local paper published these rates on gas mileage for a few new cars.
>
> Avalar can travel 480 miles on 10 gallons of gas.
>
> Sentar can travel 400 miles on 8 gallons of gas.
>
> Comstar can travel 360 miles on 9 gallons of gas.

1 Change each rate to a unit rate so that it reports miles per one gallon of gas.

    ⓐ Avalar   ⓑ Sentar   ⓒ Comstar

2 How did you calculate each unit rate?

ASK YOURSELF...
So, which car is better? Do you want the car with the lowest unit rate, like with the popcorn bags?

3 How can unit rates help you to compare these cars?

TAKE NOTE...
Make a prediction before you begin calculating, and then use ratio reasoning to answer each question.

❯ Solve each problem.

4 Guests at a dinner play sit at three tables. Each table receives large, round loaves of bread instead of individual rolls. Each person at the table shares the loaves equally.

• Table 1 has six guests and is served two loaves of bread.

• Table 2 has eight guests and is served three loaves of bread.

• Table 3 has 10 guests and is served four loaves of bread.

    ⓐ Predict at which table the guests will get the largest serving of bread.

ⓑ Determine how much bread each guest at each table will receive. Was your prediction accurate?

5 Kalida can run 3 laps in 9 minutes. Sonya can run 2 laps in 7 minutes. Who is the faster runner?

6 Peter and Kyu are making mini-cakes for the school bake sale. Peter makes 5 mini-cakes every 25 minutes. Kyu makes 3 mini-cakes every 10 minutes. If they both continue to make mini-cakes at the same rate for the same amount of time, which boy will make more cakes?

TOPIC 3

7 On Monday, the school cafeteria sold 4 chocolate milks for every 10 white milks. On Tuesday, the cafeteria sold 1 chocolate milk for every 3 white milks. On which day did the cafeteria sell more chocolate milks per number of white milks sold?

8 A tour bus drove 120 miles in 2 hours, and a school bus drove 180 miles in 3 hours. Which bus drove faster?

ACTIVITY 5

MATHia CONNECTION
• Determining and Comparing Unit Rates

Unit Rates and Conversions

TOPIC 3   LESSON 2

Getting Started   Activity   Talk the Talk
1   2   3   4   5

Problem Solving with Unit Rates

In this activity, you will use unit rates to solve problems involving constant speeds and constant pricing.

HABITS OF MIND
• Reason abstractly and quantitatively.
• Construct viable arguments and critique the reasoning of others.

1 In the spring, the gym teachers at Stewart Middle School sponsor a bike-a-thon to raise money for new sporting equipment. Students seek sponsors to pledge a dollar amount for each mile they ride.

(a) Nico can ride 12.5 miles per hour. At this rate, how far will he ride in 5 hours?

(b) If Leticia rides 56.25 miles in 5 hours, how far will she ride in 7 hours?

(c) Emil got a cramp in his leg after riding 27.5 miles in 2 hours and had to stop. If he hadn't gotten the cramp and had continued to ride at the same rate, how far would he have ridden in 3 hours?

2 Beth, Kelly, and Amy are all training for the local marathon.

(a) Beth can run 6.5 miles per hour. At this rate, how far will she run in the first 3 hours of the marathon?

(b) Kelly runs 13.5 miles in 2 hours. What is her rate?

(c) Amy wants to run the 26.2 miles of the marathon in 4.5 hours. At what rate will she have to run to reach this goal?

(d) At a workout designed to increase speed, Beth runs 800 meters in $2\frac{1}{2}$ minutes. Kelly runs 1600 meters in $4\frac{1}{2}$ minutes. Who ran faster in this workout?

3 Maya left her notebook on the bus, and her friend Ariana picked it up for her. On Saturday, they decide to meet to exchange the notebook. They live 7.5 miles from each other and plan to walk and meet between their homes. Ariana can walk 3 miles per hour; Maya can walk 4.5 miles per hour. Maya makes the suggestion, "It will take the same amount of time if you stay put, and I run 7.5 miles per hour." Is Maya's suggestion correct? **Explain your reasoning.**

4 Complete each table.

(a) A carpet store sells carpet by the square yard. Classroom carpet sells for $10.50 per square yard.

1 yd²	40 yd²	50 yd²	100 yd²
$10.50			

(b) A grocery store sells Pink Lady apples by the pound. One pound of Pink Lady apples costs $2.99.

1 lb	2 lb	5 lb	10 lb	20 lb
$2.99				

5 How did you use a unit rate to complete each table in Question 4?

TALK THE TALK

Unit Rates and
Conversions
TOPIC 3 — **LESSON 2**

Getting
Started   Activity   Talk
the Talk
1   2   3   4   5

Shopping for Cereal

Tim and Dan love cereal, but don't want to spend a lot of money. After scanning the aisle in the grocery store for the lowest prices, the boys make the following statements.

• Tim says, "I found Sweetie Oat Puffs for $0.14 per ounce. That's the cheapest cereal in the aisle!"

• Dan replies, "It's not cheaper than Sugar Hoops! The unit price for that is 6.25 oz per dollar."

Who is correct? **Explain your reasoning.**

JOURNAL

Define the term *unit rate* in your own words.

REMEMBER

When you compare unit rates, write each rate using the same units. You can use the situation to decide whether you need the larger or smaller unit rate.

PRACTICE

1 Write a unit rate for each situation.

(a) 254 words typed in 4 minutes

(b) 5 trays with 90 ice cubes

(c) 4 hot dogs eaten in 45 seconds

(d) 8 hours to drive 528 miles

(e) 10 gallons filled in 4 minutes

(f) 60 pounds of cat food in 5 bags

2 Shawna needs to buy apples to bake pies for the fair. She needs 13 pounds of apples. At one market, Shawna finds apples selling for $1.89 a pound. At another market she finds a 15-pound bag of apples for $26.99. Which market has the better deal?

3 Dylan needs to buy new contact lenses. His ophthalmologist sells 8-lens boxes in packs of 2 for $52 and 10-lens boxes in packs of 4 for $120. Which option is the better deal?

4 Pets R Us claims in their advertisement that they have the best price in town for ChowChow dog food. They sell 20-pound bags for $16.95. Stuff4Pets also claims to have the best price in town for ChowChow dog food. They are selling 30-pound bags for $24.95. Which store has a valid claim?

5 During his last race, Bryce biked 43 kilometers in 2 hours. If he maintains that same speed, how far will he travel in 3 hours?

6 Complete each table.

(a) A garden store sells topsoil by the cubic yard. The cost for 5 cubic yards of topsoil is $160.

1 yd³	5 yd³	10 yd³	18 yd³
	$160		

(b) A farmer's market sells walnuts by the pound. Three pounds of walnuts costs $14.85.

1 lb	2 lb	3 lb	10 lb	15 lb
		$14.85		

(c) Matt drives at a constant rate. He drove 390 miles in 6 hours.

1 hr	2 hr	5 hr	6 hr	9 hr
			390 miles	

STRETCH Optional

Describe how sales tax is a rate. Determine the sales tax for your state or a nearby state and calculate the costs of different items after applying the sales tax.

TOPIC 1
Ratios

TOPIC 2
Percents

TOPIC 3
Unit Rates and Conversions

| 1 | Many Ways to Measure |

| 2 | What Is the Best Buy? |

| **3** | Seeing Things Differently |

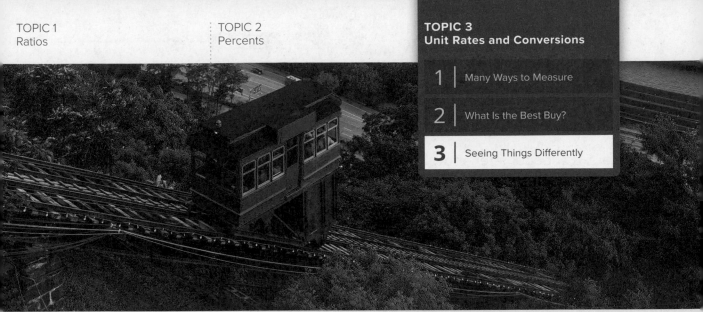

LESSON 3

Seeing Things Differently

Multiple Representations of Unit Rates

LEARNING GOALS

- Represent and identify unit rates using tables and graphs.
- Recognize that $(x, 1)$ and $(1, y)$ are both points on the graph of a unit rate.
- Graph unit rates in real-world situations involving unit pricing and constant speed.
- Compare unit rates based on their graphs.

REVIEW (1–2 minutes)

> Determine whether each graph represents equivalent ratios.
> **Explain your reasoning.**

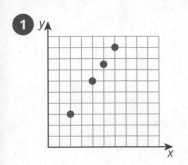

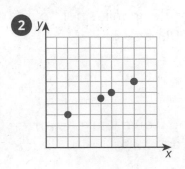

You know about special ratios called rates and have used unit rates to convert measurements, determine the better buy, and solve problems about constant speeds.

How can you identify a unit rate from a graph?

The Need...for Speed

In cars, a speedometer shows the driver the rate at which the car is moving—its speed. Many speedometers are like double number lines arranged in a circular shape. The numbers on the outside of the speedometer show the rate in miles per hour (mph), and the numbers on the inside show the rate in kilometers per hour (km/h).

❯ Use the speedometer to estimate each rate.

1 At about what rate, in kilometers per hour, is the car moving if it is traveling at 60 miles per hour?

2 At about what rate, in miles per hour, is the car moving if it is traveling at 60 kilometers per hour?

3 About how long would it take to drive 90 kilometers at 55 miles per hour? **Explain your reasoning.**

ACTIVITY 1

Unit Rates and Conversions

TOPIC 3 — LESSON 3

Getting Started

Activity 1 2 3

Talk the Talk

Graphing Rates

The Duquesne Incline opened in 1887 to move coal workers from their homes atop Mt. Washington down to the coal factories along the river in Pittsburgh, Pennsylvania. The Duquesne Incline still transports commuters who live in the area.

Jasmine takes the incline to work each morning. The incline is 800 feet long, and it takes 90 seconds to ride from the top of Mt. Washington to the bottom.

HABITS OF MIND
- Model with mathematics.
- Use appropriate tools strategically.

An incline is like a trolley that goes up and down a mountain.

TOPIC 3

1 Identify the true statements. **Explain your reasoning for each.**

(a) Jasmine travels approximately 178 feet every 20 seconds.

(b) She travels approximately 600 feet per minute.

(c) In 75 seconds, Jasmine travels approximately 750 feet.

(d) She travels approximately 44 feet every 5 seconds.

(e) She travels about 8.9 feet per second.

2 Plot the correct ratios from Question 1 on the coordinate plane. **How can you use the graph to verify correct and incorrect statements from Question 1?**

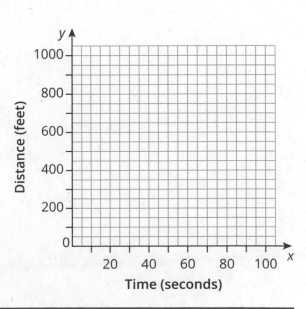

Unit Rates and Dimensions

A rhombus is considered a Golden Rhombus when the diagonals are in a particular ratio, known as φ or phi (pronounced "fi" or "fee"). Your task is to determine the ratio of the diagonals of the Golden Rhombus shown.

A Golden Rhombus

TAKE NOTE...
A diagonal is a line segment that connects opposite vertices of a polygon.

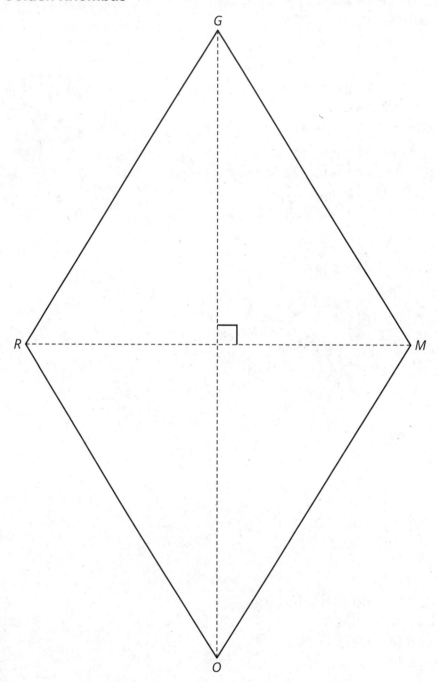

1 Use standard and non-standard tools to measure the lengths of the diagonals using 6 different units of measure and record them in the table. Be sure to include inches and centimeters as two of your units.

THINK ABOUT...

Look around your classroom to identify tools besides a ruler that you can use to measure the lengths of the diagonals.

Unit of Measure	Length of Diagonal $\overline{GO}$	Length of Diagonal $\overline{RM}$

2 Graph the lengths of the diagonals on the coordinate plane. **Then use a straightedge to connect your points.**

3 Describe the pattern in the graph. **What does this pattern tell you about the ratios?**

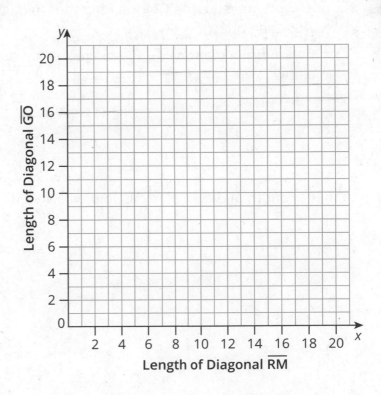

Length of Diagonal $\overline{RM}$

TOPIC 3

4 Write two unit rates that relate the length of diagonal $\overline{GO}$ and the length of diagonal $\overline{RM}$.

5 Describe where you can locate the unit rates on the graph.

6 Suppose you measure the Golden Rhombus in units called "ujeni." Use the unit rates to answer each question.

ⓐ If the length of diagonal $\overline{GO}$ is 15 ujeni, what is the length of diagonal $\overline{RM}$ in ujeni?

ⓑ If the length of diagonal $\overline{RM}$ is 15 ujeni, what is the length of diagonal $\overline{GO}$ in ujeni?

ACTIVITY 3

Unit Rates and Conversions

TOPIC 3 **LESSON 3**

Getting Started

Activity 1 2 3

Talk the Talk

Unit Rates in Tables and Graphs

HABITS OF MIND
• Reason abstractly and quantitatively.
• Construct viable arguments and critique the reasoning of others.

The 6th-grade chorus made and sold their own mixture of trail mix at soccer games to raise money for an upcoming trip. During the first soccer game, they sold 1-lb bags for $2.80. They got many requests to sell different-sized bags of their trail mix. The group decided to vary the size of the bags, but wanted to make sure that the cost-to-pounds rate stayed the same.

1 Complete the table to display the cost for various quantities of trail mix. Create a graph from your table of values.

Trail Mix Weight (lb)	Cost ($)
0.25	
0.5	
0.75	
1	
1.25	
1.5	

2 Identify two points on the graph that represent unit rates. Write each unit rate in words and explain its meaning.

3 Explain how your graph displays equivalent rates.

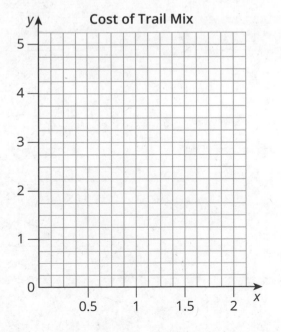

Cost of Trail Mix

TALK THE TALK

Unit Rates and
Conversions

TOPIC 3   **LESSON 3**

Getting
Started

Activity
1   2   3

Talk
the Talk

Once Upon a Unit Rate

> Write a story with unit rates that corresponds to this graph. Include three questions that someone else can answer using the graph. **Be prepared to share your story with the rest of your class.**

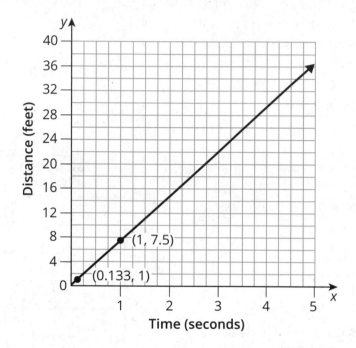

LESSON 3 ASSIGNMENT

❯ Use a separate piece of paper for your Journal entry.

PRACTICE

1. At ShopRight, Alycia spent $7.15 for $5\frac{1}{2}$ pounds of potatoes. Graph the relationship to help you answer each question.

   a. How much does 1 pound of potatoes cost?

   b. How many pounds of potatoes can you get for $1?

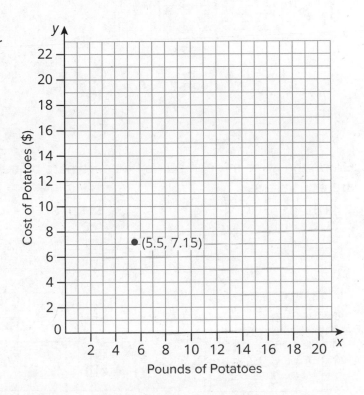

   c. About how much does 17 pounds of potatoes cost?

   d. How many pounds of potatoes can you get for $13?

❯ Determine the unit rate from each graph.

2

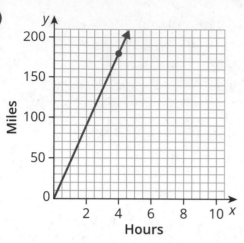

3

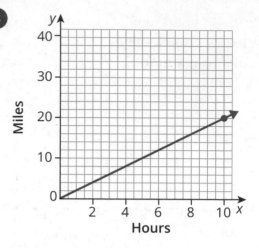

❯ Graph the rates in each pair on a coordinate plane. Explain whether or not the rates are equivalent.

4 $\dfrac{48 \text{ oz}}{3 \text{ lb}}, \dfrac{64 \text{ oz}}{4 \text{ lb}}$

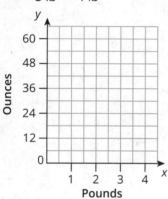

5 $\dfrac{\$4.50}{3}, \dfrac{\$7.50}{6}$

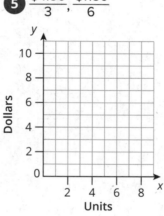

6 $\dfrac{150 \text{ mi}}{2.5 \text{ hr}}, \dfrac{525 \text{ mi}}{8.75 \text{ hr}}$

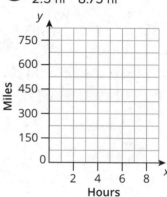

STRETCH Optional

Acceleration is a rate that compares speed with time. Gravity, for example, is acceleration at 9.8 meters per second per second, or $\dfrac{\frac{9.8m}{1s}}{1s}$. When an object is in free fall, its speed at any moment is caused by the acceleration due to gravity. How fast, in miles per hour, is a body in free fall moving after 4 seconds?

MIXED PRACTICE

❯ This Mixed Practice worksheet includes two sections: Spaced Review and End-of-Topic Review. **Use a separate piece of paper to show your work.**

Spaced Review

❯ Practice concepts from previous topics.

1 Estimate each quotient to the nearest whole number. Then calculate the quotient.

ⓐ 0.796 ÷ 9.95

ⓑ 23.84 ÷ 6.4

2 Estimate each sum to the nearest whole number. Then determine each sum.

ⓐ 4.0842 + 13.87 + 6.371

ⓑ 12.89 + 7.45 + 3.005

3 Use benchmark percents to calculate each value. Show your work.

ⓐ 7% of 26

ⓑ 28% of 90

ⓒ 35% of 142

ⓓ 22% of 864

4 For every 5 pages Morgan attempts to print, her printer messes up 3 of them. Create a ratio table to display the number of pages her printer would mess up. Then create a graph for your table of values. Be sure to label the axes and title the graph.

5 Mr. Hawkins wants to make sure that his sports goods store is stocked with enough equipment. He surveys 240 of his customers and asks them to choose the one sport that they're most likely to buy sports equipment for this season.

ⓐ How many of the surveyed customers will need baseball equipment?

ⓑ How many of the surveyed customers will need wrestling equipment?

Sport	Percent of Responses
Basketball	30%
Baseball	20%
Football	35%
Wrestling	15%

6 At Union Middle School, 99 boys, or 36% of the boys, play basketball. How many boys attend Union Middle School? Show your work.

7 The graph shows the costs of orders of stockings from an online store.

ⓐ Write each point on the graph as a ratio of number of pairs of stockings : total cost of the order.

ⓑ How much would an order of 8 pairs of stockings cost? Explain the method you used.

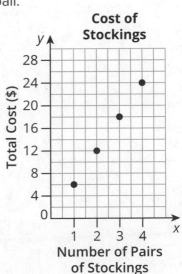

Cost of Stockings

End-of-Topic Review

AVAILABLE ONLINE
1. A **Topic Summary** reviews the main concepts for the topic.
2. A video of the **Worked Example** is provided.

> Practice concepts you learned in **Unit Rates and Conversions**.

8 A banquet hall is preparing for a wedding with 312 guests. If one table will seat 8 guests, how many tables will be needed for the wedding?

9 Determine each conversion.

(a) 24 in. = _____ cm

(b) 6 qt = _____ c

(c) 18 ft = _____ m

(d) 5 mi = _____ km

(e) 2.5 m = _____ in.

10 Determine which is the better buy.

(a) $34.95 for 5 pounds or $46.00 for 8 pounds

(b) $24.50 for 3 notebooks or 5 notebooks for $42.50

11 Determine which represents the better gas mileage.

(a) Car A: 325 miles on 13 gallons
Car B: 420 miles on 19 gallons

(b) Van A: 278 miles on 18 gallons
Van B: 158 miles on 11 gallons

12 Lynn is traveling in Mexico. She exchanges $200 for pesos. If the exchange rate is 19.29 pesos per US dollar, how many pesos should she expect to receive from the exchange?

13 Graph each rate in the given pair on a coordinate plane. Explain whether or not the rates are equivalent.

(a) $\dfrac{15 \text{ cups flour}}{8.5 \text{ cups sugar}}, \dfrac{5 \text{ cups flour}}{2.75 \text{ cups sugar}}$

(b) $\dfrac{245 \text{ mi}}{3.5 \text{ h}}, \dfrac{150 \text{ mi}}{2 \text{ h}}$

Determining Unknown Quantities

MATHia

Evaluating Numeric Expressions
- Writing and Evaluating Exponent
  Expressions
- Order of Operations
- Applying the Order of Operations
- Using Order of Operations to Evaluate
  Numeric Expressions

**Introduction to Algebraic
Expressions**
- Writing Expressions from Verbal
  Descriptions
- Patterns and One-Step Expressions
- Identifying Parts of Simple Algebraic
  Expressions
- Evaluating Algebraic Expressions

Equivalent Algebraic Expressions
- Modeling Equivalent Algebraic
  Expressions
- Exploring the Distributive Property with
  Algebraic Expressions
- Using Order of Operations to Rewrite
  Algebraic Expressions

**Using Algebraic Expressions to
Analyze and Solve Problems**
- Using Picture Algebra

**Reasoning with Algebraic
Expressions**
- Using Substitution to Identify Solutions
  to Equations

**Solving One-Step Addition and
Subtraction Equations**
- Exploring One-Step Equations with
  Double Number Lines
- Using Double Number Lines to Solve
  One-Step Addition Equations
- Solving with Addition and Subtraction)

**Solving One-Step Multiplication and
Division Equations**
- Using Double Number Lines to Solve
  One-Step Multiplication Equations
- Solving with Multiplication and Division
- Solving One-Step Equations

**Solving One-Step Equations with
Decimals and Fractions**
- Solving One-Step Equations with
  Decimals
- Solving One-Step Equations with
  Fractions

Solutions to Inequalities
- Using Substitution to Identify Solutions
  to Inequalities
- Graphing Inequalities with Positive
  Rational Numbers
- Writing Inequalities from Real-World
  Situations

**Independent and Dependent
Variables**
- Modeling Scenarios with Equations
- Analyzing Models of One-Step Linear
  Relationships

Using Graphs to Solve Problems
- Graphs of Additive and Multiplicative
  Relationships
- Comparing Additive and Multiplicative
  Relationships

**Multiple Representations of
Equations**
- Patterns and One-Step Equations
- Problem Solving Using Multiple
  Representations in the First Quadrant
- Problem Solving with Decimals

Getting Ready for Module 3
Determining Unknown Quantities

You will expand your work with numeric expressions to explore variables and algebraic expressions. You will continue to build your understanding of equivalence as you work with equations. By investigating equations and graphs, you will develop strategies to make sense of and reason about unknown quantities in real-world and mathematical problems.

The lessons in this module build on your prior experiences with patterns, inequalities, and fraction addition and subtraction.

Review these key terms and fraction addition to get ready to determine unknown quantities.

KEY TERMS

numeric pattern

A numeric pattern is a sequence, or ordered set, of numbers that is created by following a given rule.

Rule: Multiply by 2

Input	1	2	3	4
Output	2	4	6	8

inequality

An inequality is a comparison of two values that shows that one value is greater than (>), less than (<), or not equal to (≠) the second value.

Symbol	Meaning
0.3 > 0.28	0.3 is greater than 0.28
$\frac{3}{8} < \frac{3}{4}$	$\frac{3}{8}$ is less than $\frac{3}{4}$
7 ≠ 11	7 is not equal to 11

MATHia

Brush up on your skills.
If you need more practice with these skills, ask your teacher for access to corresponding workspaces in MATHia.

SKILLS YOU WILL NEED

Adding and Subtracting Fractions

When you add or subtract fractions with unlike denominators, you must first rewrite them as equivalent fractions.

What is $\frac{2}{5} + \frac{3}{10}$?

The least common denominator is 10.

$$\frac{2 \cdot 2}{2 \cdot 5} \qquad + \qquad \frac{3}{10}$$

$$\frac{4}{10} \qquad + \qquad \frac{3}{10}$$

This means that $\frac{2}{5} + \frac{3}{10} = \frac{7}{10}$.

When you subtract fractions, you follow the same steps, but subtract the numerators.

> **REVIEW**

> Calculate each sum or difference.

1 $\frac{8}{13} + \frac{3}{13}$

2 $\frac{2}{3} + \frac{1}{9}$

3 $\frac{17}{27} - \frac{8}{27}$

4 $\frac{3}{5} - \frac{1}{4}$

See the Appendix on page 719 for answers.

LESSON 1

Relationships Matter

Evaluating Numeric Expressions

Learning Goals

- Interpret a number raised to a positive integer power as a repeated product.

- Identify perfect square numbers and perfect cube numbers.

- Write and evaluate numeric expressions involving whole-number exponents.

- Model numeric expressions with two- and three-dimensional figures.

- Evaluate numeric expressions using the Order of Operations.

KEY TERMS

perfect square

evaluate a numeric expression

perfect cube

Order of Operations

REVIEW (1–2 minutes)

> Write each power of ten as a product of factors. Then calculate the product.

1 10^2

2 10^5

3 10^3

4 10^4

You have written and evaluated expressions using the four operations and the Commutative, Associative, and Distributive Properties.

Is there a conventional order for performing these operations and applying these properties?

GETTING STARTED

Expressions

TOPIC 1 — LESSON 1

Getting Started

Activity 1 2 3

Talk the Talk

A Powerful Expression

Recall that an expression in mathematics is a number or a combination of numbers and operations. You have written expressions equivalent to the area of a rectangle, length × width, and also the volume of a rectangular prism, length × width × height.

❯ Consider the area of a square and the volume of a cube.

Area of a square	**Volume of a cube**
Because all sides of a square have the same length and width, you can write the formula for the area of a square, A, as $A = s \times s$, or $A = s^2$.	Because all sides of a cube have the same length, width, and height, you can write the formula for the volume of a cube, V, as $V = s \times s \times s$, or $V = s^3$.

1 Write the area of each square as a repeated product, as a square number, and as an area in square units.

ⓐ side length = 2 in.

ⓑ side length = $\frac{1}{2}$ ft

ⓒ side length = 1.2 cm

2 Write the volume of each cube as a repeated product, as the cube of a number, and as a volume in cubic units.

ⓐ side length = 2 in.

ⓑ side length = 2 ft

ⓒ side length = $\frac{1}{3}$ cm

ACTIVITY 1
MATHia CONNECTION
• Writing and Evaluating Exponential Numeric Expressions

Expressions
TOPIC 1 — **LESSON 1**

Getting Started | Activity 1 2 3 | Talk the Talk

Writing Equivalent Expressions

Some of the areas that you wrote in the Getting Started are called **perfect squares** because you can express them as the product of two equal whole numbers.

For example, 9 is a perfect square because $3 \times 3 = 9$. Another way you can write this mathematical sentence is $3^2 = 9$.

You can use an area model to determine perfect squares.

Daniel drew on the diagram to show that the expression $(4 + 4)^2$ is equivalent to 8^2.

HABITS OF MIND
• Look for and make use of structure.
• Look for and express regularity in repeated reasoning.

TAKE NOTE...
You can read 3^2 as "3 squared."

THINK ABOUT...
How can you use the grid to determine the square of any number from 1 to 15?

$1^2 = 1$ $2^2 = 4$ $3^2 = 9$ $4^2 = 16$ $5^2 = 25$ $6^2 = 36$ $7^2 = 49$ $8^2 = 64$ $9^2 = 81$ $10^2 = 100$ $11^2 = 121$ $12^2 = 144$ $13^2 = 169$ $14^2 = 196$ $15^2 = 225$

1. Explain why $(4 + 4)^2$ is equivalent to 8^2 and not equivalent to $4^2 + 4^2$. Then use the diagram to write other expressions that are equivalent to 8^2.

TOPIC 1

2 Write two more equivalent numeric expressions for each perfect square.

    ⓐ 6^2 ⓑ 12^2

To **evaluate a numeric expression** means to rewrite the expression as a single numeric value.

3 Use the diagram to rewrite the expression $(7 - 3)^2 + (10 - 7)^2$ with fewer terms. **Explain your work.**

> **TAKE NOTE…**
> You can use parentheses to group numbers and operations. You can think about expressions inside parentheses as a single value.

A **perfect cube** is any number you can express as the product of three equal whole numbers. For example, 216 is a perfect cube because $6 \times 6 \times 6 = 216$, or $6^3 = 216$.

> **TAKE NOTE…**
> You can read 6^3 as "6 cubed."

The table shows the cubes of the first 10 whole numbers.

$1^3 = 1$	$2^3 = 8$	$3^3 = 27$	$4^3 = 64$	$5^3 = 125$
$6^3 = 216$	$7^3 = 343$	$8^3 = 512$	$9^3 = 729$	$10^3 = 1000$

4 Write two more equivalent numeric expressions for each perfect cube.

   (a) 5^3 (b) 2^3

Remember that, in general, you can represent repeated multiplication as a power.

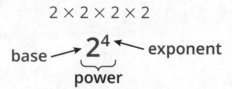

$$2 \times 2 \times 2 \times 2$$

The base of a power is the factor multiplied by itself repeatedly, and the exponent of the power is the number of times you use the base as a factor.

> **REMEMBER...**
> You can read a power in different ways: "2 to the fourth power" and "2 raised to the fourth power."

5 Identify the base and exponent in each power. Then, write each power in words.

   (a) 7^5 (b) 4^8

ACTIVITY 2

Expressions
TOPIC 1   LESSON 1

Getting
Started

Activity
1   2   3

Talk
the Talk

Modeling and Evaluating Expressions

The Expression Cards on page 355 contain a variety of numeric expressions and models that represent numeric expressions.

> Cut out the Expression Cards.

1 Consider the different structures of the expressions and the models.

(a) Sort the models in a mathematically meaningful way.

(b) Sort the expressions in a mathematically meaningful way.

(c) Explain how you sorted the Expression Cards.

HABITS OF MIND
- Model with mathematics.
- Use appropriate tools strategically.

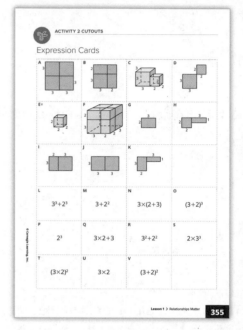

2 Match the numeric expressions with the models. **Select two pairs of cards and explain why each expression matches the model.**

Now it's your turn!

3 Think of a numeric expression involving squares or cubes, or both. Draw a model to represent that expression. Trade your model with a classmate and write the numeric expression that represents their model. When you both have written your answers, trade back and check your work!

❯ Consider the numeric expression $2 \cdot 3^2$.

Shae

I matched the expression $2 \cdot 3^2$ to
this model.

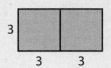

4 Explain how Shae's model represents the expression. Then evaluate the expression.

5 Doug and Miguel each evaluated the expression differently.

Miguel

$2 \cdot 3^2$

$3^2 = 9$

$2 \cdot 9 = 18$

Doug

$2 \cdot 3^2$

$2 \cdot 3 = 6$

$6^2 = 36$

ⓐ What does Miguel's solution tell you about how to evaluate a numeric expression
with both multiplication and exponents?

ⓑ What expression did Doug evaluate? Which model represents your expression?

6 Evaluate each expression on the cards you cut out. **Use the diagrams you matched
to the expression to verify your answer.**

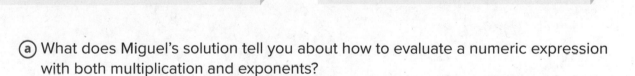

ACTIVITY 3
MATHia CONNECTION
- Order of Operations
- Applying the Order of Operations
- Using the Order of Operations to Evaluate Numeric Expressions

Expressions
TOPIC 1 — LESSON 1

Getting Started | Activity 1 2 3 | Talk the Talk

The Order of Operations

There is an *Order of Operations*, an order in which you perform operations when evaluating any numeric expression. The **Order of Operations** is a set of rules that ensures the same result every time anyone evaluates an expression.

Order of Operations Rules

1. Evaluate expressions inside parentheses or grouping symbols.

2. Evaluate exponents.

3. Multiply and divide from left to right.

4. Add and subtract from left to right.

Keep in mind that multiplication and division are of equal importance and evaluated in order from left to right. The same is true for addition and subtraction.

A mnemonic may help you remember the order. The important thing is to understand why the Order of Operations works.

> **HABITS OF MIND**
> - Attend to precision.

> **DID YOU KNOW?**
> A mnemonic is a technique that relies on key words and rhyming to remember important information.

> Consider Aimi's and Fatima's mnemonics.

Aimi
I can use "Please Excuse My Dear Aunt Sally" to remember Parentheses, Exponents, Multiplication and Division, and Addition and Subtraction.

Fatima
I like "Pink Elephants Must Dance Around Snakes" better to remember the correct Order of Operations.

❯ Evaluate each expression using the Order of Operations.

1 $28 \div 2^2 - 36 \div 3^2$

2 $12 + (25 \div 5)^2$

3 $(6^2 - 10) \times 2$

4 $168 \div 2^3 + 3^3 - 20$

5 $10 \div (5 - 3) + 2^3$

6 $3^3 - 5 \times 3 + 7$

7 $15 + 4 \times 5^2$

8 $(10 - 6) \times (7 + 3)^3$

9 $54 \div 6 + 2(8 - 3 \times 2)$

10 $(2^3 + 1)^2 - 30$

TOPIC 1

Smooth Operator

❯ Determine whether or not each expression was evaluated correctly. Show the correct work for any incorrect answers.

1 $18 \div 2 \cdot 3^2$

$18 \div 2 \cdot 9$
$18 \div 18$
1

2 $(15 + 10 \div 5) + 8$

$(15 + 2) + 8$
$17 + 8$
25

3 $60 - (10 - 6 + 1)^2 \cdot 2$

$60 - (10 - 7)^2 \cdot 2$
$60 - (3)^2 \cdot 2$
$60 - 9 \cdot 2$
$60 - 18$
42

4 $2(10 - 1) - 3 \cdot 2$

$2(9) - 3 \cdot 2$
$18 - 3 \cdot 2$
$15 \cdot 2$
30

5 Draw a model to verify that $(2 + 3)^2 \neq 2^2 + 3^2$.

Expression Cards

A

3
3
3   3

B
2
3
3   2

C
3
3
3
2
3   2   2

D
2
2
3
3

E
2
2   2

F
2
3
3   2   2   3

G
3
2

H
3
1
2
2

I
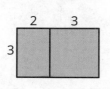
2   3
3
3   3

J
3
3   3

K
3
1
3
2

L

$3^3 + 2^3$

M

$3 + 2^2$

N

$3 \times (2 + 3)$

O

$(3 + 2)^3$

P

2^3

Q

$3 \times 2 + 3$

R

$3^2 + 2^2$

S

2×3^3

T

$(3 \times 2)^2$

U

3×2

V

$(3 + 2)^2$

Why is this page blank?

So you can cut out the cards on the other side.

LESSON 1 ASSIGNMENT

> Use a separate piece of paper for your Journal entry.

JOURNAL

Write your own mnemonic for the Order of Operations.

REMEMBER

You can evaluate numeric expressions using the Order of Operations.
1. Evaluate expressions inside parentheses or grouping symbols.
2. Evaluate exponents.
3. Multiply and divide from left to right.
4. Add and subtract from left to right.

PRACTICE

1 Draw a model to represent each numeric expression. Then evaluate the expression.

(a) $2 \cdot 5^2$

(b) $(4 + 6)^2$

(c) $5^2 + 7^2$

2 Use the Order of Operations to evaluate each numeric expression.

   (a) $4^2 \cdot 3$

   (b) $3^3 - 14 \div 2 + 5$

   (c) $17 - 2^3$

   (d) $144 \div 6^2 \cdot 8 + 2^2$

   (e) $32 \div 4^2$

   (f) $2^4 - 3 \cdot 5 + 9$

   (g) $9 + 5^2 - 2 \cdot 3^2$

   (h) $11^2 - 7 \cdot 6 - 4^3 \div 2$

STRETCH ▸ Optional

❯ Evaluate each power raised to a power.

1 $(3^2)^2$

2 $(5^2)^4$

3 $(4^3)^2$

TOPIC 1
Expressions

TOPIC 2
Equations

TOPIC 3
Graphing Quantitative Relationships

1 | Relationships Matter

2 | Into the Unknown

3 | Second Verse, Same as the First

4 | Are They Saying the Same Thing?

LESSON 2

Into the Unknown

Introduction to Algebraic Expressions

Learning Goals

- Write algebraic expressions to represent real-world and mathematical situations.

- Match algebraic and verbal expressions.

- Identify parts of an algebraic expression using mathematical terms.

- Evaluate algebraic expressions at specific values of their variables.

🔑
KEY TERMS

algebraic expression

coefficient

term

evaluate an algebraic expression

REVIEW (1–2 minutes)

❯ Determine each product, sum, difference, or quotient.

1 $\frac{1}{4}(28)$

2 $6 + 14$

3 $4 \div 12$

4 $13 - 7$

You have written and evaluated expressions made up of numbers, but often expressions are made up of numbers and variables.

How can you represent situations using numbers and variables and how do you evaluate them?

Do You Speak Math?

> Rewrite each statement using symbols.

1 Fourteen more than six

2 Six more than fourteen

3 Seven less than thirteen

4 Twenty-three subtracted from thirty

5 The quotient of twelve divided by four

6 The quotient of four divided by twelve

7 One-fourth of twenty-eight

8 Two to the seventh power

9 Seven squared

10 Two times the sum of four and six

ACTIVITY 1
MATHia CONNECTION
• Writing Expressions from Verbal Descriptions
• Patterns and One-Step Expressions

Expressions
TOPIC 1 — LESSON 2

Getting
Started   1 2 3 4   Talk
          Activity   the Talk

Writing Expressions with Variables

You can write expressions even when a number is unknown.

> **HABITS OF MIND**
> • Reason abstractly and quantitatively.
> • Construct viable arguments and critique the reasoning of others.

> A school lunch costs $3 for each student.

1 For each situation, write a numeric expression to determine how much money the school collected. Then evaluate the expression.

   (a) Fifty-five students purchase a school lunch.

   (b) One hundred twenty-six students purchase a school lunch.

   (c) One thousand five hundred twelve students purchase a school lunch.

2 Write a sentence to describe how you can determine the amount of money collected for any number of students buying school lunches.

In Question 1, there is one quantity that changes or varies—the number of students who bought school lunches. Recall, in mathematics, you often use letters to represent quantities that vary. These letters are called variables, and they help you write algebraic expressions to represent situations. An **algebraic expression** is an expression that has at least one variable.

3 Write an algebraic expression to represent the total amount of money collected for s students buying school lunches.

You call a number multiplied by a variable in an algebraic expression a **coefficient**. If a coefficient does not appear in front of a number, it is understood to be 1. So, the coefficient of x is 1.

4 Identify a coefficient in the expression you wrote in Question 3.

> The cost to rent a skating rink is $215 for a two-hour party. The cost will be shared equally among all the people who attend the party.

5 For each number of attendees, write a numeric expression to determine how much each person will pay. Then evaluate the expression.

ⓐ 1 attendee   ⓑ 215 attendees   ⓒ 10 attendees

ⓓ Write an algebraic expression to represent how much each person will pay to attend the skate party for *p* people attending the skate party.

> Jimmy has three 300-minute international calling cards.

6 Complete the table to determine how many minutes remain on each card after each call.

Minutes on Card	Duration of Call	Minutes Left on Card
300	33 min	
300	57 min	
300	1 h 17 min	

7 Write an algebraic expression that represents the number of minutes remaining on each card after a call that is *m* minutes.

8 Write an algebraic expression to represent each situation. **Identify the coefficient(s).**

(a) Ben is selling tickets to the school play. How many will he have left if he starts with *t* tickets and sells 125 tickets?

(b) A plane descends to $\frac{5}{6}$ of its cruising altitude, *a*. What is its new altitude?

(c) Game downloads cost $6 each with an additional membership fee of $10.75. What is the cost of *x* downloads?

(d) Headphones cost $35, and portable music players cost $75. How much does it cost to purchase *x* headphones and *y* portable music players?

Matching Algebraic and Verbal Expressions

> Let's play Expression Explosion!

HABITS OF MIND
- Reason abstractly and quantitatively.
- Construct viable arguments and critique the reasoning of others.

Your teacher is going to hand out cards. Your goal is to identify the written or algebraic expression that corresponds to your card. Record your pair of matching algebraic and written expressions.

1 How can you be sure that you have found the correct match?

ACTIVITY 3

MATHia CONNECTION
- Identifying Parts of Simple Algebraic Expressions

Expressions
TOPIC 1 — **LESSON 2**

Getting Started | Activity 1 2 3 4 | Talk the Talk

Parts of Algebraic Expressions

As you learned previously, an algebraic expression contains at least one variable and sometimes numbers and operations. A **term** of an algebraic expression is a number, variable, or product of numbers and variables.

HABITS OF MIND
- Look for and make use of structure.
- Look for and express regularity in repeated reasoning.

WORKED EXAMPLE

Consider the expression $3x + 4y - 7$.

The expression has three terms: $3x$, $4y$, and 7. The operation between the first two terms is addition, and the operation between the second and third terms is subtraction.

> The first term is 3 multiplied by the variable x.

> The second term is 4 multiplied by the variable y.

> The third term is a constant term of 7.

$$3x + 4y - 7$$

❯ Consider two algebraic expressions: $8 + 5x$ and $8 - 5x$.

1 What is the same in both expressions? What is different?

2 Identify the number of terms, and then the terms themselves for each algebraic expression.

ⓐ $4 - 3x$

ⓑ $4a - 9 + 3a$

ⓒ $7b - 9x + 3a - 12$

ACTIVITY 4
MATHia CONNECTION
• Evaluating Algebraic Expressions

Expressions
TOPIC 1 — LESSON 2

Getting
Started

Activity
1 2 3 4

Talk
the Talk

Evaluating Algebraic Expressions

To **evaluate an algebraic expression** means to determine the value of the expression for a given value of each variable. When you evaluate an algebraic expression, you substitute the given values for the variables, and then determine the value of the expression.

HABITS OF MIND
• Attend to precision.

1 Write a sentence to describe the meaning of each algebraic expression. Then, evaluate the algebraic expression for the given value.

REMEMBER...
Use the Order of Operations when evaluating an algebraic expression.

(a) $3x - 4$, for $x = 10$

(b) $10 - z$, for $z = 8$

(c) $5 - \dfrac{y}{4}$, for $y = 2$

(d) $5(a + 1)$, for $a = 20$

(e) $\dfrac{b^2}{4}$, for $b = 8$

(f) $11 - s^3$, for $s = 2$

2 Complete each table.

(a)

h	$3h - 2$
2	
$\dfrac{7}{3}$	
5.1	

(b)

z	$\dfrac{2z}{3} + 1$
1	
2	
5	

3 Evaluate each expression using each value in the set. Write the results as a set of numbers.

TAKE NOTE...
Use curly braces { } to show collections of numbers called sets. A set of numbers contains no repeats.

(a) $1 + m$, $\left\{ 0, \frac{2}{3}, 4 \right\}$

(b) $0.5p$, {1, 2, 5}

(c) $0 \cdot y$, {80, 92, 115}

4 Evaluate each formula for the given value.

(a) The formula $C = \frac{5}{9}(F - 32)$ shows how temperatures in degrees Celsius (C) are related to temperatures in degrees Fahrenheit (F). What is the temperature in Celsius when the temperature is 68° Fahrenheit?

(b) The formula $A = \frac{1}{2}bh$ shows how the area of a triangle is related to the measures of its base (b) and height (h). What is the area of a triangle that has a base of 8 cm and a height of 10 cm?

TOPIC 1

Expression Construction

Josh has enough time to stop at one grocery store. He needs to get 2 tubes of toothpaste, 3 frozen pizzas, and 1 bottle of dish soap. There are two grocery stores nearby that each carry the items he needs.

	Shop Right	Mixed Foods
☐ Toothpaste (1 tube)	$5	$7.13
☐ Frozen Pizza (1)	$6	$3
☐ Dish Soap (1 bottle)	$1.19	$3.50

1 Where should he shop, and how much will he spend there? **Explain your reasoning. Be sure to use an algebraic expression in your explanation.**

LESSON 2 ASSIGNMENT

> Use a separate piece of paper for your Journal entry.

JOURNAL

Describe the difference between a *coefficient* and a *term* in your own words.

REMEMBER

Whenever you perform the same mathematical process repeatedly, you can write a mathematical phrase, called an algebraic expression, to represent the situation.

PRACTICE

> Write an algebraic expression to represent each situation.

1 You have 7 folders and you want to put the same number of pages in each folder.

   a If you have a total of p pages, how many pages will be in each folder?

   b Evaluate your expression to calculate the number of pages in each folder if you have 147 pages or 245 pages.

2 You have a coupon for $5 off your total bill at Meals on Main.

   a How much will you pay after using the coupon if your bill was b dollars?

   b Evaluate your expression to calculate the amount you will pay if your bill was $23.45 or $54.83.

3 You have already read two and a half hours for the Read-a-Thon.

   a How long will you have read if you read an additional h hours?

   b Evaluate your expression to calculate the amount of time you will have read if you read 3 or $5\frac{1}{2}$ additional hours.

❯ Write an algebraic expression that represents each verbal expression.

4 Six times a number plus 3

5 A number squared divided by 2 and added to 16

6 Five plus a number and then multiplied by 8

❯ Identify the number of terms and then the terms themselves for each algebraic expression.

7 $6y + 14$

8 $7x - 3y + 12z$

9 $104a + 224b$

❯ Evaluate each algebraic expression for the given value.

10 $34 - y^2$ for $y = 5$

11 $m^3 + 18$ for $m = 2$

12 $\frac{d}{5} + 42$ for $d = 70$

STRETCH ❯ Optional

Farmer Lyndi raises chickens and goats.

1 Write an expression for the total number of animal legs on Lyndi's farm.

2 How many animal legs are on the farm if Lyndi has 16 chickens and 6 goats?

3 Suppose Lyndi counted 74 animal legs on the farm. How many of each animal might Lyndi have on the farm?

LESSON 3

Second Verse, Same as the First

Equivalent Expressions

🔑 **KEY TERM**

like terms

Learning Goals

- Model algebraic expressions with algebra tiles.
- Rewrite algebraic expressions using algebra tiles.
- Rewrite algebraic expressions using the associative, commutative, and distributive properties.
- Apply properties of operations to create equivalent expressions.
- Rewrite expressions as the product of two factors.

REVIEW (1–2 minutes)

❯ Evaluate each expression.

1 $5 \div \frac{3}{4}$

3 $\frac{(14 + 8)}{2}$

5 What do you notice about the answers to Questions 3 and 4?

2 $0.24 \div 0.6$

4 $\frac{14}{2} + \frac{8}{2}$

You have evaluated numeric expressions and written and evaluated algebraic expressions.

How do you combine algebraic expressions, like you did with numeric expressions, into as few terms as possible?

Collection Connection

The Johnson brothers collect sports gear from their favorite teams.

- Jaden has a number of jerseys and a number of caps.
- Jerome has twice as many jerseys as Jaden, but the same number of caps.
- Josh has three times as many jerseys and caps as Jaden.
- Jack has 4 times as many caps as Jaden, but no jerseys.

Your teacher has provided you with algebra tiles.

1 Use the algebra tiles to model the amount of sports gear each brother has. Use the x-tiles to represent the number of jerseys that Jaden has and the y-tiles to represent the number of caps that Jaden has. **Sketch each model you create.**

(a) Jaden

(b) Jerome

(c) Josh

(d) Jack

2 Use the algebra tiles to model the total amount of jerseys and caps the Johnson brothers have. **Sketch the model you create.**

3 Write an algebraic expression to represent the total number of jerseys and caps the Johnson brothers have.

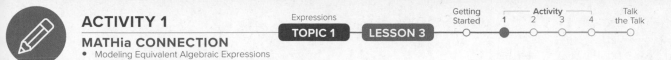

ACTIVITY 1

Expressions

TOPIC 1 **LESSON 3**

Getting Started

Activity 1 2 3 4

Talk the Talk

MATHia CONNECTION
- Modeling Equivalent Algebraic Expressions
- Exploring the Distributive Property with Algebraic Expressions

Using Algebra Tiles to Model Equivalent Expressions

HABITS OF MIND
- Model with mathematics.
- Use appropriate tools strategically.

In an algebraic expression, **like terms** are two or more terms that have the same variable raised to the same power. The coefficients of like terms can be different.

Let's start our exploration of combining like terms with a review of the properties of arithmetic and algebra that you will use to combine terms.

1 Given the algebra tile model, write an addition expression that highlights the different tiles in the model. Then, if necessary, combine like terms and write the expression using as few terms as possible.

TAKE NOTE...
All tiles that are the same size and have the same value represent like terms.

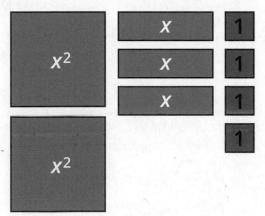

2 Analyze the last expression you wrote in Question 1.

   (a) How many terms are in your expression with the fewest terms? How does this relate to the algebra tile model?

   (b) What is the greatest exponent in the expression?

   (c) What is the coefficient of x in the expression? How does this relate to your algebra tile model?

TOPIC 1

3 Consider the model.

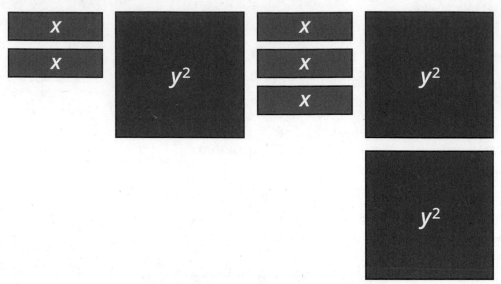

(a) Write an addition expression that highlights the different tiles in the model.

(b) Rearrange the tiles to combine all of the like tiles. How many terms does your expression have now?

(c) Write the new algebraic expression represented.

TAKE NOTE...
Combining like terms means to add or subtract terms with the same variables, such as $3x + 5x$. These terms combine to make $8x$.

4 Represent the algebraic expression $3x^2 + x + 2$ using algebra tiles and sketch your model. **How many types of tiles are needed?**

You can also use algebra tiles to represent multiplication.

> **WORKED EXAMPLE**
>
> Consider the expression $3(x + y)$.
>
> This expression has two factors: 3 and the quantity $(x + y)$. The expression means that you have three groups of the quantity $(x + y)$. The algebra tiles shown model this expression.
>
> You can use the Distributive Property to rewrite this expression. In this case, multiply the 3 by each term of the quantity $(x + y)$.
>
>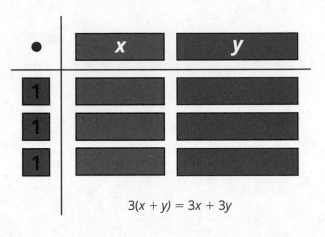
>
> $3(x + y) = 3x + 3y$

5 Analyze the parts of the mathematical expressions in the worked example. **Explain each response.**

THINK ABOUT...

This model is just adding the quantity $x + y$ three times.

(a) Which expression, $3(x + y)$ or $3x + 3y$, shows a product of two factors?

(b) How many terms are in $3x + 3y$?

(c) The number 3 is a coefficient in which expression?

6 Create a model of each expression using your algebra tiles. Then sketch the model and rewrite the expression using the Distributive Property.

(a) $4(2x + 1)$ (b) $2(x + 3)$

Algebra tiles are helpful tools for combining like terms in algebraic expressions. However, because they only represent whole number tiles, you cannot use them to model all algebraic expressions.

7 Use properties to rewrite each algebraic expression.

   (a) $2x + 3x - 4.5x$

   (b) $\frac{2}{3}(6x + 12)$

ASK YOURSELF...

Did I distribute the factor to each term in parentheses?

   (c) $5x + 2y + \frac{1}{3}x^2 - 3x$

   (d) $5 + 2(x + 3)$

   (e) $2(y + 5) + 2(x + 5)$

   (f) $\frac{1}{2}(4x + 2) + 8x$

Mr. Martin asked his class to write expressions equivalent to $7(3a + 5b)$ and got five different responses for each.

---

8 For each response, determine whether the student rewrote the original expression correctly. For those not rewritten correctly, describe the mistake the student made in rewriting the expression.

   (a) $10a + 12b$

   (b) $7(3a) + 7(5b)$

   (c) $21a + 5b$

   (d) $21a + 35b$

   (e) $7(8ab)$

ACTIVITY 2
MATHia CONNECTION
• Using Order of Operations to Rewrite Algebraic Expressions

Expressions
TOPIC 1   LESSON 3

Getting
Started   Activity   Talk
              1   **2**   3   4   the Talk

Rewriting Algebraic Expressions Involving Division

HABITS OF MIND
• Model with mathematics.
• Use appropriate tools strategically.

How do you think the Distributive Property will play a part in dividing expressions? Let's find out.

1 Consider the expression $(4x + 8) \div 4$, which you can also write as $\frac{4x + 8}{4}$.

(a) First, represent $4x + 8$ using your algebra tiles.
Then sketch the model you created.

ASK YOURSELF...
What are the 4 equally-sized groups in 4x + 8?.

(b) Next, divide your algebra tile model into four equal groups.
Then sketch the model you created.

(c) Write an expression to represent each group from your sketches in part (b).

(d) Verify you created equal groups by multiplying your expression from part (c) by 4. The product you calculate should equal $4x + 8$.

> Consider the division expression from Question 1.

WORKED EXAMPLE

You can rewrite an expression of the form $\frac{4x + 8}{4}$ using the Distributive Property.

$$\frac{4x + 8}{4} = \frac{4x}{4} + \frac{8}{4}$$
$$= 1x + 2$$
$$= x + 2$$
$$\text{So, } \frac{4x + 8}{4} = x + 2$$

TAKE NOTE...
To rewrite the expression, divide the denominator into both terms in the numerator.

The model you created in Question 1 is an example that shows that you can use the Distributive Property with division as well as with multiplication.

2 Consider the expression $\frac{2x + 6y + 4}{2}$.

  (a) Rewrite the division expression using the Distributive Property.

$$\frac{2x + 6y + 4}{2} = \frac{2x}{\boxed{}} + \frac{6y}{\boxed{}} + \frac{4}{\boxed{}}$$

  (b) Evaluate each term you wrote in part (a) to rewrite the expression.

$$\frac{2x + 6y + 4}{2} = \underline{\hspace{4cm}}$$

  (c) How can you check your answer?

Zachary wants to rewrite $\dfrac{6 + 3(x + 1)}{3}$ in as few terms as possible and proposes two different methods.

3 Analyze each correct method.

Method 1

$$\frac{6 + 3(x + 1)}{3} = \frac{6}{3} + \frac{3(x + 1)}{3}$$
$$= 2 + (x + 1)$$
$$= x + 3$$

Method 2

$$\frac{6 + 3(x + 1)}{3} = \frac{6 + 3x + 3}{3}$$
$$= \frac{3x + 9}{3}$$
$$= \frac{3x}{3} + \frac{9}{3}$$
$$= x + 3$$

(a) Explain the reasoning used in each method.

(b) When do you think it is more efficient to use each method?

❯ Consider the expression $\frac{(8x + 3)}{4}$.

Niesha

$$\frac{8x + 3}{4} = \frac{8x}{4} + \frac{3}{4}$$
$$= 2x + \frac{3}{4}$$

Eldon

$$\frac{8x + 3}{4} = \frac{1}{4}(8x + 3)$$
$$= 2x + \frac{3}{4}$$

Maeve

$$\frac{8x + 3}{4} = 2x + 3$$

4 What is the difference between Niesha's and Eldon's strategies?

5 Explain what Maeve did incorrectly when rewriting the expression.

6 Rewrite each expression using the Distributive Property.

   (a) $\frac{32 + 4x}{4}$
                                               (b) $\frac{3(x + 1) + 12}{3}$

   (c) $\frac{2x + 5(2x + 3)}{3}$

ACTIVITY 3
MATHia CONNECTION
• Using Order of Operations to Rewrite Algebraic Expressions

Expressions
TOPIC 1 | LESSON 3

Getting Started | Activity 1 2 3 4 | Talk the Talk

Factoring Algebraic Expressions

You have used the Distributive Property to multiply and divide algebraic expressions by a given value. You can also use the Distributive Property to rewrite an algebraic expression as a product of two factors: a constant and a sum of terms.

You can write any expression as a product of two factors. In many types of math problems, you often need the coefficient of a variable to be 1.

Let's explore how to use the Distributive Property—without algebra tiles—to rewrite expressions so that the coefficient of the variable is 1.

HABITS OF MIND
• Look for and make use of structure.
• Look for and express regularity in repeated reasoning.

TAKE NOTE...
Using the Distributive Property to write an expression as a product of two factors is also known as *factoring*.

1 Consider the expression $3x + 6$.

(a) Identify the coefficient of the variable term.

(b) Use the Distributive Property to rewrite the expression as the product of two factors: the coefficient and a sum of terms.

(c) How can you check your work?

In the expression $3x + 6$, you factored out the common factor of 3 from each term and rewrote the expression as $3(x + 2)$. In other words, you divided 3 from each term and wrote the expression as the product of 3 and the sum of the remaining factors, $(x + 2)$.

TAKE NOTE...
When you use the Distributive Property to rewrite the sum of two terms as the product of two factors, you are factoring expressions.

TOPIC 1

You can use the same strategy to rewrite an algebraic expression so that the coefficient of the variable is 1 even when the terms do not have common factors.

WORKED EXAMPLE

Let's rewrite the expression $4x - 7$ so the coefficient of the variable is 1.

To rewrite the expression, factor out the coefficient 4 from each term.

$$4x - 7 = 4\left(\frac{4x}{4} - \frac{7}{4}\right)$$
$$= 4\left(x - \frac{7}{4}\right)$$

The equivalent expression is the product of the coefficient and the difference of the remaining factors.

REMEMBER...

You can multiply or divide any expression by 1 and not change its value.

2 Use the Distributive Property to check that the new expression is equivalent to the original expression in the worked example.

3 Rewrite each expression as the product of two factors. **Check your answers.**

   (a) $4x + 5$ (b) $8x - 3$

   (c) $\frac{1}{2}x - 4$ (d) $0.5x + 3.5$

ACTIVITY 4
MATHia CONNECTION
• Using Picture Algebra

Expressions
TOPIC 1   LESSON 3

Getting Started   Activity   Talk the Talk
1   2   3   4

Writing Algebraic Expressions from a Scenario

HABITS OF MIND
• Attend to precision.

Jon, Jacob, Luke, and Andrew each have a number of songs downloaded on their phones.

• Jacob says: "I have twice as many songs as Jon."

• Luke says: "I have four more songs than Jacob."

• Andrew says: "I have three times as many songs as Luke."

> Write an algebraic expression that represents the number of songs for each friend. Then write an algebraic expression to describe the total number of songs for the group.

1 Let *n* represent the number of songs that Jon has.

| Jacob | Luke | Andrew | **Total** |

2 Let *w* represent the number of songs Andrew has.

| Jacob | Luke | Jon | **Total** |

3 Let *b* represent the number of songs Jacob has.

| Jon | Luke | Andrew | **Total** |

4 Let *k* represent the number of songs Luke has.

| Jon | Jacob | Andrew | **Total** |

Math Magic

❯ Consider the following number riddle.

- Choose any number.
- Add 5.
- Double the result.
- Subtract 4.
- Divide the result by 2.
- Subtract the number you started with.
- The result is 3.

1 Write the corresponding algebraic expressions for each step to show why this number trick works.

2 Create your own number trick. Then write the corresponding algebraic expressions to show why it works.

LESSON 3 ASSIGNMENT

> Use a separate piece of paper for your Journal entry.

JOURNAL

Describe 3 different ways that you can use the Distributive Property to rewrite expressions. Provide an example for each.

REMEMBER

To rewrite an algebraic expression in as few terms as possible, use the properties of arithmetic and the Order of Operations.

You can write an algebraic expression containing two terms as the product of two factors by applying the Distributive Property.

PRACTICE

1 Nelson is going on an overnight family reunion camping trip. He is in charge of bringing the wood for the campfire. He will start the fire with 6 logs and then plans to add 3 logs for each hour the fire burns.

(a) Represent the number of logs he will use as an algebraic expression.

(b) Suppose the family decides to stay for 2 nights next year. Write the expression for the number of logs they would need for 2 nights.

(c) Create a model of the situation in part (b) using your algebra tiles, and then sketch the model.

(d) Rewrite the expression in part (c) using as few terms as possible.

2 Rewrite each expression using the fewest number of terms, if possible.

(a) $4.5x + (6y - 3.5x) + 7$

(b) $\left(\frac{2}{3}y + \frac{5}{8}x + \frac{1}{4}\right) + \left(\frac{1}{4}x + \frac{1}{2}\right)$

(c) $7(2x + y) + 5(x + 4y)$

(d) $\frac{6(x + 1) + 30}{6}$

3 Rewrite each expression as a product of two factors, so that the coefficient of the variable is 1.

(a) $6x + 7$

(b) $\frac{2}{3}x + 8$

4 At the end of each school year, Evan cleans out all of the school supplies that have collected in his desk.

- He has 4 times as many markers as he has pencils.
- He has 3 more highlighters than he has markers.
- He has twice as many pens as he has highlighters.

Let p represent the number of pencils that Evan has in his desk.

(a) Write an algebraic expression that represents the number of markers in Evan's desk.

(b) Write an algebraic expression that represents the number of highlighters in Evan's desk.

(c) Write an algebraic expression that represents the number of pens in Evan's desk.

(d) Write an algebraic expression that represents the total number of writing utensils in Evan's desk.

STRETCH ▶ Optional

You can represent a three-digit number with all the same digits with an algebraic expression: $100 \times a + 10 \times a + a$.

❯ Use this fact to explain why you can evenly divide any three-digit number with all repeated digits by 37.

LESSON 4

Are They Saying the Same Thing?

Verifying Equivalent Expressions

___

Learning Goals

- Compare expressions using properties, tables, and graphs.
- Identify when two expressions are equivalent.
- Determine whether two expressions are equivalent.

REVIEW (1–2 minutes)

❯ Determine which pairs of ratios are equivalent. **Explain how you know.**

1 5 : 7 and 100 : 140

2 42 : 48 and 14 : 15

3 105 : 100 and 20 : 21

4 9 : 12 and 60 : 80

You know how to use the Distributive Property and combine like terms to write equivalent expressions.

How can you determine whether two given expressions are equivalent?

Property Sort

> Cut out the Property Cards on page 395.

On each card is one representation of a property of numbers or operations that you have used in the past to rewrite and evaluate numeric expressions.

1 Sort the cards according to the property named or illustrated on the cards. Create a table that shows your final sorting.

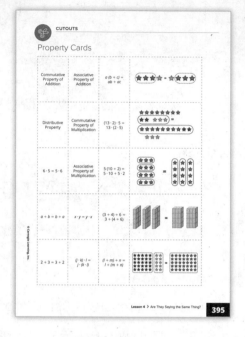

2 Using complete sentences, write an explanation for how each picture illustrates its property.

ACTIVITY 1

Expressions
TOPIC 1 — LESSON 4

Getting Started
Activity 1
Talk the Talk

Determining Whether Expressions Are Equivalent

HABITS OF MIND
- Model with mathematics.
- Use appropriate tools strategically.

Two algebraic expressions are **equivalent expressions** if, when any values are substituted for the variables, the results are equal.

While it's not realistic to test each expression for every possible value for the unknown, you can examine the characteristics of each expression in the different representations:

- a table of values

- a graph of both expressions

- rewritten expressions using the properties

Consider the two expressions $2(x + 2) + 3x$ and $5x + 4$.

❯ Let's explore each representation.

1 Complete the table of values for each value of x.

x	$2(x + 2) + 3x$	$5x + 4$
0		
1		
2		
3		

ⓐ What can you determine based on the set of values in the table?

ⓑ What do you need to know to verify that the two expressions are equivalent?

TOPIC 1

You can also use a graph to determine or verify whether two expressions are equivalent.

2 Consider your completed table of values from Question 1.

x	2(x + 2) + 3x	5x + 4
0	4	4
1	9	9
2	14	14
3	19	19

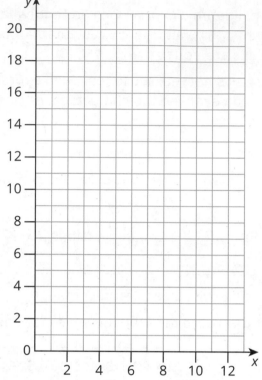

ⓐ Plot the values for each expression on the coordinate plane. **Then connect the results for each expression with a line.**

ⓑ How does the graph demonstrate that the two expressions are equivalent?

3 Rewrite the given expression and identify the property applied at each step.

$2(x + 2) + 3x$ _____ Given

$= 2x + \underline{\quad} + 3x$ _____

$= \underline{\qquad}$ _____ Combine Like Terms, Addition

4 Are the two expressions equivalent? **Explain your reasoning.**

Consider the two expressions $2x + 5$ and $2(x + 5)$.

5 Complete the table of values for each value of x.

x	$2x + 5$	$2(x + 5)$
0		
2		
4		
5		

6 Use the table of values to sketch the graph of both expressions on the coordinate plane.

(a) Plot the values for each expression on the coordinate plane.

Use a □ to represent the values from the first expression and a △ for the values from the second expression.

Then, connect the results for each expression with a line.

(b) What does the graph tell you about the equivalence of the two expressions?

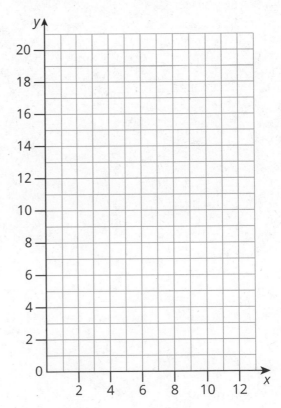

7 Use the Distributive Property to rewrite the expression $2(x + 5)$.

8 Are the two expressions equivalent? **Explain your reasoning.**

9 Use a table, properties, and a graph to determine whether the expressions $x + 3(2x + 1)$ and $7x + 3$ are equivalent. **Explain whether the expressions are equivalent using all three representations.**

x	x + 3(2x + 1)	7x + 3
0		
1		
2		

$x + 3(2x + 1)$ Given

$= x +$ _____

$=$ _____

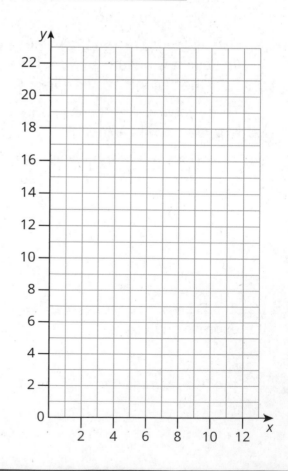

Property Management

❯ Identify the property or operation used to rewrite each equivalent expression.

1 $10 \cdot 4x + 3(2x + 1)$ Given

    $= (10 \cdot 4)x + 3(2x + 1)$

    $= 40x + 3(2x + 1)$ Multiplication

    $= 40x + 6x + 3$

    $= 46x + 3$

2 $20 + (6 + x) + 7$ Given

    $= 20 + (x + 6) + 7$

    $= 20 + x + (6 + 7)$ Associative Property of Addition

    $= 20 + x + 13$

    $= x + 20 + 13$

    $= x + 33$

3 $7x + \dfrac{12x - 8}{4} + 5x$ Given

    $= 7x + 3x - 2 + 5x$

    $= 10x - 2 + 5x$

    $= 10x + 5x - 2$

    $= 15x - 2$

4 Rewrite $\dfrac{2(x+5)-4}{2} - x$ using the fewest terms possible. Justify each step with a property or operation. Then verify using another representation that your expressions are equivalent.

Property Cards

Commutative Property of Addition

Associative Property of Addition

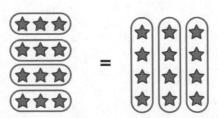

$a\,(b + c) = ab + ac$

Distributive Property

Commutative Property of Multiplication

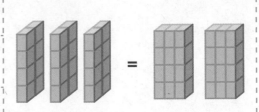

$(13 \cdot 2) \cdot 5 = 13 \cdot (2 \cdot 5)$

$6 \cdot 5 = 5 \cdot 6$

Associative Property of Multiplication

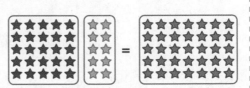

$5\,(10 + 2) = 5 \cdot 10 + 5 \cdot 2$

$a + b = b + a$

$x \cdot y = y \cdot x$

$(3 + 4) + 6 = 3 + (4 + 6)$

$2 + 3 = 3 + 2$

$(j \cdot k) \cdot l = j \cdot (k \cdot l)$

$(l + m) + n = l + (m + n)$

Why is this page blank?

So you can cut out the cards on the other side.

> ❯ Use a separate piece of paper for your Journal entry.

REMEMBER ❯

To determine whether two expressions are
equivalent, you can create a table of values, graph
the expressions, or rewrite the expressions using
number properties.

PRACTICE ❯

> ❯ Determine whether each pair of expressions are equivalent. Use properties, a table,
> and a graph in each problem to verify your answer.

1 $2(3x + 2) - 2x$ and $4x + 2$

x	$2(3x + 2) - 2x$	$4x + 2$

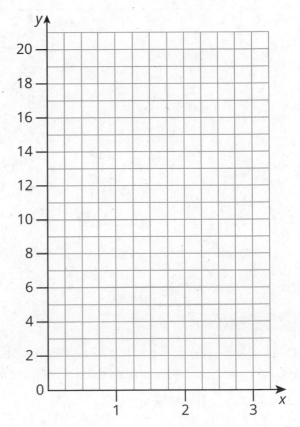

2 $2x + 1$ and $2\left(x + \frac{1}{2}\right)$

x	$2x + 1$	$2\left(x + \frac{1}{2}\right)$

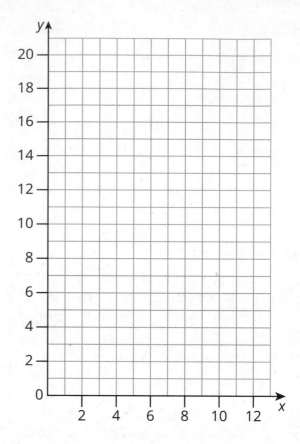

STRETCH Optional

> Determine whether each pair of expressions are equivalent. Use properties, a table, and a graph in each problem to verify your answer.

1 $(x + 5)(2x + 1)$ and $2x^2 + 5$

2 $(x + 1)(x - 1)$ and $x^2 - 1$

MIXED PRACTICE

❯ This Mixed Practice worksheet includes two sections: Spaced Review and End-of-Topic Review. **Use a separate piece of paper to show your work.**

Spaced Review

❯ Practice concepts from previous topics.

1 Calculate each conversion.

   (a) 4 grams = _____ milligrams

   (b) 6400 ounces = _____ pounds

2 Determine each sum.

   (a) $\frac{6}{7} + 3\frac{1}{5}$

   (b) $1\frac{2}{3} + 4\frac{1}{4}$

3 Determine the least common multiple (LCM) of each pair of numbers.

   (a) 6 and 10

   (b) 7 and 12

4 Determine each whole for the percent and part given.

   (a) 68 is 32% of what number?

   (b) 16 is 80% of what number?

5 Determine which is the better buy.

   (a) $12.99 for 42 ounces or $2.99 for 10 ounces

   (b) 3 pounds for $5.00 or $1.50 per pound

6 Determine at least two equivalent ratios for each given ratio.

   (a) $\frac{2 \text{ eggs}}{5 \text{ cups of milk}}$

   (b) $\frac{20 \text{ red}}{12 \text{ blue}}$

7 Calculate the volume of the solid formed by rectangular prisms.

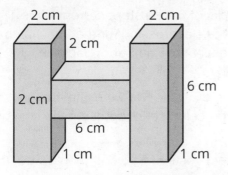

8 In Ms. Romano's math class of 25 students, 8 of the students play a musical instrument. What percent of the class plays a musical instrument?

End-of-Topic Review

AVAILABLE ONLINE

1. A **Topic Summary** reviews the main concepts for the topic.
2. A video of the **Worked Example** is provided.

❯ Practice concepts you learned in **Expressions**.

9 Evaluate each numeric expression.

   (a) $56 \div 8 + 3 \cdot 6$

   (b) $9 \cdot 8 - 29 + 30 \div 15 - 15$

10 Use the Distributive Property and combine like terms to rewrite each expression.

   (a) $9(6m + 3) + 6(1 - 4m)$

   (b) $\dfrac{3(4x + 8y)}{6} + 2y - x$

11 Rewrite each expression as the product of two factors, so that the coefficient of the variable is 1.

   (a) $3x - 5$

   (b) $\frac{3}{4}x + 9$

12 Write an algebraic expression to represent each verbal expression.

   (a) One-third the sum of a number and two and one hundredths.

   (b) Sixteen and two-tenths subtracted from two times a number.

13 Miguel has three times as many books as Jose. Write an expression to represent the number of books Miguel has if j represents the number of books Jose has.

14 Rosa has 5 fewer bracelets than Maria. Write an expression to represent the number of bracelets Rosa has if m represents the number of bracelets Maria has.

15 Sheldon Elementary School has a school store. The parent association is in charge of buying items for the store.

   (a) The store sells scented pencils that come in packs of 24. Write an algebraic expression that represents the total number of scented pencils it has available to sell. Let p represent the number of packs of scented pencils.

   (b) The store sells animal-themed folders that come in packs of 6. The store currently has 4 packs in the store and is ordering more. Write an algebraic expression for the total number of folders it has after ordering more folders. Let x represent the number of packs of folders ordered.

   (c) The store sells animal-shaped rubber bracelets that come in packs of 24. Write an algebraic expression that represents the cost of each bracelet. Let c represent the cost of a pack of 24 bracelets.

16 Darian's band made $500 on one night. They had to subtract costs of $80 and then divide the remaining money among the band members. If there are 4 members in the band, which numeric expression correctly shows the amount that each member will make? Explain your answer using the Order of Operations.

Expression A	Expression B
$500 - 80 \div 4$	$(500 - 80) \div 4$

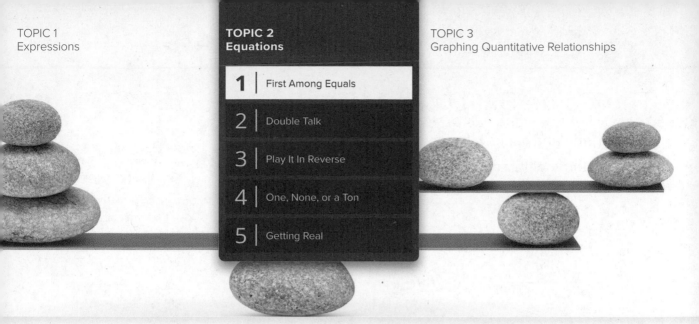

LESSON 1

First Among Equals *SKIP*

Reasoning with Equal Expressions

- Compose and decompose numeric and algebraic equations.

- Substitute values into equations to determine whether they make the equation true.

- Construct and analyze equations using Properties of Equality.

> **REVIEW** (1–2 minutes)

> Rewrite each number as an addition, subtraction, multiplication, or division expression. Use each operation once.

1 24

2 $\frac{1}{2}$

3 0

4 100

You have learned about both numeric and algebraic expressions and how they describe situations and relationships among quantities.

What properties do equal expressions have and how can you use these properties to reason about solutions?

The Same But Different

You can write the same value in more than one way.

1 Write three different expressions equal to 4.

_____ = 4

4 = _____

4 = _____

2 Now write three different expressions equal to 4 + 5.

4 + 5 = _____

_____ = 4 + 5

4 + 5 = _____

3 What can you do to one of the expressions you wrote in Question 1 to make it equal to one of the expressions you wrote in Question 2?

ACTIVITY 1
MATHia CONNECTION
• Using Substitution to Identify Solutions to Equations

Equations
TOPIC 2   LESSON 1

Getting Started   Activity 1   2   Talk the Talk

Using Substitution to Understand Equality

HABITS OF MIND
• Model with mathematics.
• Use appropriate tools strategically.

Recall that an equation is a statement of equality between two expressions. An equation can contain numbers, variables, or both in the same mathematical sentence.

> Consider the equation $8 + 4 =$ _____ $+ 5$. It has an unknown number.

One way to determine the unknown number in the equation is to rewrite the expressions on both sides of the equals sign until they match.

> Consider the reasoning of Rylee, Clover, and Fiona to determine the unknown number.

Rylee

The equals sign tells me to perform the operation on the left in the equation.
$8 + 4 = 12$
$12 + 5 = 17$
Therefore, the unknown number is 17.

Fiona

I can determine the unknown number by rewriting both expressions.
$8 + 4 =$ _____ $+ 1 + 4$
$7 + 1 + 4 =$ _____ $+ 1 + 4$
Therefore, the unknown number is 7.

Clover

The equals sign means that the expressions on each side have the same value. I can take 1 from 8 and give it to the 4 and keep the value of the expressions the same.
$(8 - 1) + (4 + 1) =$ ___ $+ 5$
$7 + 5 =$ ___ $+ 5$
Therefore, the unknown number is 7.

DID YOU KNOW?

The **Reflexive Property of Equality** states that a number is always equal to itself. If a is a number, then $a = a$. So, when both sides of an equation look exactly the same, their values are equal.

1 What is the unknown number in the equation 8 + 4 = _____ + 5? **Explain why this makes sense.**

2 Explain the error in Rylee's reasoning.

3 How are Fiona's reasoning and Clover's reasoning similar? How are they different?

4 Consider the equation 31 + 67 = _____ + 12.

   a Determine the unknown number by rewriting the expressions on either side of the equals sign until they match.

   b How did you use reasoning to determine the unknown number?

   c How can you check your answer to make sure it is correct?

5 Use your number sense reasoning to determine each unknown number. **Show your work.**

   a 85 + 45 = _____ + 60   **b** 9 + 23 = _____ + 14

ACTIVITY 2

Equations

TOPIC 2 — LESSON 1

Getting Started

Activity 1 2

Talk the Talk

Using Properties of Equality

Equations come in many forms. Because expressions are either numeric or algebraic, you can make equations that have just numbers or both numbers and variables.

The **Addition Property of Equality** states that if two values a and b are equal when you add the same value c to each, the sums are equal.

The **Subtraction Property of Equality** states that when you subtract the same value c from equal values a and b, the differences are equal.

Properties of Equality	For all numbers a, b, and c
Addition Property of Equality	If $a = b$, then $a + c = b + c$
Subtraction Property of Equality	If $a = b$, then $a - c = b - c$

A double number line is a model used to show that two expressions are equal. It helps make visible the equivalent relationship between expressions. Expressions that are at the same location have the same value. We refer to the line connecting expressions as a "barbell."

❯ Consider the equation $x = 15$ represented on the double number line.

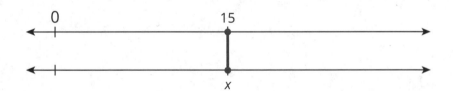

1 Use the Property of Equality stated to write at least three equations with the same *solution*. **Represent each equation on the double number line.**

   ⓐ The Addition Property of Equality

TAKE NOTE...
A **solution** to any equation is any value that makes the equation true.

(b) The Subtraction Property of Equality

2 Consider the equation $x + 5 = 10$ represented on the double number line. Use the Property of Equality stated to write at least three equations with the same solution. **Represent each equation on the double number line.**

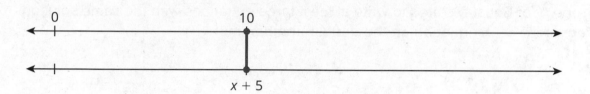

(a) The Addition Property of Equality

(b) The Subtraction Property of Equality

The **Multiplication Property of Equality** states that if two values a and b are equal, when you multiply each by the same value c, the products are equal.

The **Division Property of Equality** states that when you divide equal values a and b by the same value c, the quotients are equal. The Division Property of Equality is true only if c is not equal to 0.

Properties of Equality	For all numbers a, b, and c
Multiplication Property of Equality	If $a = b$, then $a \cdot c = b \cdot c$.
Division Property of Equality	If $a = b$ and $c \neq 0$, then $a \div c = b \div c$.

3 Consider the equation $x = 5$ represented on the double number line. Use the Property of Equality stated to write at least three equations with the same solution. **Represent each equation on the double number line.**

   ⓐ The Multiplication Property of Equality

   ⓑ The Division Property of Equality

4 Consider the equation $\frac{1}{2}x = 10$ represented on the double number line. Use the Property of Equality stated to write at least three equations with the same solution. **Represent each equation on the double number line.**

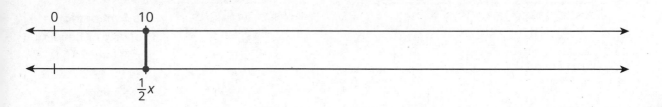

(a) The Multiplication Property of Equality

> **REMEMBER...**
> Properties of Equality allow you to maintain balance and rewrite equations.

(b) The Division Property of Equality

5 How do you know that all the equations on each double number line are equivalent?

TOPIC 2

TALK THE TALK

Equations
TOPIC 2 — **LESSON 1**

Getting Started

Activity 1 — 2

Talk the Talk

Shaking Your Symmetry

❯ Consider each equation shown and identify which are equivalent to $x = 3$. State the Property of Equality used to create each equivalent equation.

1 $x + 3 = 3 + 3$

2 $x + 8 = 11$

TAKE NOTE...
The **Symmetric Property of Equality** states that if $a = b$, then $b = a$. So, $x = 3$ is the same as $3 = x$.

---

3 $x - 1 = 4$

4 $5x = 15$

5 $x - 2 = 1$

6 $\frac{x}{1} = 2$

7 $10x = 13$

8 $\frac{x}{5} = \frac{3}{5}$

> Use a separate piece of paper for your Journal entry.

JOURNAL

Complete each statement with the correct term.

1 The _____ states that if two values a and b are equal, when you multiply each by the same value c, the products are equal.

2 The _____ says that when both sides of an equation look exactly the same, their values must be equal.

3 An _____ is a mathematical sentence created by writing two expressions with an equals sign between them.

REMEMBER

Properties of Equality allow you to maintain balance and rewrite equations.

For all numbers a, b, and c:

Addition Property of Equality
If $a = b$, then $a + c = b + c$.

Subtraction Property of Equality
If $a = b$, then $a - c = b - c$.

Multiplication Property of Equality
If $a = b$, then $ac = bc$.

Division Property of Equality
If $a = b$, and $c \neq 0$, then $\frac{a}{c} = \frac{b}{c}$.

PRACTICE

> Determine each unknown value.

1 $9 - 3 =$ _____ $+ 1$

2 $4 \cdot$ _____ $= 20$

3 $81 \div 1 = 9($ _____ $)$

4 _____ $+ 17 = 17 + 38$

5 _____ $\div 3 = 21$

6 _____ $+ 4 = 9 + 2$

7 $8 +$ _____ $= 5 + 8$

8 $99 =$ _____ $- 1$

❯ Consider the equation $x = 12$ represented on the double number line. Use the Property of Equality stated to write at least three equations with the same solution. Represent each equation on the double number line.

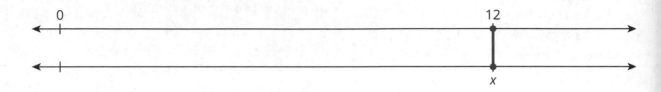

9 The Addition Property of Equality

10 The Division Property of Equality

The equation shows a two-digit number added to x to equal another two-digit number.

$[\ \ ][\ \ ] = x + [\ \ ][\ \ ]$

1 Enter a digit (from 1 to 9) in each box, using each digit only once. What two-digit numbers give x the greatest possible value?

LESSON 2

Double Talk

Solving One-Step Addition Equations

- Reason about addition equations.
- Use double number lines to represent and solve one-step addition equations.
- Use inverse operations to solve one-step addition equations.

REVIEW (1–2 minutes)

> Determine each sum or difference.

1 $5.67 + 8.73$

2 $8.73 - 5.67$

3 $\frac{3}{7} + \frac{4}{5}$

4 $\frac{20}{3} - \frac{15}{4}$

Throughout this course, you have used various tools, strategies, and properties to solve mathematical problems.

What tools can you use to solve equations?

This Open Road

The double number line shows three equivalent equations.

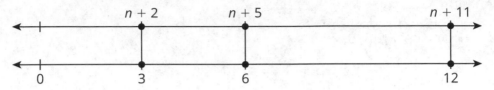

1 Write the equations represented on the double number line.

2 What is the value of *n* that makes all the equations true?

3 How can you check that the value you determined in Question 2 makes all the equations true?

ACTIVITY 1
MATHia CONNECTION
• Exploring One-Step Equations with Double Number Lines
• Using Double Number Lines to Solve One-Step Addition Equations

Equations
TOPIC 2 — LESSON 2

Getting Started
Activity 1 2 3
Talk the Talk

Reasoning About Addition Equations

When you determine the value of a variable that makes an equation true, you solve the equation. Recall that a solution to an equation is a value for the variable that makes the equation true.

You can use a double number line to represent and determine the solution to an equation.

TOPIC 2

WORKED EXAMPLE

Solve the equation $x + 10 = 15$.

First, draw a model to set up the equation.

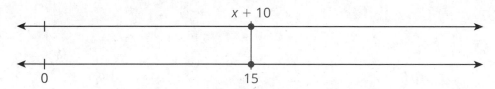

You want to determine the value of x so the expression $x + 10$ is equal to 15. You can move the barbell **10 units left** to locate x, this means subtracting 10: $x + 10 - 10$ is x.

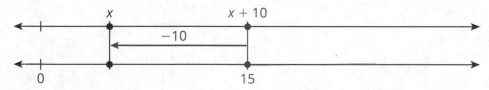

Since the barbell represents that the two expressions form an equation, you have to subtract 10 from 15 also: $15 - 10$ is 5.

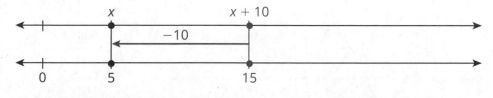

1 How can you check that $x = 5$ is the solution to the equation?

2 Which Property of Equality did you use?

3 Use a double number line to determine a value that makes each equation true. Identify the Property of Equality that you use for each equation. **Check your solution.**

(a) $p + 10 = 17$

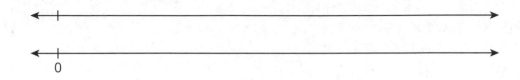

(b) $14 + q = 32$

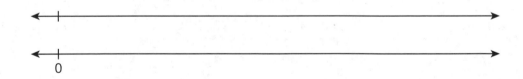

(c) $90 = x + 64$

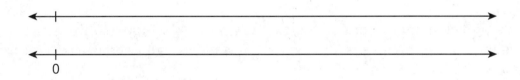

ACTIVITY 2
MATHia CONNECTION
• Solving with Addition and Subtraction

Equations
TOPIC 2 — LESSON 2

Getting Started   Activity 1 2 3   Talk the Talk

Solving Addition Equations

You have now solved one-step equations.

A **one-step equation** is an equation you can solve using only one operation.

You can use reasoning to determine the value for the variable that makes an equation true. You can also use properties and inverse operations. **Inverse operations** are pairs of operations that reverse the effects of each other. For example, subtraction and addition are inverse operations.

HABITS OF MIND
• Model with mathematics.
• Use appropriate tools strategically.

WORKED EXAMPLE

Solve the equation $h + 6 = 19$.
You can use a double number line to solve for h.

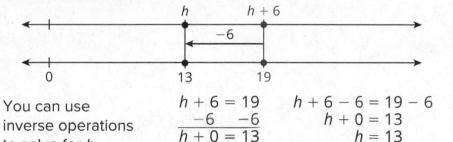

You can use inverse operations to solve for h.

$$h + 6 = 19$$
$$\underline{-6 \quad -6}$$
$$h + 0 = 13$$
$$h = 13$$

$$h + 6 - 6 = 19 - 6$$
$$h + 0 = 13$$
$$h = 13$$

REMEMBER...
The Additive Identity Property states that for any number m, $m + 0 = m$. In other words, when you add 0 to any number, it stays the same. It keeps its identity!

TOPIC 2

---

1 Examine the worked example.

ⓐ What is the solution to $h + 6 = 19$? **Check your solution.**

ⓑ Which property was used to maintain equality while solving the equation?

ⓒ Are there other solutions to the equation? **How do you know?**

2 Use the same strategy to solve each equation. **Check your solution.**

ⓐ $t + 24 = 85$

ⓑ $35 = 12 + m$

ACTIVITY 3

Equations
TOPIC 2 **LESSON 2**

Getting
Started

Activity
1   2   3

Talk
the Talk

Reasoning About More Interesting Addition Equations

You can use the same reasoning you have learned to solve more complicated equations.

HABITS OF MIND
• Look for and make use of structure.
• Look for and express regularity in repeated reasoning.

1 Think about each algebraic equation. Use reasoning to describe a relationship between c and d that makes the mathematical sentence true.

ASK YOURSELF...
Is a double number line helpful in reasoning about any of these equations?

(a) $c + 23 = d + 14$

(b) $45 + c = 66 + d$

(c) $c + 3d = 2c$

(d) $4c + d + 10 = 8c + 2d$

2 Braeden thinks that he can use a double number line to reason about more complicated equations, such as $4x = 20 + 3x$. Is Braeden correct? **Show your work.**

It All Adds Up

In this lesson, you used double number lines to reason about the solutions to equations and used inverse operations to solve one-step equations.

1 What does it mean to solve an equation?

2 Describe how to solve any one-step addition equation. How do you check to see whether a value is the solution to an equation?

TOPIC 2

3 Solve each equation. **Check your solution.**

(a) $120 + y = 315$

(b) $b + 5.67 = 12.89$

(c) $2356 = a + 1699$

(d) $\frac{7}{12} = g + \frac{1}{4}$

(e) $w + 3.14 = 27$

(f) $19 + p = 105$

LESSON 2 ASSIGNMENT

❯ Use a separate piece of paper for your Journal entry.

JOURNAL ❯

Write a definition for each term in your own words.

- one-step equation
- solution
- inverse operations

REMEMBER

A solution to an equation is the value or values for the variable that makes the equation true. To solve a one-step addition equation, use number sense or the Subtraction Property of Equality to determine the value of the variable.

PRACTICE ❯

❯ Use a double number line to solve each equation. Check your solution.

1 $x + 7 = 15$

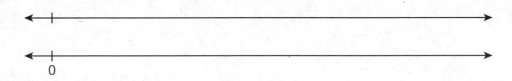

2 $19 = x + 13$

3 $14.5 = 6 + y$

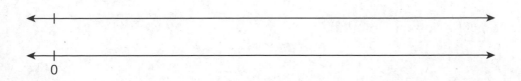

4 $a + \frac{1}{2} = 4\frac{3}{4}$

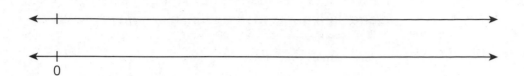

> Solve each equation. Check each solution.

5 $34 = x + 17$

6 $a + 25 = 92$

7 $7\frac{3}{5} + b = 10\frac{3}{4}$

8 $24\frac{1}{2} = t + 5\frac{1}{4}$

9 $r + 3.4 = 13.1$

10 $4.21 = 2.98 + s$

STRETCH Optional

> Solve each equation. Check each solution.

1 $34 = x - 17$

2 $a - 25 = 92$

3 $r - 3.4 = 13.1$

4 $24\frac{1}{2} = t - 5\frac{1}{4}$

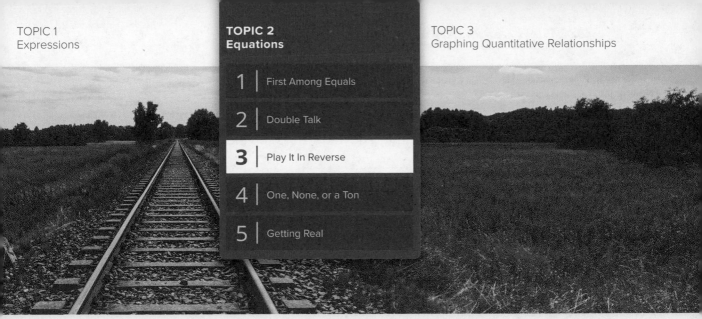

TOPIC 1
Expressions

TOPIC 2
Equations

1 | First Among Equals

2 | Double Talk

3 | Play It In Reverse

4 | One, None, or a Ton

5 | Getting Real

TOPIC 3
Graphing Quantitative Relationships

LESSON 3

Play It In Reverse

Solving One-Step Multiplication Equations

- Use double number lines to represent one-step multiplication equations.
- Use inverse operations to solve one-step multiplication equations.
- Reason about multiplication equations.
- Connect double number lines to the algorithm for solving multiplication equations.
- Solve one-step multiplication equations.

REVIEW (1–2 minutes)

> Determine the unknown product or factor that makes each statement true.

1 $\frac{4}{5} \cdot \frac{5}{4} =$ _____

2 $5 \cdot$ _____ $= 1$

3 _____ $\cdot \frac{23}{7} = 1$

4 $\frac{1}{12} \cdot 12 =$ _____

You have solved one-step addition equations using double number lines and inverse operations.

How can you use similar strategies to solve one-step multiplication problems?

Play It Again, Sam

❯ Consider the double number line that shows three equivalent equations.

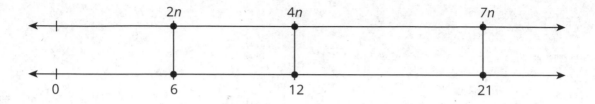

1 Write the equations represented on the double number line.

2 What is the value of *n* that makes all the equations true?

3 How can you check that the value you determined in Question 2 makes all the equations true?

ACTIVITY 1

Equations
TOPIC 2 LESSON 3

Getting
Started 1 2 **Activity** 3 4 5 Talk
the Talk

Representing Multiplication Equations on a Double Number Line

HABITS OF MIND
• Reason abstractly and quantitatively.
• Construct viable arguments and critique the reasoning of others.

TOPIC 2

Just as with addition equations, solving multiplication equations involves determining the value for the variable that makes the statement true.

WORKED EXAMPLE

Consider the multiplication equation $2x = 6$.

This equation states that for some value of x, the expression $2x$ is equal to 6.

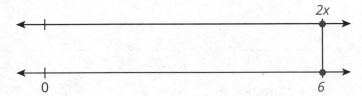

You can decompose the distance of $2x$ into two equal parts to determine the location of x. The expression $1x$, or x, is halfway between 0 and $2x$.

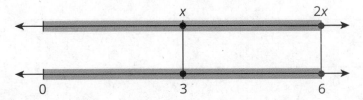

Since the expressions are connected as an equation, you also need to locate the point that is halfway between 0 and 6.

By examining the double number line, you can see that $x = 3$.

❯ Use the double number line to decompose the distance of the variable term into equal parts to determine the location of x. **Identify and check your solution.**

1 $3x = 12$

2 $7x = 63$

ACTIVITY 2
MATHia CONNECTION
• Using Double Number Lines to Solve One-Step Multiplication Equations

Equations
TOPIC 2 LESSON 3

Getting Started 1 **2** 3 4 5 Talk the Talk
Activity

Making Sense of Multiplication Equations

Multiplication equations often include numbers other than whole numbers.

❯ Consider the equation $\frac{1}{3}x = 2$.

1 Explain how the variable term in this equation compares to the variable terms in the previous activity.

REMEMBER...
There are different ways to write equivalent expressions.
$\frac{1}{3}x = \frac{x}{3}$

WORKED EXAMPLE

Consider the multiplication equation $\frac{1}{3}x = 2$.

The equation states that for some value of x, the expression $\frac{1}{3}x$ is equal to 2.

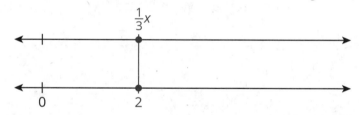

One way to solve this equation for x is to compose three distances equal to $\frac{1}{3}x$ to create the distance x.

Then to maintain equivalence, compose three distances equal to 2.

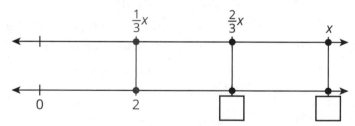

---

2 Complete the worked example by filling in the unknown values. Then write the solution to the equation $\frac{1}{3}x = 2$.
Check your solution.

THINK ABOUT...
Because you start with a fractional amount of x, you have to compose to get a whole x.

❯ Compose the distance of the variable term into the appropriate equal parts to determine the location of x. **Then identify and check the solution.**

3 $\frac{1}{4}x = 7$

4 $\frac{1}{2}x = 5$

5 Vanessa used a double number line to solve $\frac{2}{3}x = 8$. **Analyze her strategy.**

Vanessa

I created my double number line and represented the equation and x.

Then I labeled the bottom number line of numbers to identify the value of x.

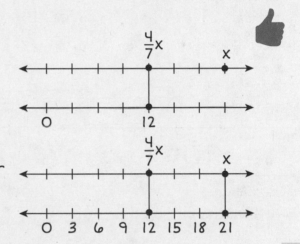

ⓐ Why did Vanessa set up her double number line in this way?

ⓑ Identify and check her solution.

TOPIC 2

❯ Use Vanessa's strategy and the double number line to solve each equation.
   Check your solution.

6 $\frac{4}{5}x = 12$

7 $\frac{3}{4}x = 8$

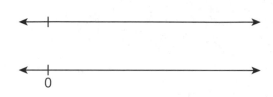

8 $\frac{8}{5}x = 64$

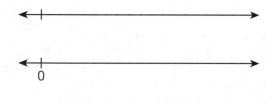

THINK ABOUT...
Think about
the relationship
between the
algebraic
expression and the
constant. Will the
unknown value be
greater than or less
than the constant?

❯ Reflect on the equations you solved in this activity.

9 How were they similar? What was common in how you used the double
   number lines?

Reasoning with Fractional Coefficients to Solve Equations

HABITS OF MIND
- Reason abstractly and quantitatively.
- Construct viable arguments and critique the reasoning of others.

❯ Consider the equation $\frac{4}{5}x = \frac{1}{10}$.

1 How is this equation different from the equation you solved in the previous activity?

❯ Compare the solution strategies proposed by Zoe and Landon.

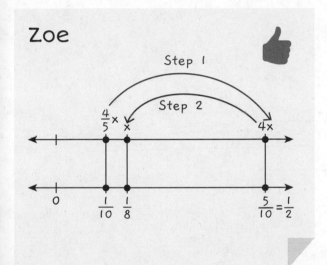

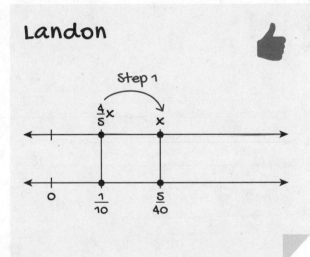

2 On the double number lines of each student's work, show the operation performed in each step of their solution strategies.

❯Use a double number line to solve each equation. **Check your solution**.

3 $\frac{3}{4}x = \frac{2}{5}$

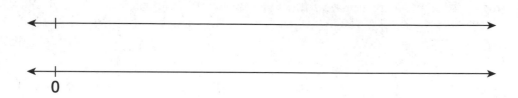

0

4 $\frac{2}{7}x = \frac{4}{9}$

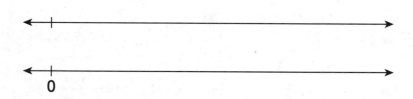

0

You learned to solve addition equations by first reasoning with double number lines and then with inverse operations. Now you have solved multiplication equations by reasoning with double number lines.

5 How do you think that you can solve these equations without using the double number lines?

ACTIVITY 4
Equations
TOPIC 2 — LESSON 3

Getting Started   Activity   Talk the Talk
1 2 3 4 5

MATHia CONNECTION
• Solving with Multiplication and Division
• Solving One-Step Equations with Decimals
• Solving One-Step Equations with Fractions

Solving Multiplication Equations Without Models

You reasoned with multiplication equations made up of a variable term and a constant. You can also use Properties of Equality and inverse operations to solve this type of equation. Which operation is the inverse of multiplication?

HABITS OF MIND
• Look for and make use of structure.
• Look for and express regularity in repeated reasoning.

TOPIC 2

WORKED EXAMPLE

Use Properties of Equality to solve the equation $4r = 32$.

Strategy 1

$4r = 32$

$\dfrac{4r}{4} = \dfrac{32}{4}$ Use inverse operations to isolate the variable.

$1r = 8$ Perform division.

$r = 8$ Identity Property of Multiplication

Strategy 2

$4r = 32$

$\dfrac{1}{4} \cdot 4r = \dfrac{1}{4} \cdot 32$

$1r = 8$

$r = 8$

---

1 Check the solution to $4r = 32$ shown in the worked example.

REMEMBER...

The Identity Property of Multiplication states that for any number m, $m \cdot 1 = m$. In other words, when you multiply by 1, the number stays the same.

---

2 Use one of the strategies from the worked example to solve each equation.

(a) $8a = 72$

(b) $11t = 132$

3 Write the properties that justify each step.

(a) $6w = 90$

$\dfrac{6w}{6} = \dfrac{90}{6}$ _____

$1w = 15$ _____

$w = 15$ _____

(b) $6w = 90$

$\dfrac{1}{6} \cdot 6w = \dfrac{1}{6} \cdot 90$ _____

$1w = 15$ _____

$w = 15$ _____

4 Diego and Venita are solving the equation $5 = \dfrac{p}{7}$.

(a) Diego says that to solve $5 = \dfrac{p}{7}$, he would divide by 7. The value of p that makes the equation true is $\dfrac{5}{7}$. Venita disagrees and says that they should divide by $\dfrac{1}{7}$, and the solution is 35. Who is correct?

(b) How can Diego and Venita check to see whose answer is correct?

5 Compare the solution strategies used by Sydney and Sam. **What do you notice?**

Sydney

$$\frac{2}{5}x = 20$$

$$\frac{\frac{2}{5}x}{\frac{2}{5}} = \frac{20}{\frac{2}{5}}$$

$$1x = 20\left(\frac{5}{2}\right)$$

$$x = 50$$

Sam

$$\frac{2}{5}x = 20$$

$$\left(\frac{5}{2}\right)\frac{2}{5}x = \left(\frac{5}{2}\right)20$$

$$1x = 50$$

$$x = 50$$

6 Solve each equation. **Check to ensure that your solution makes the original equation a true statement.**

(a) $\frac{n}{4} = 7$

(b) $18 = 3y$

(c) $\frac{3}{2}h = \frac{5}{2}$

(d) $3.14s = 81.012$

(e) $3\frac{1}{3} = \frac{3}{10}w$

(f) $4.2k = 14.7$

TOPIC 2

Reasoning About More Interesting Multiplication Equations

HABITS OF MIND
- Look for and make use of structure.
- Look for and express regularity in repeated reasoning.

Recall that you can create an equation by writing two expressions with an equals sign between them.

❯ Consider the equation $7c = 28d$.

1 How is this equation different from the equations you have solved in this lesson?

2 Generate at least 3 pairs of values for c and d that make the equation true. **What patterns do you notice?**

3 Jesse and Dominic each proposed a solution for the equation $7c = 28d$. Who's correct?

Jesse   Dominic

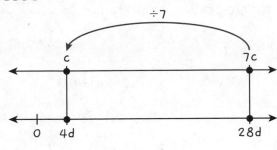

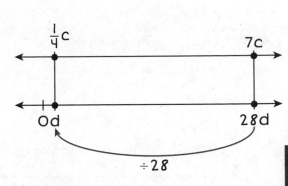

> Use reasoning to solve each equation for one of the variables.

4 $18m = 54n$

5 $12s = \frac{1}{2}t$

TALK THE TALK

Equations

TOPIC 2   LESSON 3

Getting Started   Activity
1   2   3   4   5

Talk the Talk

What's Your Strategy?

This lesson shows each equation written as $px = q$, where p and q are positive rational numbers and x is the unknown. You have investigated different strategies to solve these equations.

> Analyze each given equation.

$2n = 12$ $\frac{2}{5}x = 14$ $3x = 55$ $1.1m = 5.5$

$1.45r = 5.9$ $7h = 35$ $\frac{x}{4} = \frac{3}{8}$ $8r = \frac{3}{4}$

1 Sort each equation according to the solution strategy you think is most efficient.

Division Property of Equality	Multiplication Property of Equality

2 Provide a rationale for your choice of solution strategy or strategies.

> Use a separate piece of paper for your Journal entry.

JOURNAL

Explain how to solve the equation $px = q$ for x. Be sure to include the properties you use in the process.

REMEMBER

A solution to an equation is the value or values for the variable that makes the equation true. To solve a one-step multiplication equation, isolate the variable using number sense, the Division Property of Equality, or the Multiplication Property of Equality.

PRACTICE

1 Use the double number line to solve each equation. Check your solution.

ⓐ $3x = 10$

ⓑ $\frac{x}{5} = 6$

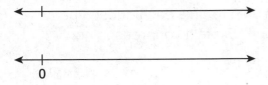

ⓒ $\frac{3}{5}x = 12$

ⓓ $\frac{5}{4}x = \frac{2}{3}$

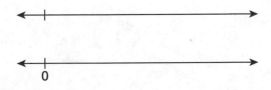

2 Solve each equation. Check your solutions.

(a) $2.1 = 0.5y$

(b) $4r = 26$

(c) $\frac{2}{9}h = 8$

(d) $\frac{4}{3} = \frac{8}{3}b$

(e) $14 = \frac{s}{3}$

(f) $3.8x = 2.736$

3 Bertrand invites 21 people to his party and wants to give each guest 3 party favors. If n is the total number of party favors he will need to order, the equation that represents this situation is $\frac{n}{21} = 3$.

(a) If Bertrand orders 58 party favors, will he be able to give each guest 3 party favors? That is, is 58 a solution to the equation? Explain your reasoning.

(b) How many party favors does Bertrand need to order? Use the equation to determine the solution. State the inverse operation needed to isolate the variable. Then, solve the equation. Check your solution.

STRETCH Optional

Like double number lines, you can use balances to model equation solving. Consider the balances shown.

On balance A, a water pitcher balances with a juice bottle. On balance B, the water pitcher balances a cereal bowl and plate. On balance C, three plates balance two juice bottles.

1 How many cereal bowls will balance a water pitcher?

TOPIC 1
Expressions

TOPIC 2
Equations

TOPIC 3
Graphing Quantitative Relationships

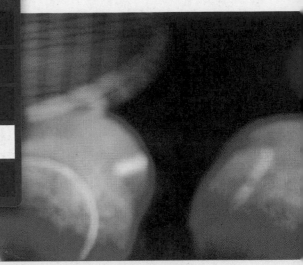

LESSON 4

One, None, or a Ton

Solutions to Equations and Inequalities

- Determine the number of solutions of an equation or inequality.
- Analyze, write, and graph inequalities.

REVIEW (1–2 minutes)

❯ Solve each equation.

1 $x + 37 = 37$

2 $\frac{1}{4}x = \frac{1}{4}$

3 $x + 0 = 225$

4 $58x = 0$

KEY TERMS

Zero Property of Multiplication

Identity Property of Multiplication

Identity Property of Addition

graph of an inequality

solution set of an inequality

You have used Properties of Equality to determine solutions to one-step addition and multiplication equations.

How can you use these properties to reason about solutions to equations and inequalities?

Game, Set, Match

❯ Consider these three equations and the set of values.

$x + 1 = 5$ $x + 1 = x + 1$ $x = x + 1$

$$\{0, 1, 2, 3, 4\}$$

1 Determine which values from the set, if any, make each equation true.

(a) $x + 1 = 5$

(b) $x + 1 = x + 1$

(c) $x = x + 1$

ACTIVITY 1

MATHia CONNECTION
- Using Substitution to Identify Solutions to Inequalities

Equations

TOPIC 2   **LESSON 4**

Getting Started   Activity 1   2   Talk the Talk

Identifying Solutions

Equations come in many forms. Because expressions are either numeric or algebraic, equations can be made of just numbers or both numbers and variables.

Equations are statements—they may always be true, never be true, or be true only for one or more values of the variable.

Always true	Never true	True for certain values of the variable
$6 = 10 - 4$ $x = x$	$10 = 20$ $x = x + 2$	$x = 5$ $x + 2 = 12$

When you determine that an equation is never true, you can make it a true statement by using the symbol $\neq$. For example, you should write $10 = 20$ as $10 \neq 20$.

1 Use the list of given expressions to write the type of equation described.

(a) Write an equation using two expressions that has no possible solution. **Explain why the equation has no solution.**

Expressions
$6 - 2$
x
4
$3 + x$
$x + 3$
0

(b) Write an equation using two expressions that is true no matter what number you substitute for the variable. **Explain why there are an infinite number of solutions.**

TOPIC 2

2 Analyze each equation and identify whether it has one solution, no solutions, or an infinite number of solutions. Then solve the equation. **Explain your reasoning.**

(a) $\frac{5}{8} = x + \frac{1}{2}$

(b) $x \cdot 1 = x$

(c) $11 + x = 11$

(d) $\frac{x}{10} = 0.1$

(e) $x + 5 = x + 4$

(f) $x + 0 = x$

(g) $10x = 30$

(h) $x + 8 = x$

(i) $x + 3.5 = 14.75$

(j) $0x = 0$

Equations that have an infinite number of solutions are equations that are true no matter what value you assign to the variable. The structure of these equations often describes important properties of numbers.

❯ Consider each property.

- The **Zero Property of Multiplication** states that the product of any number and 0 is 0.

- The **Identity Property of Multiplication** states that the product of any number and 1 is the number.

- The **Identity Property of Addition** states that the sum of any number and 0 is the number.

3 Analyze the equations you solved in Question 2.

　　ⓐ Which equation states the Zero Property of Multiplication?

　　ⓑ Which equation states the Identity Property of Multiplication?

　　ⓒ Which equation states the Identity Property of Addition?

4 For each solution, write a different equation with that solution.

　　ⓐ $x = \frac{1}{4}$

　　ⓑ $x = 6$

　　ⓒ $x = 0.1$

ACTIVITY 2

Equations

Getting Started

Activity 1 2

Talk the Talk

TOPIC 2 LESSON 4

MATHia CONNECTION
* Graphing Inequalities with Positive Rational Numbers
* Writing Inequalities from Real-World Situations

Inequalities

You have studied equations, which are mathematical sentences formed by relating two equivalent expressions. In this lesson, you will analyze inequalities, which are mathematical sentences that show one expression is greater or less than another expression.

HABITS OF MIND
* Model with mathematics.
* Use appropriate tools strategically.

You can use a number line to represent inequalities. The **graph of an inequality** in one variable is the set of all points on a number line that make the inequality true. The set of all points that make an inequality true is the **solution set of the inequality**.

1 Consider the graphs of the inequalities $x > 3$ and $x \geq 3$.

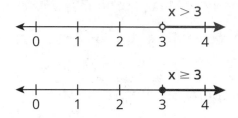

THINK ABOUT...

Why does one graph show an open circle and the other one a closed circle?

ⓐ Describe each number line representation.

ⓑ Describe the solution set for each inequality.

ⓒ How does the solution set of the inequality $x \geq 3$ differ from the solution set of $x > 3$?

2 Consider the graphs of the inequalities $x < 3$ and $x \leq 3$.

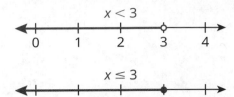

$x < 3$

0 1 2 3 4

$x \leq 3$

0 1 2 3 4

(a) Describe each number line representation.

(b) Describe the solution set for each.

(c) How does the solution set of the inequality $x \leq 3$ differ from the solution set of $x < 3$?

You can represent the solution to any inequality on a number line by a ray. A ray begins at a starting point and goes on forever in one direction.

A closed circle means that the starting point is part of the solution set of the inequality. An open circle means that the starting point is not part of the solution set of the inequality.

ACTIVITY 2 Continued

3 Write the inequality represented by each graph.

(a)
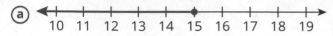
10 11 12 13 14 15 16 17 18 19

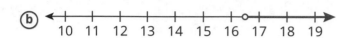

<blockquote>
TAKE NOTE...
For solution sets that don't start on an exact number, make your best approximation.
</blockquote>

(b)
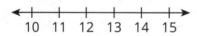
10 11 12 13 14 15 16 17 18 19

(c)
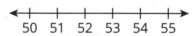
30 31 32 33 34 35 36 37 38 39

(d)

20 21 22 23 24 25 26 27 28 29

4 Graph the solution set for each inequality.

(a) $x \leq 14$

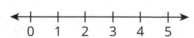
10 11 12 13 14 15

(b) $x < 55$

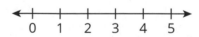
50 51 52 53 54 55

(c) $2\frac{1}{2} \leq x$

0 1 2 3 4 5

(d) $x > 3.3$

0 1 2 3 4 5

(e) $x \neq 4.2$

0 1 2 3 4 5

5 Consider the inequalities in Questions 1 through 4.

(a) How many solutions does each inequality have?

(b) Can you write an inequality that has no solutions? **Explain your reasoning.**

(c) Can you write an inequality that has just one solution? **Explain your reasoning.**

6 Define a variable and write a mathematical statement to represent each situation. Then sketch a graph of each inequality.

(a) The maximum load for an elevator is 2900 pounds.

(b) A car can seat up to 8 passengers.

(c) No persons under the age of 18 are permitted.

(d) You must be at least 13 years old to join.

TOPIC 2

Not All Variables Are Created Equal

A point at a is plotted on the number line shown.

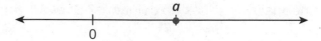

1. Plot a point to the right of this point and label it b.

   (a) Write three different inequalities that are true about a and b.

   (b) What can you say about all points to the right of point a on the number line?

2. Plot a point to the left of a and label it c.

   (a) Write three different inequalities that are true about a and c.

   (b) What can you say about all the points to the left of point a on the number line?

3. Describe the position of all the points on the number line that are:

   (a) greater than a.   (b) less than a.

JOURNAL

Describe how the graph of an inequality represents the solutions to the inequality.

REMEMBER

Equations can have one solution, no solutions, or an infinite number of solutions.

The set of all points that make an inequality true is the solution set of the inequality.

PRACTICE

❯ Identify whether each equation has one solution, no solutions, or an infinite number of solutions, and explain your reasoning. Then solve each equation.

1 $x = x + 6$

2 $4 \cdot x = 20$

3 $\frac{x}{3} = 21$

4 $1x = x$

5 $8 + x = x + 8$

6 $99 = x - 1$

7 $81 = 9x$

8 $x + 17 = 55$

> Write the inequality represented by each graph.

9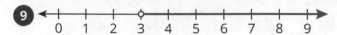

10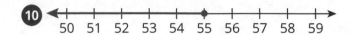

11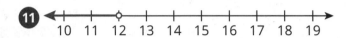

12

> Graph the solution set for each inequality.

13 $x > 12$

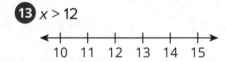

14 $1.8 \geq x$

15 $x \geq 3\frac{3}{4}$

16 $x \neq 13.5$

STRETCH Optional

> Model each equality or inequality situation. Then determine each solution.

1 Najid is taller than Emily and shorter than Daniel. Who is the tallest?

2 Sophie is now as old as Jasmine was 6 years ago. Who is older?

TOPIC 1
Expressions

TOPIC 2
Equations

TOPIC 3
Graphing Quantitative Relationships

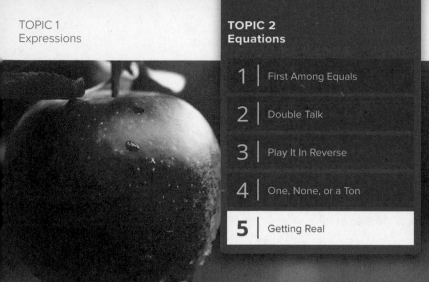

LESSON 5

Getting Real

Solving Equations to Solve Problems

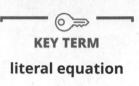

KEY TERM

literal equation

Learning Goals

- Use variables to represent quantities in expressions describing real-world values.
- Solve problems by writing and solving equations.

REVIEW (1–2 minutes)

> For each situation, define variables and write an equation that represents the situation.

1 Val has three times as many comic books as Chad.

2 It rained 15 more days in April than in May.

You know about expressions and equations and how they often represent the structure of real-world situations.

How can you apply your knowledge to write equations and solve real-world and mathematical problems?

Equations, Literally

You have already learned a lot of important equations in mathematics. Some of these equations are *literal equations*. A **literal equation** is an equation in which the variables represent specific measures. You most often see literal equations when you study formulas.

For example, the formula for the area of a triangle, $A = \frac{1}{2}bh$, is a literal equation. The variables in this equation represent the measures of the area, base, and height of the triangle.

1 Think about the formula for the area of a parallelogram.

   (a) Write the formula for area, A. Use b to represent the base and h to represent the height.

   (b) Solve the equation for b.

   (c) Solve the equation for h.

2 You can calculate the distance, d, of an object traveling at a constant rate by multiplying the rate, r, by the time, t. Write an equation in terms of each quantity.

   (a) Distance

   (b) Rate

   (c) Time

ACTIVITY 1

Equations
TOPIC 2 — LESSON 5

Getting Started
Activity 1
Talk the Talk

Using Equations to Solve Problems

You can use what you know about writing algebraic expressions to write equations that represent the values in a problem. You can then use your equation to determine a solution.

❯ Write and solve an equation for each problem. Show your work and label your answers. Describe the strategy you used to determine each solution.

1 Raul's sister is 6 years older than he is. What is Raul's age if his sister is 19 years old?

2 Approximately $\frac{1}{10}$ of the mass of a medium-sized apple is sugar. What is the approximate mass of a medium-sized apple that contains 19 grams of sugar?

3 Oscar made brownies for his class. He tripled the recipe he normally uses. If he made 36 brownies for his class, how many brownies does his original recipe make?

TOPIC 2

4 In June of 2016, for every 20 total emails a person received, they could expect to get 11 spam emails. If a person received 300 spam emails in one month, how many total emails did they receive?

5 In Jaden's town, the middle school has 443 more students than the high school. If the middle school has 817 students, how many students are at the high school?

6 The average height of an ostrich, the tallest bird, is 121 inches. The average height of a bee hummingbird, the smallest bird, is 2.75 inches. How many times taller is the ostrich than the bee hummingbird?

> Write an equation to represent each situation and then solve it to answer the question. A situation may require more than one equation.

7 Kendra bought some back-to-school supplies for $10.70 and showed them to her friend Naya. She bought 2 erasers for 55 cents each and 5 markers for 90 cents each. Kendra also bought 8 notepads, but she forgot how much she paid for them.

Naya said that she was not charged the right amount. How did she know?

8 The Bermuda Triangle is an imaginary triangle connecting Miami, Florida, to San Juan, Puerto Rico, to Bermuda. The Bermuda Triangle covers an area of 454,000 square miles. The dashed line on the map shows a distance of about 926 miles.

What is the approximate distance from Bermuda to Puerto Rico?

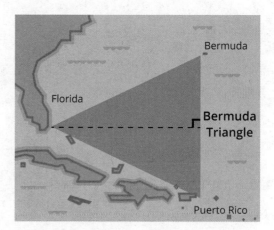

9 There are two routes Amit can take when he bikes home from school—the long way and the short way. The long way is $1\frac{1}{2}$ times as far as the short way. Over 5 days, he biked a total of 30 miles from school to home. He took the short way three times.

What is the distance of the short way?

Write Your Own

In this lesson you used the values given in a word problem to write and solve equations to answer questions posed about the scenario. Now you are going to work backwards from a given equation to create a word problem that you can solve with the equation.

1 Write your own word problem that someone can solve with the equation $2.4 + x = 5$.

2 Write your own word problem that someone can solve with the equation $4x = 8$.

❯ Use a separate piece of paper for your Journal entry.

Write a definition of *literal equation* in your own words.

REMEMBER

You can use the relationships described in real-world problems to write equations to solve for unknown values and use those solutions to answer questions. You can also substitute given values for variables in literal equations to solve for unknown values.

PRACTICE

1 The total cost, t, of an online order is the cost of the items, c, plus the cost of shipping, s.

   ⓐ Write an equation to represent the total cost.

   ⓑ Solve the equation for the cost of the items.

   ⓒ Solve the equation for the cost of shipping.

2 Solve each equation. **Show your work.**

   ⓐ $3g = 6.3$ ⓑ $5x = 12 + 18$

   ⓒ $2(4m) = 72$ ⓓ $2(a + 2a) = 90$

❯ Write an equation to represent each situation and then solve it to answer the question. A situation may require more than one equation.

3 A rectangular pool has a width of 24 feet. A second rectangular pool has a perimeter of 48 feet, which is $\frac{1}{3}$ the perimeter of the first pool. What is the length of the first pool?

4 The local firefighters collect toys to distribute at various give-away events. They have 4569 toys and will sponsor 129 give-away events. How many toys can they give away at each event? How many toys, if any, will be left over?

STRETCH Optional

You read a report that says that only $\frac{7}{100}$ of all people who own car dealerships in the country are women.

1 There are about 20,000 people who own car dealerships in the country. How many of them are female?

2 In a group of 2000 people who own car dealerships attending a conference, about how many would you expect to be female?

3 How did you determine the number of women car dealers, given the total number of car dealers? Use complete sentences to explain your answer.

4 Write an expression to represent the number of women car dealers, given the total number of car dealers.

5 Write an equation that you can use to determine the total number of car dealers in a certain city, given that the number of women car dealers in the city is 14.

6 Use the equation to determine the total number of car dealers in the city.

MIXED PRACTICE

❯ This Mixed Practice worksheet includes two sections: Spaced Review and End-of-Topic Review. **Use a separate piece of paper to show your work.**

Spaced Review

❯ Practice concepts from previous topics.

1 Determine each unknown.

   (a) $\frac{5}{6} = \frac{x}{30}$

   (b) $\frac{90}{x} = \frac{9}{2}$

2 Rewrite each expression as a single term.

   (a) $\frac{2}{3}x + \frac{4}{5}x$

   (b) $\frac{1}{3}\left(\frac{2}{5}x\right)$

3 Rewrite each expression as the product of a constant and a sum of terms with a coefficient of 1.

   (a) $2x + 5$

   (b) $\frac{1}{2}x + \frac{3}{5}$

4 Rewrite each algebraic expression by applying the Distributive Property.

   (a) $3.5(2x + 1)$

   (b) $\frac{1}{2}(3 - 4a)$

5 Determine the conversion.

   (a) 6 inches = _____ centimeters   (b) 10 kilometers = _____ miles

6 Define variables and write an algebraic expression to represent each situation.

   (a) Terrance has one fewer sibling than Casey. Kolbie has three more siblings than Terrance.

   (b) Connor has half as many comic books as Devyn. Isaac has 4 more comic books than Connor.

7 Write a different division problem that has the same quotient as the one given.

   (a) $36.5 \div 0.005$ (b) $63.196 \div 14.8$

8 In planning for the upcoming regional girls' tennis tournament, Coach McCarter looked at her players' statistics from the previous 2 months.

- Sarah: 7 matches won, 3 matches lost
- Sophie: 6 matches won, 4 matches lost
- Grace: 7 matches won, 4 matches lost

Based on their records, which player should Coach McCarter choose to attend the regional tournament?

9 Analyze each solution strategy. Which solution correctly evaluates the expression? Determine the error that was made in the incorrect solution.

Solution A	Solution B
$25 \times 20^2 - 4000$	$25 \times 20^2 - 4000$
$25 \times 400 - 4000$	$500^2 - 4000$
$10{,}000 - 4000$	$250{,}000 - 4000$
6000	$246{,}000$

End-of-Topic Review

> **AVAILABLE ONLINE**
> 1. A **Topic Summary** reviews the main concepts for the topic.
> 2. A video of the **Worked Example** is provided.

> Practice concepts you learned in **Equations**.

10 Solve each equation. Check your solutions.

    (a) $2.6 + j = 7.1$ (b) $\frac{21}{5} = b + \frac{3}{4}$ (c) $4x = 30$ (d) $\frac{3}{5}x = 21$

11 Identify whether each equation has one solution, no solutions, or an infinite number of solutions.

    (a) $x + 4.5 = x$ (b) $6x = 4x + 2x$

    (c) $\frac{3}{4}x = 9$ (d) $0x = 45$

12 Graph the solution set for each inequality.

    (a) $x \geq 6$ (b) $x < 14$

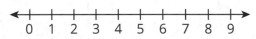

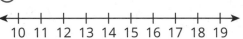

13 A builder requires a certain number of bricks each time he builds a brick structure. To make sure he has enough bricks, he always orders 50 additional bricks.

    (a) Define variables for the quantities in the situation.

    (b) Write an equation for the total number of bricks ordered.

    (c) Suppose the builder calculated that he needed 1275 bricks. How many bricks did he order?

14 Use the Properties of Equality to write an equation that has the given solution. Identify which Property of Equality you used.

    (a) $j = 3$

    (b) $8 = m$

15 Write and solve an equation to determine each unknown measurement.

    (a) The area of a triangle is 12.5 square feet and the height is 6 feet. Determine the base of the triangle.

    (b) The area of a parallelogram is 74.8 square feet and the base is 22 feet. Determine the height of the parallelogram.

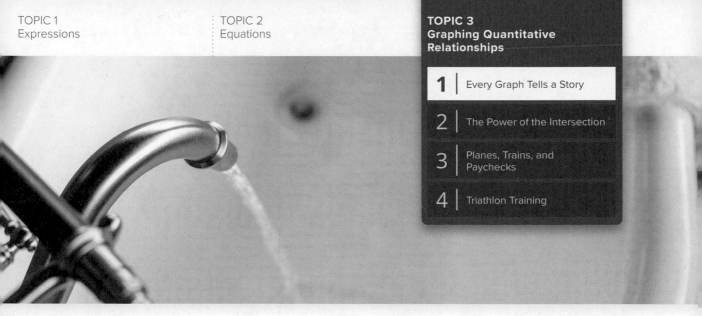

LESSON 1

Every Graph Tells a Story
Independent and Dependent Variables

Learning Goals

- Identify the graphs of situations.
- Determine whether graphs are discrete or continuous.
- Identify and use variables to define independent and dependent quantities in real-world problems.
- Write an equation in terms of two quantities.

KEY TERMS

discrete graph

continuous graph

dependent quantity

independent quantity

independent variable

dependent variable

REVIEW (1–2 minutes)

❯ Use the given rule to complete each table.

1 **Rule:** Multiply by 3

Input (*x*)	2		4	
Output (*y*)		9		15

2 **Rule:** Add 12

Input (*x*)	6		10	
Output (*y*)		20		23

You have analyzed quantities in a variety of ways. Often, the equation you write with variables depends on the question you are answering.

How do you know which variable is the focus of a mathematical question?

GETTING STARTED

Graphing Quantitative
Relationships
TOPIC 3 | LESSON 1

Getting
Started
1 | 2 | 3 | 4 | 5 | Talk
the Talk

Activity

It's Not a Tall Tale!

❯ Write a story to describe the situation represented by each graph.

1 The Water Level in the Bathtub

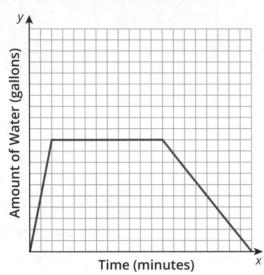

2 Walking Home From School

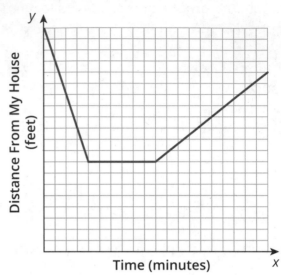

_____
_____
_____
_____
_____
_____
_____
_____
_____
_____
_____
_____
_____
_____
_____
_____

ACTIVITY 1

Graphing Quantitative
Relationships

TOPIC 3   LESSON 1

Getting
Started

Activity
1   2   3   4   5

Talk
the Talk

Match and Analyze

In this activity, you will match a specific graph to a real-world problem situation.

> Cut out the graphs and scenarios located on pages 477 through 485.

1 Tape each graph in the box with the appropriate scenario. Label the axes with appropriate quantities and units.

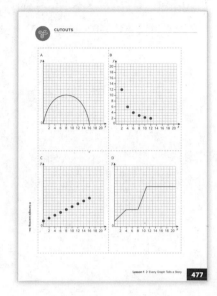

2 How did you determine which graph matched which scenario?

TAKE NOTE...
Even though only certain points make sense in the situation, you can draw a line to model the shape of the data.

TOPIC 3

A **discrete graph** is a graph of isolated points. Often, the coordinates of those points are counting numbers. A **continuous graph** is a graph with no breaks in it. Each point on a continuous graph, even those with fractional numbers as coordinates, represents a solution to the graphed scenario.

3 Which graphs are discrete graphs and which are continuous graphs? How does the scenario inform you that the graph will display discrete points or be continuous?

4 Which graph(s) represent equivalent ratios? How does the scenario inform you that the graph(s) will display equivalent ratios?

5 Consider the graph in the Rainy Day scenario. Assume that 2 hours after you left home, 1.5 inches of rain had fallen.

(a) Explain how the graph illustrates that the rain fell faster later in the day than at the beginning of the day.

(b) Describe when it was not raining in terms of the time, t.

6 Consider the graph in the Toy Rocket scenario. The rocket reaches a maximum height of 256 feet.

(a) Describe the shape of the graph.

(b) Describe when the rocket was rising into the air in terms of the time, t.

7 Consider the graph of the T-shirt Sales scenario. Suppose there is a minimum order total of $100 when you are ordering the T-shirts. Describe the number of shirts, n, that you must order to meet the minimum order requirement. **Explain your reasoning.**

TAKE NOTE...
There are lots of graphs that are not lines!

> Be sure to keep your graphs and scenarios. You will use them in the next activity.

TOPIC 3

ACTIVITY 2

Graphing Quantitative
Relationships

TOPIC 3   LESSON 1

Getting
Started

Activity
1   2   3   4   5

Talk
the Talk

Quantities That Change

HABITS OF MIND
• Attend to precision.

When one quantity depends on another in a real-world problem situation, it is said to be the **dependent quantity**. The quantity on which it depends is called the **independent quantity**.

The variable that represents the independent quantity is called the **independent variable**, and the variable that represents the dependent quantity is called the **dependent variable**.

> Consider the scenarios from the previous activity.

1 Use the Team Party scenario to answer each question.

   (a) Which two quantities are changing in this situation?

   (b) Which quantity depends on the other?

   (c) Define variables for each quantity and label them appropriately as the independent and dependent variables.

ASK YOURSELF...

Which quantity depends on the other?

2 Noel wrote an equation to represent the Fish Tank scenario.

> ### Noel
>
> 10 gallons per minute drain from a
> 200-gallon fish tank: w = 200 - 10t.

(a) What do the variables *w* and *t* represent in Noel's equation?

(b) Which two quantities are changing in this situation?

(c) Which quantity is the independent quantity, and which is the dependent quantity?

3 Identify the independent quantity and the dependent quantity in each of the four remaining scenarios.

(a) Rainy Day

   Independent Quantity:
   Dependent Quantity:

(b) Toy Rocket

   Independent Quantity:
   Dependent Quantity:

(c) Movie and Game Rentals

   Independent Quantity:
   Dependent Quantity:

(d) T-shirt Sales

   Independent Quantity:
   Dependent Quantity:

ASK YOURSELF…
Do you see any connection between the independent and dependent variables and the graph?

TOPIC 3

ACTIVITY 3
MATHia CONNECTION
• Modeling Scenarios with Equations

Graphing Quantitative Relationships
TOPIC 3   LESSON 1

Getting Started   Activity   Talk the Talk
1   2   **3**   4   5

Total Price and Profit

A store makes a 20% profit on the total price of all the items they sell.

HABITS OF MIND
- Reason abstractly and quantitatively.
- Construct viable arguments and critique the reasoning of others.

❯ Analyze the situation.

1 Name the two quantities that are changing.

TAKE NOTE...
Profit is the extra money for selling items, over and above the cost of producing the items.

2 Describe which value depends on the other.

❯ Let t represent the total price of all items sold in dollars, and let p represent the profit in dollars.

3 Write an equation to represent the relationship between these variables.

4 Identify the independent and dependent variables in this situation.

5 Complete the table.

	Independent Quantity	Dependent Quantity
Quantity Name		
Unit of Measure		
Variable		
	25.00	
	50	
	100	

6 Use the table to complete the graph.

Profit Earned Given Total Price

ASK YOURSELF...

Why do you think the total price is on the horizontal axis and profit is on the vertical axis?

7 Is this a discrete graph or a continuous graph?
Explain your reasoning.

8 On which axis is the independent variable? The dependent variable?

TOPIC 3

ACTIVITY 4

Graphing Quantitative
Relationships

TOPIC 3 — **LESSON 1**

Getting
Started

Activity
1 2 3 4 5

Talk
the Talk

Profit and Total Price

Let's think about the problem situation in a
different way.

HABITS OF MIND
• Reason abstractly and quantitatively.
• Construct viable arguments and
  critique the reasoning of others.

Suppose you are operating this store, and you know how much profit you make on
each item.

1 Name the two quantities that are changing. Describe which value depends on
the other.

❯ Let *p* be equal to the profit, and let *t* be equal to the total price of
all items sold.

2 Write an equation to represent the relationship between
these variables.

THINK ABOUT...

Now, we need
to isolate the
OTHER variable.
This is just solving
a multiplication
equation!

3 Identify the independent and dependent variables in
this situation.

4 Complete the table.

	Independent Quantity	**Dependent Quantity**
Quantity Name		
Unit of Measure		
Variable		
	8	
	10	
	20	

5 Use the table to complete the graph.

6 Is this a discrete graph or a continuous graph? **Explain your reasoning.**

ASK YOURSELF...

Why are the labels on your axes different from the previous graph?

7 On which axis is the independent variable? On which axis is the dependent variable?

ACTIVITY 5
MATHia CONNECTION
• Analyzing Models of One-Step Linear Relationships

Graphing Quantitative Relationships
TOPIC 3 — **LESSON 1**

Getting Started   Activity 1 2 3 4 5   Talk the Talk

The Question Matters

The situations in the previous activities are similar but presented in two different ways.

1 Complete each summary statement.

Total Price and Profit
The _____ depends on the _____.
Equation: _____

Profit and Total Price
The _____ depends on the _____.
Equation: _____

2 What do you notice about the two equations?

TAKE NOTE...
It's important to determine the goal of the problem before you start working.

3 How does examining this same situation from different perspectives affect the independent and dependent variables?

4 What can you conclude about the designation of a variable as independent or dependent?

5 Compare the two graphs in the last two activities.

(a) How are they similar and how are they different?

(b) What do you notice about the independent and dependent variables?

> Consider another scenario.

Dawson purchased a diesel-powered car that averages 41 miles per gallon.

6 Suppose Dawson is interested in how far the car travels on a given amount of gas.

(a) Identify the independent and dependent quantities.

(b) Define variables for each quantity and identify which is the independent variable and which is the dependent variable.

(c) Write an equation to represent the relationship between the two variables.

TOPIC 3

7 Suppose, instead, that Dawson runs out of gas on a regular basis. He is interested in how many gallons of gas he has used when he knows how many miles he has driven. Use the same variables you defined in Question 6.

(a) Identify which variable represents the independent quantity and which variable represents the dependent quantity.

(b) Write an equation to represent the relationship between the two variables.

8 How would you expect the graphs of the two situations to be similar? How would they be different?

Spring Fling

Nadja is coordinating the neighborhood Spring Fling. She asks Matthew to blow up balloons for the event. The graphs shown represent his efforts.

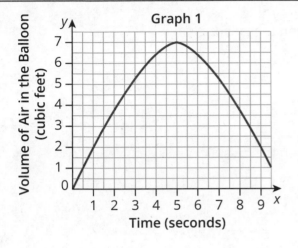

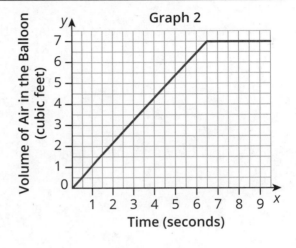

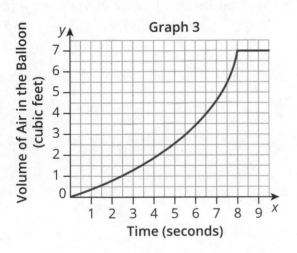

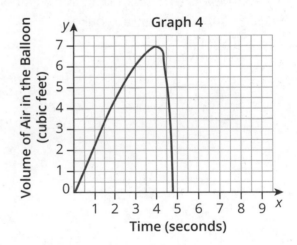

1 Analyze each graph shown, and then answer each question.

  a Which quantity is represented on the *x*-axis in each graph? The *y*-axis?

  b Which quantity is the independent quantity and which is the dependent quantity?

2 Match each description with the appropriate graph.

ⓐ Matthew blows air into a balloon at a steady rate, then ties it off when it is full.

ⓑ Matthew blows air into a balloon, and then the balloon pops!

ⓒ Matthew blows air into a balloon, and then lets the air out.

ⓓ Matthew blows air into a balloon slowly. As the balloon stretches out, he is able to blow more air into the balloon. He then ties off the balloon when it is full.

A

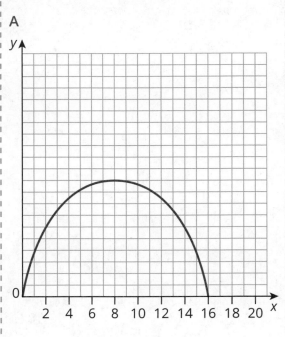

B

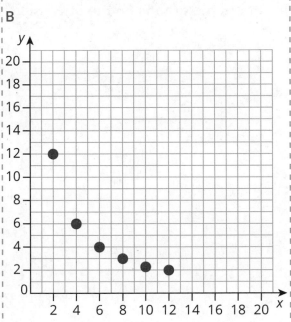

C

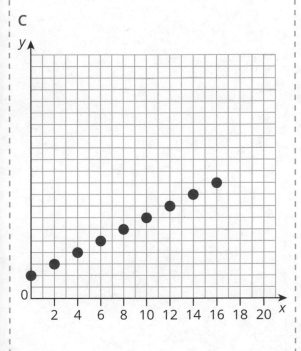

D

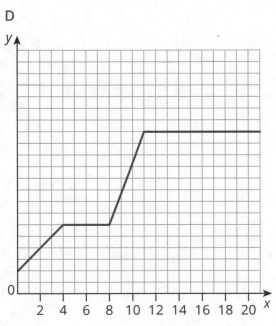

Why is this page blank?

So you can cut out the graphs on the other side.

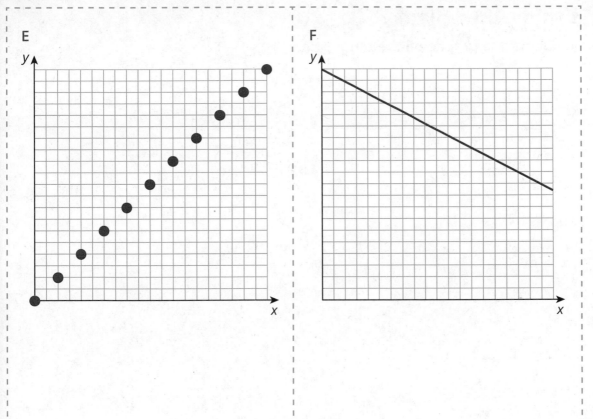

E

F

Why is this page blank?

So you can cut out the graphs on the other side.

Team Party

You have cookies for your team party, but you don't know how many of your teammates will show up. How many cookies will each teammate receive if everyone receives the same number of cookies?

Fish Tank

You are draining a 200-gallon fish tank at a rate of 10 gallons per minute. How much water remains in the tank at a specific time?

Why is this page blank?
So you can cut out the situations on the other side.

Rainy Day

When you left home, the rain was falling at a steady rate. Then it stopped raining for a few hours before a sudden downpour. Finally, it stopped raining. How many inches of rain had fallen at different points of the day?

Toy Rocket

You launch a toy rocket into the air from the ground and observe its height through its entire flight. How many feet high was the rocket at a specific time after launch?

Why is this page blank?

So you can cut out the situations on the other side.

Movie and Game Rentals

The video kiosk charges $2.00 for movie and game rentals. How many movies and games can you rent for different amounts of money?

T-Shirt Sales

Your club is selling T-shirts. There is a $25 design charge plus the cost per T-shirt. What is the total cost to order different numbers of T-shirts?

Why is this page blank?

So you can cut out the situations on the other side.

LESSON 1 ASSIGNMENT

> Use a separate piece of paper for your Journal entry.

JOURNAL

Describe the difference between the independent and dependent quantities in a situation in your own words.

REMEMBER

You know which quantity depends on the other based on the mathematical or real-world question asked. When graphing, you represent the independent quantity on the horizontal axis and the dependent quantity on the vertical axis.

PRACTICE

1 Determine the independent variable and the dependent variable in each given equation.

  (a) The equation $T = 75 - d$ is used to calculate the water temperature, T, at a depth, d, in a particular lake.

  (b) The equation $p = \frac{t}{3}$ is used to calculate the individual profit, p, made by each of three brothers operating a lemonade stand with a total profit, t.

2 An online ticket broker charges $6.50 per ticket. You are interested in the total amount of money you must pay for a given number of tickets.

  (a) Name the two quantities that are changing in this situation.

  (b) Define variables for each quantity and identify which represents the independent quantity and which represents the dependent quantity.

  (c) Write an equation for the relationship between the two variables.

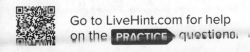

Go to LiveHint.com for help on the **PRACTICE** questions.

3 Jana runs about 8 miles an hour. She logs the distance she runs over time.

ⓐ Define variables for each changing quantity and identify each as the independent or dependent variable. Then write an equation to represent the situation.

ⓑ Use your equation to complete the table of values for this situation. Then use your equation and table to create a graph. Remember to label your axes.

	Independent Quantity	Dependent Quantity
Quantity Name		
Unit of Measure		
Variable		
	0.5	
	1	
	1.5	

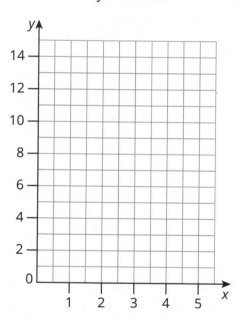

STRETCH ▶ Optional

1 Create two different scenarios that use time as a varying quantity. In one scenario, use time as the independent quantity. In the other, use time as the dependent quantity. Write a question that could be answered in each case. Create a graph for each situation.

TOPIC 1
Expressions

TOPIC 2
Equations

TOPIC 3
Graphing Quantitative
Relationships

1 | Every Graph Tells a Story

2 | The Power of the Intersection

3 | Planes, Trains, and Paychecks

4 | Triathlon Training

LESSON 2

The Power of the Intersection

Using Graphs to Solve Problems

Learning Goals

- Analyze the relationship between the independent and dependent variables in a graph and relate the variables to an equation.
- Use graphs to solve one-step real-world problems.
- Use an inequality of the form $x > c$ or $x < c$ to represent constraints when solving a real-world problem.

REVIEW (1–2 minutes)

❯ Determine which equations represent proportional relationships. **Explain how you know.**

1 $c = 2.5n$

2 $l = w + 25$

3 $d = \frac{1}{3}t$

4 $T = 100 - d$

You have graphed equivalent ratios and used those graphs to solve problems.

How can you use graphs to solve one-step real-world problems?

Selling Pretzels

Nic sells pretzels for $1.25 each at the morning events held at the Community Center. At the end of the events he is supposed to report the number of pretzels he sold and the total amount of money collected.

Nic sold pretzels on three different mornings, but he only reported either the number of pretzels sold or the dollar amount collected.

ASK YOURSELF...
What are the independent and dependent quantities in this situation?

1 Calculate each missing piece of information from his daily reports.

Pretzel Sales			
	Friday	Saturday	Sunday
Pretzels Sold	16	40	
Amount Collected ($)			40

2 Define the quantities and write an equation to represent the relationship between the number of pretzels sold and the amount of money collected in dollars.

3 Does this situation represent a proportional relationship? **Justify your answer.**

ACTIVITY 1

Graphing Quantitative
Relationships

TOPIC 3   LESSON 2

Getting   Activity   Talk
Started   1   2   the Talk

Using a Graph to Determine Unknown Quantities

HABITS OF MIND
- Model with mathematics.
- Use appropriate tools strategically.

In the Getting Started, you used an equation to represent the relationship between the number of pretzels Nic sold at the Community Center and the amount of money he collected.

You can also use a graph to represent this relationship. The graph shows the ordered pairs corresponding to the amounts you determined in Question 1 of the Getting Started, and the corresponding equation is $y = 1.25x$.

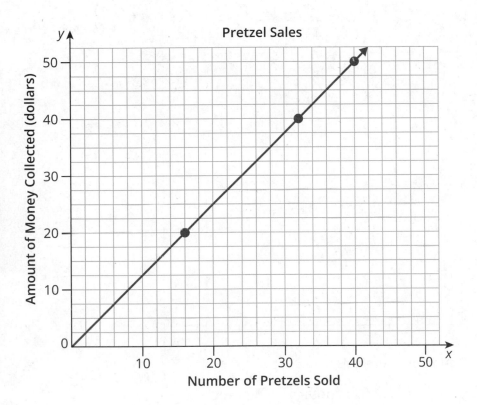

TAKE NOTE...

One way to analyze the relationship between ordered pairs displayed on a graph is to draw a line.

In some problem situations, when you draw a line all the points will make sense. In other problem situations, like this one, not all the points on the line will make sense.

TOPIC 3

1 Label the three ordered pairs shown on the graph.

2 What does each ordered pair represent?

3 Identify the unit rate in this situation. **Plot and label it on the graph.**

You can use a graph to determine an independent quantity given a dependent quantity.

WORKED EXAMPLE

You can use the graph to determine how many pretzels Nic sold if he collected $10.

First, locate 10 on the *y*-axis and draw a horizontal line. This shows that $10 is the amount of money collected.

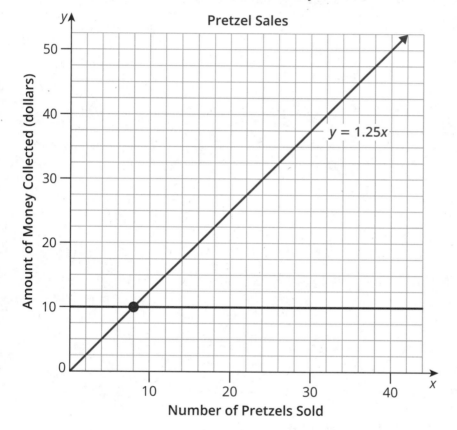

Pretzel Sales

$y = 1.25x$

Amount of Money Collected (dollars)

Number of Pretzels Sold

The *x*-value of the point where your horizontal line intersects with the graph of 1.25*x* is the number of pretzels sold for $10.

REMEMBER...

The solution to an equation is any value that makes the equation true. The graph of an equation is the set of all its solutions plotted on a coordinate plane.

4 How many pretzels did Nic sell when he collected $10?

❯ Use the graph in the worked example to answer each question.

5 How many pretzels did Nic sell when he collected:

ⓐ $25.00?

ⓑ $33.75?

ⓒ $40.00?

ⓓ more than $45.00?

ⓔ at least $50.00?

6 Nic reported that on Saturday morning he sold 13 pretzels and collected $16.25, and on Saturday afternoon he sold 42 pretzels and collected $47.50.

Do you think he reported accurately? **Explain your reasoning.**

Graphing Quantitative
Relationships

TOPIC 3   LESSON 2

Getting   ⌐ Activity ⌐   Talk
Started   1   2   the Talk
○────────○────────●────────○

ACTIVITY 2

MATHia CONNECTION
- Graphs of Additive and Multiplicative Relationships
- Comparing Additive and Multiplicative Relationships

Shipping Charges

> An online site sells a single closeout item each day. The items and prices change daily. The company charges a flat fee of $6.00 for shipping.

The graph shown represents a model of this problem situation.

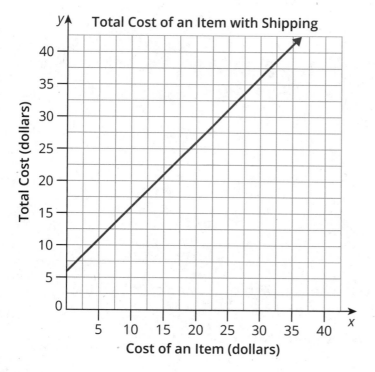

DID YOU KNOW?

A flat fee is a one-time charge on each order, regardless of how many items are ordered.

1 Write an equation to represent the relationship between the cost of an item, x, and the total cost, y. **Label the graph of the line with your equation.**

ASK YOURSELF...

In this problem situation, do all the points on the line make sense?

2 Does this situation represent a proportional relationship? **Justify your answer.**

❯ Use the graph or your equation to answer each question.

3 What is the total cost when the cost of the item is:

    ⓐ $18.00?

    ⓑ $25.00?

    ⓒ $32.50?

    ⓓ $75.00?

THINK ABOUT...

How does your strategy change if the dependent value is not visible on the graph?

4 Suppose the flat fee for shipping changed to $6.80. How would the graph change? How would the equation change? Would that change the way you could use the graph to determine values?

5 How would the graph change if there was free shipping on all orders where the cost of the item is greater than $20.00? **Sketch the graph.**

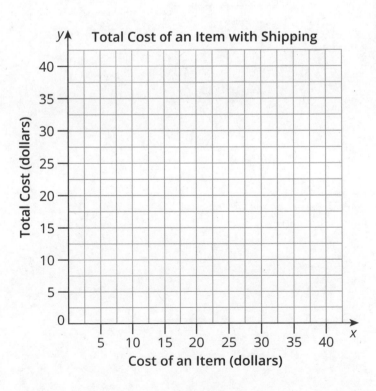

TOPIC 3

TALK THE TALK

Graphing Quantitative
Relationships

TOPIC 3   LESSON 2

Getting
Started

Activity
1   2

Talk
the Talk

Plus or Times?

1 Describe the similarities and differences between the pairs of equations.

$y = 5x$ and $y = x + 5$

$y = \frac{1}{2}x$ and $y = \frac{1}{2} + x$

$y = 4.95x$ and $y = x + 4.95$

2 Describe the similarities and differences among the graphs shown. Write an equation for each graph.

Graph A

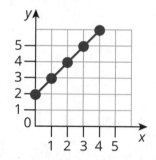

Graph B

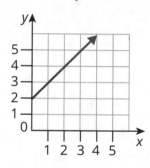

Graph C

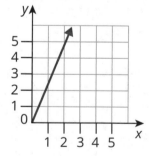

Graph D

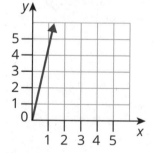

LESSON 2 ASSIGNMENT

❯ Use a separate piece of paper for your Journal entry.

JOURNAL ❯

Describe the similarities and differences between the graphs of equations represented in the form $y = nx$ and $y = x + n$, where n is any positive rational number and x and y are unknown quantities.

REMEMBER

Graphs are powerful visual representations of the relationship between quantities. You can use a graph to estimate a solution. You can also formally solve equations to determine exact values.

PRACTICE ❯

A shuttle space suit, including the life support system, weighs about 310 pounds. The break in the y-axis represents the values from 0–300.

1 What does each ordered pair on the line represent?

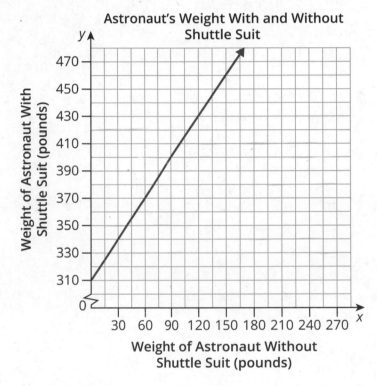

Astronaut's Weight With and Without Shuttle Suit

2 Write an equation to represent the relationship shown in the graph.

3 Is this a proportional relationship? Justify your answer.

4 In this problem situation, do all the points on the line make sense? Explain your reasoning.

5 Determine the weight of an astronaut without the shuttle suit given the astronaut's weight while wearing the shuttle suit.

ⓐ 480 lb   ⓑ 467 lb   ⓒ 520 lb

The gravitational pull of the Moon is not as great as that on Earth. In fact, if a person checks their weight on the Moon, it will be only $\frac{1}{6}$ of their weight on Earth.

6 What does each ordered pair on the line represent?

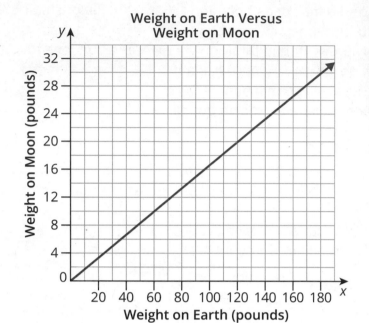

Weight on Earth Versus Weight on Moon

7 Write an equation to represent the relationship shown in the graph.

8 Is this a proportional relationship? Justify your answer.

9 In this problem situation, do all the points on the graph make sense?

10 Determine the weight of a person on Earth given his weight on the Moon.

ⓐ 12 lb   ⓑ 21 lb   ⓒ 36 lb

STRETCH Optional

1 Write an equation to represent each of the three segments of the graph shown. List any restrictions in the possible *x*-values.

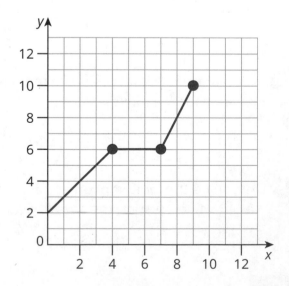

TOPIC 1
Expressions

TOPIC 2
Equations

TOPIC 3
Graphing Quantitative Relationships

1 | Every Graph Tells a Story

2 | The Power of the Intersection

3 | Planes, Trains, and Paychecks

4 | Triathlon Training

LESSON 3

Planes, Trains, and Paychecks
Multiple Representations of Equations

Learning Goals

- Write and solve equations that represent relationships given in tables, graphs, and situations.

- Identify independent and dependent quantities represented in tables, graphs, and scenarios.

- Analyze the relationship between the independent and dependent quantities in a situation using graphs, tables, and equations.

- Determine whether the data represented in a graph of an equation are discrete or continuous.

REVIEW (1–2 minutes)

> State which quantity in the situation depends on the other.

1 Snow is falling at a rate of 3 inches per hour.

2 The outside temperature is increasing at an average of 10 degrees each day.

You have identified independent and dependent quantities in relationships and have expressed these relationships using equations.

How can you use different representations to relate independent and dependent quantities?

GETTING STARTED

Graphing Quantitative
Relationships

TOPIC 3 — LESSON 3

Getting
Started — Activity —
1 2 3 4

Talk
the Talk

To the Equation-Mobile!

A mobile (MO-beel) is hanging art. It features all kinds of different objects suspended from string or wire. Balance is important to the visual effect of mobiles.

> Determine what value each shape represents in each mobile.

1

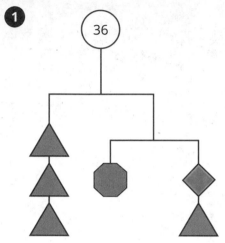

2

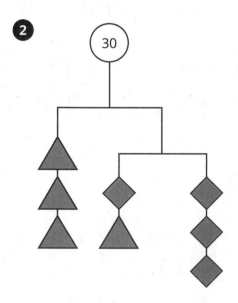

ACTIVITY 1
MATHia CONNECTION
• Patterns and One-Step Equations

Graphing Quantitative
Relationships

TOPIC 3   LESSON 3

Getting
Started

Activity
1   2   3   4

Talk
the Talk

Analyzing Relationships in Tables

SnapSmart charges the same price for each 3 inch by 4 inch picture print.

1 The table shows a few orders and the cost of each.

(a) What is the cost of one print? **Explain how you determined the cost.**

Number of Prints	Cost ($)
10	1.20
32	3.84
45	5.40
50	6.00

(b) Define variables for the quantities in this situation. Then write an equation that models the relationship between these quantities.

(c) Create a graph for this situation.

(d) Tell whether the quantities in the SnapSmart scenario are discrete or continuous. **Explain your reasoning.**

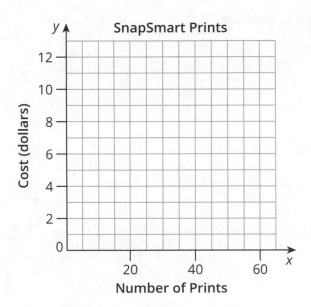

SnapSmart Prints

Cost (dollars)

Number of Prints

(e) Draw a line to show the shape of the graph. **Do all the points on the line make sense in this scenario?**

TOPIC 3

Number of Items	Cost ($)
1	6
8	48
16	96
5	30

The table shows the cost of a particular item.

2 Describe how the cost is related to the number of items.

3 Define variables for the quantities in this situation. Then write an equation that models the relationship between these quantities.

4 Explain whether the quantities in this situation are discrete or continuous.

5 Create a graph for this situation.

6 What do you notice about the shape of the graph? **Connect the points to see the shape**.

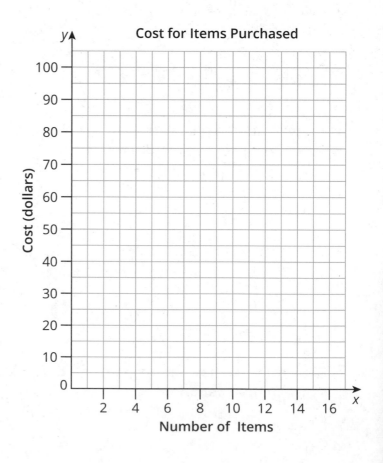

7 Analyze each table of values. Identify the independent and dependent quantities in each. **Then, write an equation that models the relationship between the quantities.**

(a)

Total Profit Made ($)	Profit Made by Each Person ($)
21	7.00
25.50	8.50
45	15.00

(b)

Boxes of Cookies Sold	Total Profit ($)
3	7.50
5	12.50
7	17.50

(c)

Number of Tiles Required	75	95	115
Number of Tiles Ordered	90	110	130

ACTIVITY 2
MATHia CONNECTION
Graphing Quantitative Relationships
TOPIC 3   LESSON 3
Getting Started
Activity
1   2   3   4
Talk the Talk

ACTIVITY 2
MATHia CONNECTION
• Problem Solving Using Multiple Representations in the First Quadrant

Analyzing Relationships in Graphs

The graph shows the relationship between the distance of a train from the station and the time in minutes since noon.

1 Complete the table using the points from the graph.

Time Since Noon (minutes)	Distance (miles)

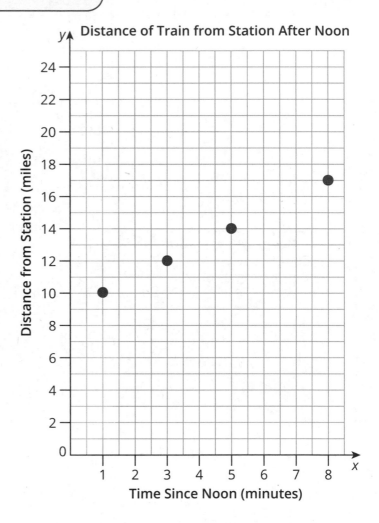

Distance of Train from Station After Noon

2 Define variables and write an equation to represent the relationship between the quantities.

3 How far is the train from the station 20 minutes after noon?

4 Connect the points to show the shape of the graph. **Do all of the values on the line make sense in this situation?**

The graph shows the relationship between the height of a plane and its distance from the airport in miles.

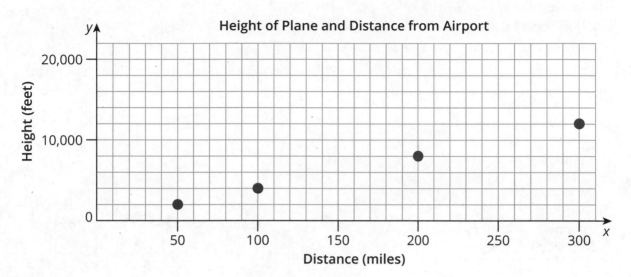

Height of Plane and Distance from Airport

5 Complete the table using the points from the graph.

Distance (mi)	Height (ft)

6 Write an equation to represent the relationship between the quantities.

7 What is the height of the plane at 150 miles? **Use the graph to justify your answer.**

8 Connect the points to show the shape of the graph. **Do all of the values on the line make sense in this situation?**

TOPIC 3

Analyzing Relationships in Scenarios

HABITS OF MIND
• Look for and make use of structure.
• Look for and express regularity in repeated reasoning.

> Jake's dog eats an average of 40 pounds of dry dog food in one month.

1 Write an equation to model the relationship between the number of pounds of dog food and the number of months.

2 Complete the table and graph.

Time (months)	Dog food (pounds)
0	
1	
2	
	120
	160
	200

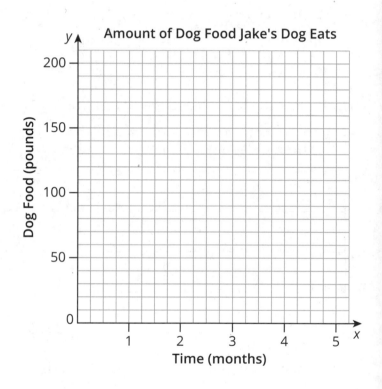

Amount of Dog Food Jake's Dog Eats

3 Connect the points to show the shape of the graph. **Do all of the points on the line make sense in this situation?**

ACTIVITY 4

MATHia CONNECTION
- Problem Solving with Decimals

Solving Problems Using Graphs, Tables, and Equations

HABITS OF MIND
- Model with mathematics.
- Use appropriate tools strategically.

> Your friend Aidan got a job working at the local hardware store. He created the graph shown to track how much money he makes for a given number of hours.

1 Create a table of values for Aidan's graph.

Hours Worked	Pay ($)
0	
5	
10	
15	

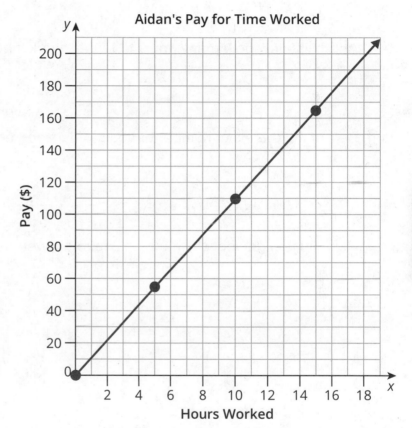

Aidan's Pay for Time Worked

2 How can you tell, by looking at the graph, whether the graph displays equivalent ratios? If it does, what is the ratio, or rate, displayed in the graph?

3 Define variables for the hours worked and Aidan's pay.

4 Write an equation to describe Aidan's graph.

5 Use the tool of your choice—equation, graph, or a table—to answer each equation.

(a) Approximately how much money did Aidan make if he worked 17 hours this week?

(b) Determine the exact amount of money Aidan made if he worked 12 hours this week.

(c) Approximately how many hours did Aidan work if he made $120 this week?

(d) Determine the exact number of hours Aidan worked if he made $178.75 this week.

(e) How did you decide which tool to use to answer each question?

TALK THE TALK

Graphing Quantitative
Relationships

TOPIC 3   LESSON 3

Getting   Activity
Started   1   2   3   4   Talk
the Talk

Let Us Organize the Ways

Multiple representations—including drawings or diagrams, verbal descriptions, tables, graphs, and equations—can be useful in analyzing and solving problems.

1 Complete the graphic organizer by describing the advantages of each representation.

- verbal

- table

- graph

- equation

Multiple Representations

Verbal

Table

Graph

Equation

> Use a separate piece of paper for your Journal entry.

JOURNAL

Create an algebraic equation. Represent the equation using a word problem, a table, and a graph.

REMEMBER

You can use a table of values, a graph, or an equation to show the relationship between independent and dependent quantities.

PRACTICE

1 Lashawna works at a candy shop that sells bulk candy. Before calculating the price, Lashawna must subtract the weight of the plastic bucket customers put the candy in. The candy bucket weighs 0.72 pound.

(a) Complete the table.

(b) Write an equation that models the relationship between the quantities in this situation.

Total Weight (lb)	Weight of Candy (lb)
2.84	
3.00	
	0.71
0.98	
	1.71
	1.13

(c) Use the table to create a graph of the relationship.

(d) Explain whether all points on the line make sense.

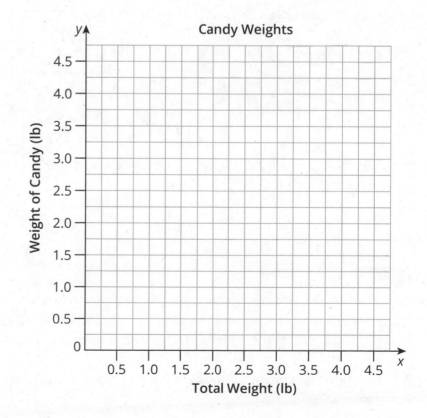

Candy Weights

Weight of Candy (lb) — y-axis: 0.5, 1.0, 1.5, 2.0, 2.5, 3.0, 3.5, 4.0, 4.5

Total Weight (lb) — x-axis: 0.5, 1.0, 1.5, 2.0, 2.5, 3.0, 3.5, 4.0, 4.5

2 Lashawna is packaging some bulk candy for a sale. The price is $3.98 per pound.

(a) Write an equation to model the relationship between the total cost (*t*) and the weight of the candy (*c*).

(b) Complete the table. Then use the table to create a graph of the relationship.

Weight of Candy (lb)	Total Cost ($)
2.50	
3.20	
	4.98
1.97	
	9.47
	13.93

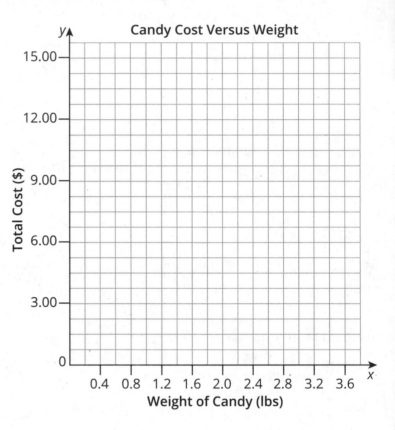

Candy Cost Versus Weight

(c) Explain whether it makes sense to connect the points on your graph.

STRETCH

A cryptarithm is a puzzle which replaces digits with letters. Your job is to use reasoning to determine what digits the letters stand for. When two letters are the same, they represent the same digit. When the letters are different, they represent different digits.

1 In this famous cryptarithm, the sum is correct. Can you solve it?

```
    S  E  N  D
+   M  O  R  E
_____
 M  O  N  E  Y
```

LESSON 4

Triathlon Training

Relating Distance, Rate, and Time

Learning Goals

- Use multiple representations to solve one-step real-world and mathematical problems.

- Analyze the relationship between independent and dependent quantities using graphs, tables, and equations.

- Summarize the relationship between distance, rate, and time.

REVIEW (1–2 minutes)

❯ Express each time in the requested representation.

1 3 hours and 15 minutes as a decimal

2 3 hours and 15 minutes in terms of minutes

3 2.75 hours in terms of hours and minutes

4 2.75 hours in terms of minutes

You have graphed and analyzed a variety of relationships between two quantities. You will notice a frequent grouping of some quantities, such as distance, rate, and time.

What relationship exists between these quantities?

GETTING STARTED

Graphing Quantitative
Relationships

TOPIC 3 · LESSON 4

Getting
Started
Activity
1 2 3
Talk
the Talk

Gearing Up for the Olympics

Deazia has her sights set on competing in the triathlon in a future Summer Olympics. A triathlon includes three sports: swimming, cycling, and running. Deazia must build up her endurance to be able to complete all three events in quick succession!

As part of her training, Deazia will participate in a variety of triathlons over the next year. The table provides the distances for each leg of five different triathlons.

	Island Escape	Kid Zone	Olympic Style	Sprint	SuperTri
Swim	1.5 mi	0.6 km	1.5 km	0.75 km	2.4 mi
Cycle	18 mi	15 km	40 km	20 km	112 mi
Run	8 mi	5 km	10 km	5 km	26.2 mi

1 What is the total distance in miles and kilometers covered in each triathlon?

TAKE NOTE...

You might need to convert units. Remember that 1 km ≈ 0.62 mi.

2 If Deazia completes all 5 triathlons in one year, how many miles will she swim during these competitions? How many miles will she cycle? How many miles will she run?

ACTIVITY 1

Graphing Quantitative
Relationships

TOPIC 3 — LESSON 4

Getting
Started

Activity
1   2   3

Talk
the Talk

Swimming Rate

Swimming is the first leg of the triathlon, so Deazia has trained with a coach to improve her chance of getting off to a great start.

Deazia's coach plotted her times and distances from her last few training sessions. Based on the data, the coach drew in a line to represent an approximation of her average speed.

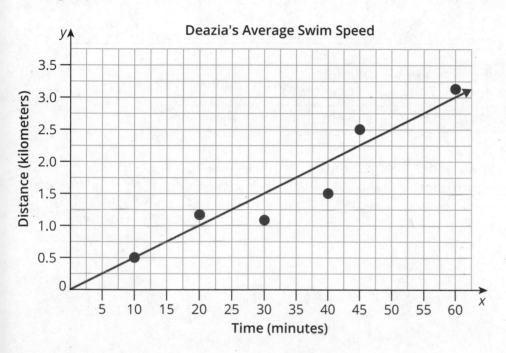

Deazia's Average Swim Speed

1 Deazia's little sister thinks that all of the points should be on the line drawn by her coach. Is she correct? **Explain your reasoning.**

2 Use the graph to determine Deazia's average swimming rate.

3 Write an equation to represent the amount of time, *t*, required for Deazia to swim a given distance, *d*, in kilometers.

4 Write another form of the equation to represent the distance, *d*, in kilometers Deazia can swim for a given amount of time, *t*.

Deazia wants to know how long it will take her to complete the swimming segment of each triathlon.

	Island Escape	Kid Zone	Olympic Style	Sprint	SuperTri
Swim	1.5 mi	0.6 km	1.5 km	0.75 km	2.4 mi

5 Assuming Deazia swims at her average rate, determine how long it should take her to complete the swimming segment of each triathlon.

ⓐ Island Escape

ⓑ Kid Zone

ⓒ Olympic Style

ⓓ Sprint

ⓔ SuperTri

ASK YOURSELF...

Which form of the equation should you use to answer this question?

6 Deazia's coach surprised her with an entry into a secret triathlon, the Mystic, last weekend. If she swam at her average rate and completed the swim segment in 45 minutes, how long was the swim segment? **Explain your reasoning.**

ACTIVITY 2

Graphing Quantitative
Relationships

TOPIC 3 — LESSON 4

Getting
Started

Activity
1   2   3

Talk
the Talk

Cycling Rate

Deazia cycles at a constant rate as a regular part of her training schedule.

Deazia records her distances and times in table shown.

1 Write an equation to determine the amount of time required for Deazia to cycle a given distance.

Distance Biked (kilometers)	Time (minutes)
5	15
35	105
90	270

2 Assuming she cycles at the same average rate, how long should it take Deazia to complete the cycling segment of each triathlon?

	Island Escape	Kid Zone	Olympic Style	Sprint	SuperTri
Cycle	18 mi	15 km	40 km	20 km	112 mi

ⓐ Island Escape

ⓑ Kid Zone

ⓒ Olympic Style

ⓓ Sprint

ⓔ SuperTri

ACTIVITY 3

Graphing Quantitative
Relationships

TOPIC 3   LESSON 4

Getting
Started

Activity
1   2   3

Talk
the Talk

Running Rate

Deazia runs every day as part of her training routine. She averages 9 minutes per mile.

HABITS OF MIND
- Model with mathematics.
- Use appropriate tools strategically.

1 Write an equation to determine the amount of time required to run a given distance.

2 Use your equation to determine how long it will take Deazia to complete the running segment of each triathlon.

	Island Escape	Kid Zone	Olympic Style	Sprint	SuperTri
Run	8 mi	5 km	10 km	5 km	26.2 mi

ⓐ Island Escape

ⓑ Kid Zone

ⓒ Olympic Style

ⓓ Sprint

ⓔ SuperTri

3 Use your equation and the results from Question 2 to create a graph of time, in minutes, that Deazia runs versus her distance, in miles. Connect the plotted points.

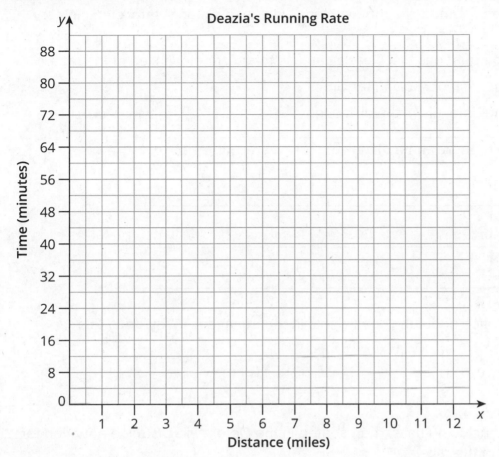

Deazia's Running Rate

Time (minutes) / Distance (miles)

4 After competing in the Mystic triathlon, Deazia reports that it took her 87 minutes to complete the running segment. Use the graph to estimate the length of the running segment of this triathlon.

THINK ABOUT...
Assume that Deazia runs at her average rate in this triathlon.

5 Rewrite the equation in Question 1 to determine the distance traveled for a given amount of time.

6 Use your new equation to determine the actual length of the running segment of the Mystic.

TALK THE TALK

Graphing Quantitative
Relationships

TOPIC 3 • LESSON 4

Getting
Started

Activity
1   2   3

Talk
the Talk

Reflecting on Triathlon Training

To analyze the three segments of the triathlons, you used distances traveled, times traveled, and rates.

1 Record the two equations that Deazia can use to describe each leg of the race.

- Determine the distance, given the time.
- Determine the time, given the distance.

	Determine Distance	**Determine Time**
Swim		
Cycle		
Run		

2 What do you notice about the coefficients in the equations? **Why does this make sense?**

3 Write the ratio, including units, represented in the *Determine Distance* equation for each segment of the race.

4 Explain why the ratios, or rates, listed in Question 3, not their reciprocals, are the appropriate rates to use in determining distance.

LESSON 4 ASSIGNMENT

> Use a separate piece of paper for your Journal entry.

REMEMBER

The equation that relates distance, rate, and time is $d = rt$.

PRACTICE

1 An airplane takes off and climbs at a constant rate of 1400 feet per minute.

(a) Write an equation to model the relationship between the plane's altitude and the time in minutes.

(b) Complete the table.

(c) Use the equation to determine the plane's altitude after 11 minutes.

Time (min)	Altitude (ft)
1	
1.5	
2	
2.5	

2 A car travels on the interstate at a constant speed. The table shows the distances the car traveled.

(a) Determine the car's rate in miles per hour and hours per mile.

(b) Write an equation to determine the amount of time required to travel a given distance.

Distance (miles)	Time (hours)
16.25	0.25
32.5	0.5
260	4
390	6

(c) Use the table to create a graph of the time versus the distance traveled.

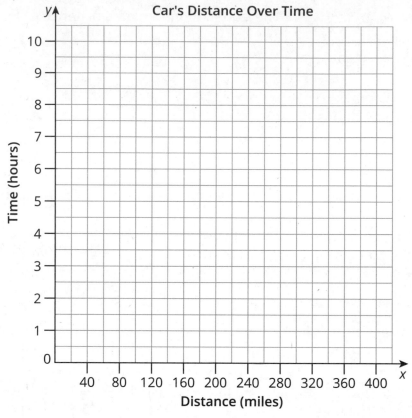

Car's Distance Over Time

(d) Determine how many minutes it will take the car to travel 43 miles.

STRETCH Optional

Alison and her friend are traveling home from New Jersey on Route 28.

- Alison thinks that taking Route 66 to Route 80 is a faster way home.

- Alison's friend says that staying on Route 28 is shorter, so they will make it home faster.

1 Who's correct? Which path is faster? By how much?

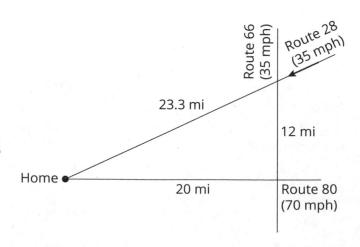

> This Mixed Practice worksheet includes two sections: Spaced Review and End-of-Topic Review. **Use a separate piece of paper to show your work.**

Spaced Review

> Practice concepts from previous topics.

1 Use long division to determine each quotient.

(a) 1968 ÷ 12

(b) 2363 ÷ 139

2 Write each statement as an algebraic expression.

(a) five less than twice a number

(b) seven and one half more than a number

3 Write the two possible unit rates for each ratio.

(a) 8 cups of sugar for every 2 tablespoons of vanilla

(b) $3.56 for 24 ounces

4 Determine which rate is faster.

(a) 185 miles in 3 hours or 490 miles in 8 hours

(b) 70 miles per hour or 100 kilometers per hour

5 Calculate the area of each triangle.

(a)

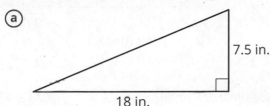

7.5 in.

18 in.

(b)

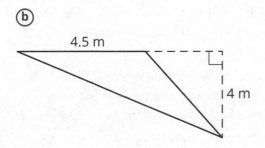

4.5 m

4 m

6 Determine each answer using the given formula.

(a) The formula $P = 4s$ is used to calculate the perimeter, P, of a square with a side length, s. Calculate the length of a side of the square if its perimeter is 34.56 inches.

(b) The formula $P = a + b + c$ is used to calculate the perimeter, P, of a triangle with side lengths a, b, and c. Calculate the unknown side length for a triangle with a perimeter of 52.81 inches and two sides measuring 16.32 inches each.

7 Solve each equation and state the inverse operation you used.

(a) $t + 4\frac{3}{4} = 8$

(b) $22 = \frac{11}{7}y$

(c) $20 = 6x$

(d) $p - 15.5 = 44$

8 In a video game, a character needs to shine a light through two spinning wheels that have holes in them. The first wheel makes a complete rotation in 7 seconds. The second wheel makes a complete rotation in 9 seconds. The holes are lined up at 0 seconds. How many seconds will pass before they are lined up again?

End-of-Topic Review

❯ Practice concepts you learned in **Graphing Quantitative Relationships**.

9 Use the graph to estimate each solution.

(a) How long did it take Serena to travel 70 miles?

(b) How long did it take to burn 100 calories?

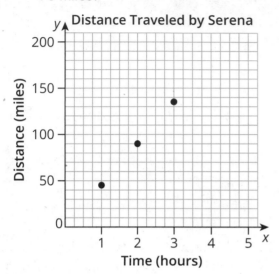

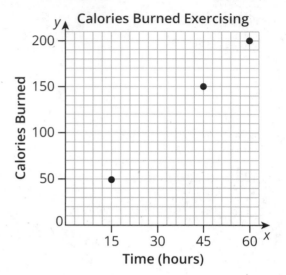

10 Determine the independent and dependent quantities in each scenario.

(a) Selena is driving to her grandmother's house. She travels an average of 60 miles per hour.

(b) On her way to work each morning, Sophia purchases a cup of coffee for each of her colleagues and pays $2.25 per cup of coffee.

11 A mountain climber is ascending a mountain at a rate of 5 feet per minute. Define variables and write an equation that represents the situation. Graph the equation on a coordinate plane.

12 A business subtracts $7.50 from each employees' gross weekly pay to cover the cost of their uniforms.

(a) Define variables for this situation.

(b) Write an equation that models the relationship between the variables.

(c) Graph the equation. Is the graph discrete or continuous?

(d) Calculate the gross weekly pay when the pay after the uniform fee is $67.23.

13 Name the two quantities that are changing in each and determine which quantity is the dependent quantity and which is the independent quantity.

(a) Terrence types 80 words per minute.

(b) To determine the total weekly wages of his employees, Mr. Jackson multiplies the total number of hours his employees work by $12.

Moving Beyond Positive Quantities

TOPIC 1 Signed Numbers	TOPIC 2 The Four Quadrants

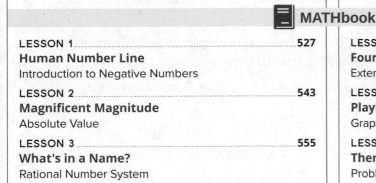 **MATHbook**

MATHia

Introduction to Negative Numbers
- Introduction to Negative Numbers
- Representing Integers on Number Lines
- Graphing Inequalities with Rational Numbers

Absolute Value
- Using Absolute Value

Rational Number System
- Classifying Rational Numbers

Extending the Coordinate Plane
- Exploring Symmetry on the Coordinate Plane
- Identifying and Interpreting Ordered Pairs
- Plotting Points

Graphing Geometric Figures
- Drawing Polygons on the Coordinate Plane

Problem Solving on the Coordinate Plane
- Writing an Expression from a Scenario, Table, or Graph
- Solving One-Step Equations Using Multiple Representations in Four Quadrants

Getting Ready for Module 4
Moving Beyond Positive Quantities

You will investigate the numbers to the left of zero on the number line, identifying the opposite of a number and ordering rational numbers. Building on your knowledge of distance, you will define *absolute value*. You will extend the coordinate plane and use it to create polygons, calculate horizontal and vertical distances, and solve problems.

The lessons in this module build on your prior experiences with coordinate planes, lines of symmetry, and comparing numbers.

Review these key terms and strategies to order decimal and fraction values to get ready to move beyond positive quantities.

KEY TERMS

coordinate plane

A plane formed by the intersection of a vertical number line called the *y*-axis, and a horizontal number line called the *x*-axis is a coordinate plane.

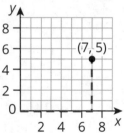

line of symmetry

A line of symmetry is an imaginary line that passes through a shape or object and divides it into two identical halves

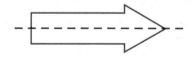

MATHia

Brush up on your skills.
If you need more practice with these skills, ask your teacher for access to corresponding workspaces in MATHia.

SKILLS YOU WILL NEED

Ordering Positive Rational Numbers

Plotting numbers on a number line will help you compare values and order the numbers.

$$1\frac{1}{2} \quad 0.6 \quad \frac{13}{10} \quad \frac{4}{5}$$

Notice that 0.6 is the farthest to the left, making 0.6 less than (<) the other numbers. Also, $1\frac{1}{2}$ is farthest to the right, making it greater than (>) the other numbers.

To order the values from least to greatest, record them in order from left to right.

$$0.6 \quad \frac{4}{5} \quad \frac{13}{10} \quad 1\frac{1}{2}$$

REVIEW

> Use the coordinate plane to answer the questions.

1 Write the coordinates.

   (a) Point A.

   (B) Point B.

2 Plot each point

   (a) (7, 5)

   (B) (0, 2)

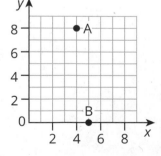

See the Appendix on page 719 for answers.

LESSON 1

Human Number Line

Introduction to Negative Numbers

🔑 KEY TERMS

negative numbers

infinity

Learning Goals

- Use positive and negative numbers to describe quantities having opposite directions.

- Explain the meaning of 0 in contexts represented by positive and negative numbers.

- Identify and represent a number and its opposite on a number line.

- Represent, interpret, and order positive and negative integers and other rational numbers using number lines and inequality statements.

> **REVIEW** (1–2 minutes)

❯ Use the number line to plot and compare each pair of numbers. Then, insert a > or < symbol to make each inequality statement true.

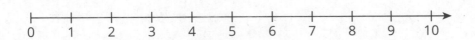

0   1   2   3   4   5   6   7   8   9   10

1 $\frac{3}{4}$ __ $1\frac{1}{2}$

2 5.5 __ 5.06

3 7.65 __ 6.75

You have used numbers equal to or greater than 0 to represent real-world situations.

How can you use numbers less than 0 to describe real-world situations?

Time Travel

In this activity, you will use a number line to represent time.

Your teacher will assign students to participate in the activity.

❯ Record what happens on the number line.

1 For each student, plot and label the point where the student stands on the number line. Also identify what time the point represents.

- **Student A:** Stand at 0 to represent the time right now.
- **Student B:** Stand at the point that represents 3 hours from now.
- **Student C:** Stand at the point that represents 3 hours ago.
- **Student D:** Stand at the point that represents 5 hours from now.
- **Student E:** Stand at the point that represents 2 hours ago.
- **Student F:** Stand at the point that represents 7 hours ago.

Investigating Time on a Number Line

You can reflect the positive numbers on a number line across 0 to create a number line with *negative numbers*.

Negative numbers are to the left of 0 on the number line.

Positive numbers extend to positive *infinity*, and negative numbers extend to negative *infinity*. **Infinity**, represented by the symbol ∞, means a quantity with no end or bound.
The number line goes on forever in both directions!

TAKE NOTE...
You write a negative number with a negative sign. You can write a positive number with a positive sign or without any sign.

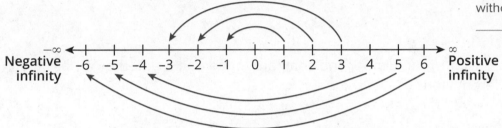

Negative infinity $-\infty$ −6 −5 −4 −3 −2 −1 0 1 2 3 4 5 6 ∞ Positive infinity

1 Describe the change in the values of the numbers as you move to the right on the number line.

2 Describe the change in the values of the numbers as you move to the left on the number line.

> Consider your class time number line.

3 Describe the locations of the points that represent time in the future.

4 Describe the locations of the points that represent time in the past.

5 How would labels on your number line compare to the one created by a class that starts at a different time?

> Think about where you plot a given number of hours before or after time 0. What do you notice about its distance from 0?

6 What do you notice about where you plot a time 3 hours before and 3 hours after now? Or 6 hours before and 6 hours after now?

ACTIVITY 2
MATHia CONNECTION
• Introduction to Negative Numbers

Signed Numbers
TOPIC 1   LESSON 1

Getting Started | Activity 1 2 3 4 5 | Talk the Talk

Representing Opposites on a Number Line

HABITS OF MIND
• Look for and make use of structure.
• Look for and express regularity in repeated reasoning.

Let's think more about both sides of 0 on a number line.

Your teacher will model a number line.

1 Create and label a number line according to the model.

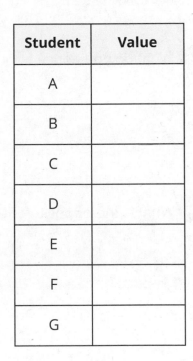

2 Plot and label the location where each student stands on the number line. In the table, identify the value represented by the location where the student is standing.

- **Student A:** Stand at 0.
- **Student B:** Stand at 4.5.
- **Student C:** Stand at the opposite of 4.5.
- **Student D:** Stand at −6.
- **Student E:** Stand at the opposite of −6.
- **Student F:** Stand at a location between 2 and 3.
- **Student G:** Stand at the location that is the opposite of Student F.

Student	Value
A	
B	
C	
D	
E	
F	
G	

3 Describe the number line relationship of the students who were opposites of each other.

TOPIC 1

Opposite numbers are reflections of each other across 0 on the number line.

- The opposite of a positive number is a corresponding negative number.
- The opposite of a negative number is a corresponding positive number.

THINK ABOUT...

There is only one number that is its own opposite.

Attaching a negative sign to a number means reflecting that number across 0 on the number line.

4 Use symbols to represent the opposite of each number and the value it represents.

   (a) $-(4.5)$ = _____   (b) $-(-6)$ = _____

5 What do you notice about the distance from 0 of corresponding opposite numbers?

6 What is the opposite of 0?

7 Name the opposite of each number. Then plot each number and its opposite on the number line.

   (a) $1\frac{1}{2}$ (b) -5 (c) -9.9

REMEMBER...

Don't forget to label the number line!

<----+---->
                            0

ACTIVITY 3

Signed Numbers

TOPIC 1   LESSON 1

Getting Started   Activity   Talk the Talk
1   2   **3**   4   5

TOPIC 1

Representing Money on a Number Line

The value 0 can have different meanings depending on how you interpret a situation.

HABITS OF MIND
- Reason abstractly and quantitatively.
- Construct viable arguments and critique the reasoning of others.

Alyson and her friends are trying to decide whether they can go to the movies. Each ticket costs $9.00. Each friend comments on how much money they have.

- Alyson: I have $2.50 more than the movie costs.
- Sharon: Oh, I don't have enough money. I'm $4.00 short.
- Brian: Not only can I buy a ticket, but I have just enough money to buy the $8.00 snack combo!
- Eileen: If I can find one more quarter, I can go.

Myron and Paulie created different number lines to represent the scenario.

Myron

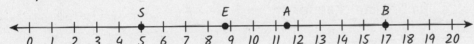

Paulie

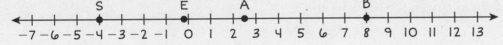

> Analyze each representation of the scenario.

1 What does each point represent on Myron's number line?

2 What does each point represent on Paulie's number line?

3 Myron and Paulie are thinking about 0 differently. Explain what 0 represents on each number line.

4 Suppose the four friends decide to go to a matinee instead, where the ticket price is $7.50.

    a How would Myron's number line change?

    b How would Paulie's number line change?

DID YOU KNOW?
A matinee is a movie played at a theater in the afternoon.

Temperature Connection

In this activity, you will use a vertical number line to analyze temperatures.

1 Record each temperature on the thermometer shown.

(a) The highest temperature on record in the United States is 134°F. It occurred in 1913 in Death Valley, California.

(b) The lowest temperature on record is −80°F. It occurred at Prospect Creek Camp, Alaska.

(c) The lowest temperature recorded in the contiguous 48 states is −70°F. It occurred in Rogers Pass, Montana.

(d) The highest winter average temperature in the United States is 78°F, which occurs in Honolulu, Hawaii.

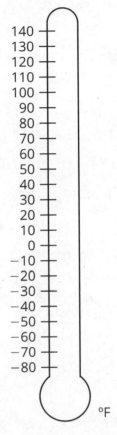

2 Which is colder, the lowest temperature recorded in Alaska or the lowest temperature recorded in Montana? **How do you know?**

3 Yadi and Eric were comparing 25 degrees to –27 degrees.

- Yadi wrote 25 < –27 and justified her comparison by stating that the further a number is from zero, the greater the number.

- Eric wrote 25 > –27 and justified his comparison by stating that the greater temperature is above the lower temperature on a thermometer.

Who is correct? **Explain your choice.**

4 Plot each set of temperatures on the thermometer. Then insert a > or < symbol to make each number sentence true.

(a) –26°F _____ –31°F

(b) –6°F _____ –17°F

(c) –9°F _____ 8°F

```
50 ┼
40 ┼
30 ┼
20 ┼
10 ┼
 0 ┼
−10 ┼
−20 ┼
−30 ┼
−40 ┼
−50 ┼
        °F
```

5 Order the temperatures from least to greatest.

25°F   –33°F   0°F   105°F   –40°F   –5°F   67°F

ACTIVITY 5

MATHia CONNECTION
- Representing Integers on a Number Line
- Graphing Inequalities with Rational Numbers

Signed Numbers
TOPIC 1   LESSON 1

Getting Started | Activity 1 2 3 4 5 | Talk the Talk

Comparing and Ordering Rational Numbers

HABITS OF MIND
- Reason abstractly and quantitatively.
- Construct viable arguments and critique the reasoning of others.

Helen and Grace started a company called Top Notch. The table shown represents their first 10 weeks of operation. A number in parentheses represents a loss for the week. Amounts that are not in parentheses represent a profit for the week.

Week	1	2	3	4	5	6	7	8	9	10
Profit/Loss	$159	($201)	$231	($456)	($156)	($12)	$281	$175	$192	$213
+/− Number										

1 Use the table and number line to answer each question.

(a) Write each profit or loss as a positive or negative number and then plot the number on the number line.

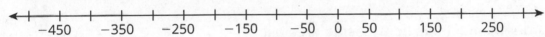

(b) What does 0 represent in this situation?

(c) In which week did the company have:
- The greatest profit?
- The greatest loss?

2 For each pair of weeks, write an inequality statement to compare the positive and negative numbers. **Interpret the statement in context.**

(a) Week 1 and Week 5

(b) Week 4 and Week 6

You can compare different types of numbers by plotting the numbers on a number line.

3 Use the number line to answer each question.

(a) Plot each value on the number line.

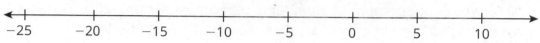

$-6\frac{2}{3}$ -20 0 10.5 $-17\frac{1}{2}$ -7.98 12 -3 -13

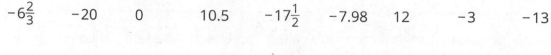

-25 -20 -15 -10 -5 0 5 10

(b) Which of the numbers has the least value? **How do you know?**

(c) Which of the numbers has the greatest value? **How do you know?**

ASK YOURSELF...
How do you know which rational number is greater by looking at the number line?

(d) Order the numbers from least to greatest.

4 Plot each rational number on the number line. Then insert a >, <, or = symbol to make each number sentence true.

(a) -10.25 _____ $-15\frac{2}{3}$

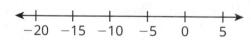

-20 -15 -10 -5 0 5

(b) -17 _____ -17

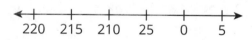

220 215 210 25 0 5

(c) $5\frac{2}{3}$ _____ -8.28

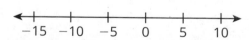

-15 -10 -5 0 5 10

TALK THE TALK

Signed Numbers
TOPIC 1 — **LESSON 1**

Getting Started
Activity
1 2 3 4 5
Talk the Talk

TOPIC 1

Putting It All Together

In this lesson, you used a number line to represent positive numbers, negative numbers, and zero.

1 What does 0 mean on a number line?

2 What does *opposite* mean in terms of a number line?

3 Compare the types of numbers. Use what you know about number lines to explain your reasoning.

(a) Which is greater—a negative or a positive rational number?

(b) Which is greater—zero or any positive rational number?

(c) Which is greater—zero or any negative rational number?

(d) How do you decide which of two numbers is greater when both numbers are positive?

(e) How do you decide which of two numbers is greater when both numbers are negative?

④ Your sixth-grade cousin goes to school in a different state. His math class has not yet started comparing integers. Write him an email explaining how to compare any two numbers. **Be sure to include 1 or 2 examples and enough details that he will be able to explain it to his class.**

LESSON 1 ASSIGNMENT

> Use a separate piece of paper for your Journal entry.

JOURNAL

Write a sentence or two to explain the relationship between *opposites* and *negative numbers*.

REMEMBER

You can use the rational number line to represent positive numbers, negative numbers, and zero. The values to the left of zero on the number line are reflections of the values on the right across 0.

PRACTICE

1 Plot each number and its opposite on the number line.

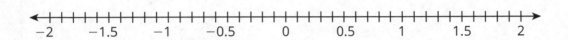

(a) -1

(b) 0.4

(c) $1\frac{3}{4}$

(d) -1.9

(e) 0.09

2 Insert a >, <, or = symbol to make each number sentence true.

(a) -5 ___ $-5\frac{2}{3}$

(b) -3.5 ___ $-3\frac{1}{2}$

(c) -18 ___ 9

(d) -6.75 ___ -2.25

3 Order the numbers from least to greatest.

0.125 $1\frac{1}{5}$ $-\frac{4}{9}$ $\frac{4}{11}$ $-\frac{3}{2}$ -2.75

4 The Ravine Flyer II is a steel and wood roller coaster that takes advantage of the terrain in Erie, PA, to make the ride more exciting. Although the coaster is only 80 feet high, it follows the line of a cliff that drops to −35 feet (0 represents the height of the cliff).

(a) Plot the highest and lowest points of the roller coaster on the vertical number line.

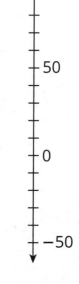

(b) Explain why a vertical number line better represents the problem context than a horizontal number line.

(c) How many total feet does the roller coaster drop?

5 The Monster is a roller coaster that uses a design similar to the Ravine Flyer II. The Monster reaches a height of 120 feet, but then drops to −25 feet. Order the highest and lowest points of the two roller coasters from least to greatest.

6 An amusement park wants to design a coaster that rises 60 feet above ground and then drops the same distance below ground through a tunnel. Represent the underground depth with a number, and explain its relationship with the above ground height.

STRETCH Optional

> Create a new situation, similar to Activity 3 *Representing Money on a Number Line*, in which zero can have two different meanings.

TOPIC 1
Signed Numbers

TOPIC 2
The Four Quadrants

1	Human Number Line
2	Magnificent Magnitude
3	What's in a Name?

LESSON 2

Magnificent Magnitude

Absolute Value

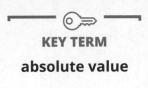

Learning Goals

- Explain the meaning of the absolute value of a rational number as its distance from 0 on a number line.

- Interpret the meaning of absolute value as the magnitude for a positive or negative quantity in a real-world context.

- Evaluate the absolute value of a quantity.

- Compare and order numbers expressed as absolute value and distinguish absolute value comparisons from statements about order.

REVIEW (1–2 minutes)

❯ Plot each set of numbers on the number line and describe the relationship between the numbers.

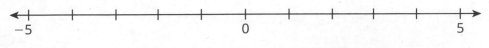

1 5 and −5

2 $2\frac{3}{4}$ and $-2\frac{3}{4}$

You can describe numbers by their distance from 0 on the number line.

How can you use these distances to solve real-world problems?

Going the Distance

> Use the number line to answer each question.

1 Plot a point at −7 on the number line.

2 Describe the distance from −7 to 0.

3 Plot as many other points as possible on the number line that are the same distance from 0 as −7.

4 How many numbers did you plot? **Why do you think this is true?**

Absolute Value as Magnitude

Let's revisit the number line from the *Human Number Line* lesson. Your teacher will assign students to participate in the activity.

> Record what happens on the number line.

- **Student A:** Stand on 0 and hold one end of a piece of string.
- **Student B:** Take the other end of the string and locate a point on the number line that represents the length of the string.
  Now, while still holding onto the string, locate another point on the number line that represents the same length.
- Repeat this process with two more pieces of string of different lengths and two additional students, Students C and D. Student A will hold the 0 end of each string.

HABITS OF MIND
- Look for and make use of structure.
- Look for and express regularity in repeated reasoning.

TOPIC 1

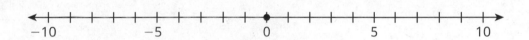

1 Compare the locations where each student stood.

   (a) What do you notice about the distances each time the students moved?

   (b) What do you notice about the approximate values for the numbers where each stood?

The magnitude, or **absolute value**, of a number is its distance from zero on a number line. The symbol for absolute value is | |. You read the expression |*n*| as "the absolute value of a number *n*."

TAKE NOTE...
Because distance is never negative, the absolute value of a number is always positive or 0.

2 Plot the values 5 and −7.2 on the number line. Then describe each value's distance from 0 and complete the statement.

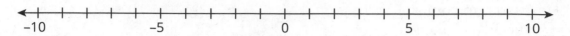

(a) How far is 5 from 0?

(b) |5| = _____

(c) How far is −7.2 from 0?

(d) |−7.2| = _____

3 Explain what each statement means. Name any other values that have the same absolute value, if possible.

(a) |−5|

(b) $|1\frac{5}{6}|$

(c) |0.75|

(d) |−1.36|

❯ Use your investigation and a number line to answer each question.

4 Can two different numbers have the same absolute value? **If so, provide examples.**

5 What can you say about the absolute value of each type of number?

(a) Positive numbers

(b) Negative numbers

(c) Zero

Interpreting Absolute Value Statements

You can use absolute values in real-world applications when you have an interest in only the number and not in the sign of the number. When you look at temperature changes, you could say the temperature "fell by," "decreased by," or "increased by" an absolute value.

1 Complete the table with an appropriate situation, absolute value statement, or number. For the last row, assign the correct units to the number based on your situation.

Situation	Absolute Value Statement	Numeric Example (with units)
The temperature went from 55°F to 5°F.	The temperature fell by 50°F.	–50°F
The bank account balance went from $2500 to $2250.		
The bank account balance went from $495 to $615.		$120
	The water level increased by 4.9 feet.	
During the hike, the elevation went from 1125 feet to 1750 feet.		
		–10 _____

TOPIC 1

You also use absolute value statements to describe how numbers compare with other numbers. You often use these statements without thinking about "less than" or "greater than." Rather, you use words like "debt," "lost," "colder," "depth," "above," "hotter," or "below."

2 Complete the table with an appropriate situation, absolute value statement, or example. For the last row, assign the correct units to the numeric example based on your situation.

Situation	Absolute Value Statement	Numeric Example (with units)
A water level less than $-2\frac{1}{2}$ feet	More than $2\frac{1}{2}$ feet below a full pool	–3 feet
An account balance less than –$30	A debt greater than $30	
A weight less than –7.5 pounds of previous weight	Lost more than 7.5 pounds	
	Deeper than 350 feet below the water	
	Colder than 10 degrees below 0	
	A depth greater than 15 m	
	A golf tournament stroke total more than 7 strokes below	
		–100 _____

ACTIVITY 3
MATHia CONNECTION
• Using Absolute Value

Signed Numbers
TOPIC 1 — LESSON 2

Getting Started   Activity 1 2 3   Talk the Talk

Using Absolute Value to Solve Real-World Problems

In this activity, you will use absolute value to solve real-world problems.

HABITS OF MIND
• Reason abstractly and quantitatively.
• Construct viable arguments and critique the reasoning of others.

TOPIC 1

In the building Melanie works in, the lobby is on the ground floor, or floor zero, with 10 floors of offices above it. The building also has 4 floors of garage below the lobby.

Melanie has an office on the 9th floor and parks on the 3rd floor below the ground floor.

1 Taylor and Cecelia determine how many floors Melanie must go up from her car to reach her office.

- Taylor represents the 9th floor as 9 and the 3rd floor below ground as –3. She says that since 9 – 3 = 6, Melanie travels 6 floors to get from her car to her office.

- Cecelia says that the ground floor to the 9th floor is 9 floors, and from the ground floor to the 3rd garage level is 3 floors, so Melanie travels |9| + |– 3|, or 9 + 3, floors. This is a total of 12 floors.

Who is correct? **Explain your reasoning.**

❯ Write a numeric expression using absolute values that would represent each situation. Then calculate the answer.

2 Caleb parks his car on the 2nd floor below ground and works on the 7th floor. How many floors must he go up from his car to reach his office?

3 Lucinda is working on the 8th floor. At lunch, she goes to her car on the 4th floor below ground, and then back up to the lobby. How many total floors does Lucinda travel?

4 If Damon goes from his office on the 10th floor to a meeting on the 5th floor, how many floors does he travel and in which direction?

The table shows the Top Notch company's balance sheet for the first 8 weeks of operation. Amounts within parentheses represent a negative balance.

5 Use estimation to enter the gains/losses between consecutive weeks in the table.

6 Between which two weeks did Top Notch have the largest gain in money? What was the actual gain?

7 Between which two weeks did Top Notch have the largest loss in money? What was the actual loss?

8 What was the difference between the company's lowest balance and its highest balance?

Week	Balance	Gain/Loss
1	($159)	
2	($201.35)	
3	$231.57	
4	($456.45)	
5	($156)	
6	($12.05)	
7	$281.34	
8	$175	

9 Order the estimated gains and losses that you determined in Question 5 from least to greatest. **Use a negative sign to indicate losses.**

10 Order the estimated gains and losses that you determined in Question 5 from least to greatest according to their absolute values. What does the absolute value mean in the context of this problem?

11 Why are the orders different in Questions 9 and 10?

> As part of a long-term science experiment, scientists connected two rulers at zero and used that to measure a pond's water level. They placed the connected rulers in the pond so that the water level aligned at zero. The scientists measured the water level each week for 10 weeks.

Week	1	2	3	4	5	6	7	8	9	10
Water Level	$2\frac{3}{4}$	$-2\frac{1}{8}$	$1\frac{7}{8}$	$-\frac{3}{4}$	$\frac{3}{4}$	$1\frac{1}{8}$	$-\frac{7}{8}$	$1\frac{1}{4}$	-2	$-\frac{3}{16}$

12 What do the positive numbers represent? What do the negative numbers represent?

13 Between which two weeks did the water level change the most? What was the change?

14 Between which two weeks did the water level change the least? What was the change?

TOPIC 1

You Absolutely MUST Compare These!

❯ Insert a >, <, or = symbol to make each statement true. **Justify each answer in terms of the definition of absolute value and number lines.**

1 $|-4.67|$ _____ $|3|$

2 $|-15|$ _____ $|15|$

3 $\left|25\frac{9}{10}\right|$ _____ $\left|-33\frac{2}{3}\right|$

4 $|13.45|$ _____ $|-27|$

5 $|-15.34|$ _____ $\left|-1\frac{11}{12}\right|$

6 $\left|-19\frac{1}{2}\right|$ _____ $|5.5|$

LESSON 2 ASSIGNMENT

> Use a separate piece of paper for your Journal entry.

JOURNAL

Explain the relationship between a number, its opposite, and its absolute value.

REMEMBER

The absolute value of a rational number is its distance from zero on a number line. You can use absolute value expressions to calculate the distance between positive and negative numbers.

PRACTICE

1 The lobby, or floor zero, of an office building built into the side of a hill is at street level. There are a number of floors above the lobby and a number of floors below the lobby that are below street level. The directory lists the location of different departments and locations by floor number. A floor with a B before the number is that many floors below street level.

Write a numeric expression using absolute values that would represent each situation. Then calculate the answer.

Directory	Floor
Accounting	7
Board Room	12
Cafeteria	B4
Conference Room	10
Customer Service	1
Human Resources	B2
Lobby	0
Marketing	5
Storage	B5

a Ronnie visits a friend that works in human resources before attending a meeting in the board room. How many floors must she travel to reach the board room?

b Ursula works in accounting. At lunch, she goes to the cafeteria. She then heads to the conference room for a meeting. How many total floors does Ursula travel?

c Jeremy gets something out of storage before heading back up to marketing. How many floors does he travel and in which direction?

d A visitor enters the lobby and goes to customer service. He decides to grab a snack at the cafeteria before returning to the lobby to leave. How many total floors does the visitor travel?

Go to LiveHint.com for help on the PRACTICE questions.

Lesson 2 > Magnificent Magnitude **553**

2 The table shown tracks the movements of people in an office building. Complete the table to explain the changes.

Situation	Absolute Value Statement	Rational Number
Zanna went from the 14th floor to the 9th floor.	Her position decreased by 5 floors.	
Drew went from the 2nd floor to the 8th floor.		6 floors
Sebastian went from the 17th floor to the 8th floor.		

3 Tyler marked a rain gauge with values from −6 inches to +6 inches and filled the gauge with water to the zero mark. The table shows the levels in the rain gauge over 8 days.

@ Between which two consecutive readings did it rain the most? How many inches were recorded? Show your work.

b Between which two consecutive readings was evaporation the greatest? How many inches of water evaporated? Show your work.

Days	Gauge Reading (in.)
1	0.5
2	−1.3
3	3.7
4	4.2
5	2.1
6	−0.9
7	−2.4
8	5.6

STRETCH Optional

❯ Write a scenario to represent each rational number.

1 −12 **2** $-4\frac{1}{2}$ **3** 7.3 **4** −0.7

TOPIC 1
Signed Numbers

1 | Human Number Line

2 | Magnificent Magnitude

3 | What's in a Name?

TOPIC 2
The Four Quadrants

LESSON 3

What's in a Name?

Rational Number System

Learning Goals

- Classify numbers according to their number systems.
- Apply and extend an understanding of whole numbers and integers to the system of rational numbers.
- Understand ordering of rational numbers.

REVIEW (1–2 minutes)

❯ Represent each decimal or percent as a fraction in lowest terms.

1 0.3

2 2.8

3 $\frac{3}{4}$%

4 212%

You use many different types of numbers in math class and in your everyday life, including whole numbers, fractions, and decimals, both positive and negative.

How can you organize and classify different types of numbers?

Sort It Out!

> Cut out the cards found on page 563. Then analyze and sort the numbers into different groups. You may group them in any way you feel is appropriate, but you must sort the numbers into more than one group.

1 For each of your groups,

- Create a title that fits the numbers in that group.
- List the numbers included.
- Write a rationale for why you group those particular numbers.

CUTOUTS

Number Cards

0	−5.78	$2\frac{15}{16}$	$\frac{3}{4}$%	−452
$\frac{1}{2}$	24	9	$\frac{6}{7}$	$-\frac{6}{7}$
−0.5	0.5	$-\frac{1}{2}$	2.5%	5.78
−3	|−3|	$-\frac{2}{3}$	$\frac{1}{1000}$	0.001
−6.41	|6.41|	−(−9)	|−452|	−0.3
255%	$6\frac{1}{4}$	25%	0.25%	$\left\|\frac{215}{16}\right\|$

TOPIC 1

© Carnegie Learning, Inc.

Lesson 3 > What's in a Name?   563

2 Compare your sort with your classmates' sorts. Create a list of the different ways your class grouped the numbers.

Analyzing Number Sorts

❭ Consider the numbers on the cards from the Getting Started.

1 Suzanne grouped these numbers together. Why do you think she put these numbers in the same group?

0	−452	9	24
|−3|	−3	−(−9)	|−452|

2 Zane had a group similar to Suzanne's but he did not include −452 and −3. Why do think Zane omitted these numbers from his group?

3 Amelia said that she created two groups: Group 1 contains all the numbers that she can write as fractions and Group 2 contains all the numbers that she cannot write as fractions. Analyze Amelia's sorting idea.

   (a) Which numbers do you think Amelia placed in Group 2?

   (b) Justine is not sure about Amelia's sort. She thinks that you can write all of the numbers as fractions. Is Justine correct? **Explain why or why not.**

TOPIC 1

You have used different sets of numbers, including the set of natural, or counting, numbers and the set of whole numbers.

4 Identify the numbers from the sort that are in each set.

    ⓐ Natural numbers

    ⓑ Whole numbers

Throughout this topic, you have been learning about the set of *integers*. The set of **integers** includes the set of whole numbers with their opposites. You can represent the set of integers as $\{\ldots, -3, -2, -1, 0, 1, 2, 3, \ldots\}$.

> **TAKE NOTE...**
> The three periods before and after specific numbers in the set are called an **ellipsis,** and you use them to represent infinity in a number set.

5 Identify the numbers from the sort that you can include in the set of integers.

Now that you know about the set of integers, we can now define the set of *rational numbers*. The set of **rational numbers** is the set of numbers you can write as $\frac{a}{b}$, where a and b are integers and $b \neq 0$.

6 Identify the numbers from the sort that you can include in the set of rational numbers.

ACTIVITY 2
MATHia CONNECTION
• Classifying Rational Numbers

Signed Numbers
TOPIC 1   **LESSON 3**

Getting Started | ⎯ Activity ⎯ | Talk the Talk
| 1 **2** 3 |

Classifying Numbers

There are many ways you can classify numbers. As you saw in the previous activity, many of the classifications are subsets of other classifications. The diagram shows the different sets of numbers you have encountered in your mathematical experiences.

• Natural numbers are a subset of whole numbers.

• Whole numbers are a subset of integers.

• Integers are a subset of rational numbers.

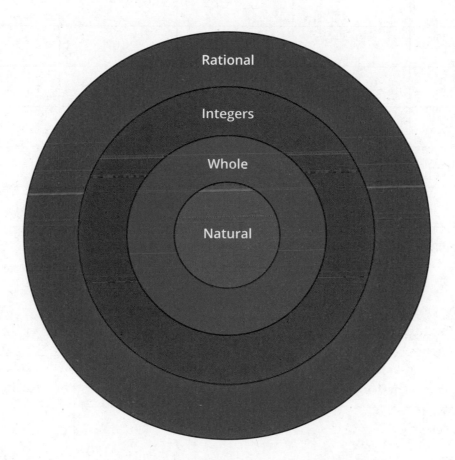

❯ Pin the number on the bullseye! Your teacher will direct students to pin (or tape) a number card to its correct location in the diagram of the rational number set.

1 For each value, check all of the number sets to which it belongs.

Number	Natural Number	Whole Number	Integer	Rational Number
3				
3.222				
0				
−4.5				
$-\frac{3}{5}$				
54				
−5				
$\frac{23}{3}$				
0.667				
−1,364,698				

2 Complete the table with the missing examples and descriptions.

	Natural Numbers	Whole Numbers	Integers	Rational Numbers
Examples	{1, 2, 3, ...}		{...,−3, −2, −1, 0, 1, 2, 3,...}	
Description	Counting numbers	Natural numbers and 0		

Density

HABITS OF MIND
• Attend to precision.

The set of rational numbers has different properties that are not true for natural numbers, whole numbers, or integers. The **Density Property** states that between any two rational numbers is another rational number.

1 Plot the given rational numbers. Then plot and label a rational number between each pair of rational numbers.

(a) $4\frac{1}{3}$ and $4\frac{2}{3}$

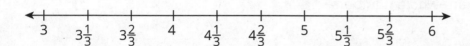

(b) 5.5 and 5.6

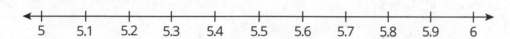

(c) 0.45 and 0.46

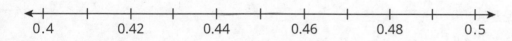

(d) −0.45 and −0.46

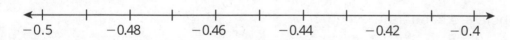

2 How many numbers are between any two rational numbers?

TOPIC 1

TALK THE TALK

Signed Numbers
TOPIC 1 — **LESSON 3**

Getting
Started

Activity
1   2   3

Talk
the Talk

Do They Always Belong?

> Determine whether each statement is true or false. **Justify your answer using definitions or examples.**

1 All whole numbers are rational numbers.

2 All rational numbers are whole numbers.

3 All rational numbers are integers.

4 All integers are rational numbers.

5 All whole numbers are integers.

6 All integers are whole numbers.

Number Cards

0	−5.78	$2\frac{15}{16}$	$\frac{3}{4}\%$	−452
$\frac{1}{2}$	24	9	$\frac{6}{7}$	$-\frac{6}{7}$
−0.5	0.5	$-\frac{1}{2}$	2.5%	5.78
−3	$\lvert -3 \rvert$	$-\frac{2}{3}$	$\frac{1}{1000}$	0.001
−6.41	$\lvert 6.41 \rvert$	−(−9)	$\lvert -452 \rvert$	−0.3
255%	$6\frac{1}{4}$	25%	0.25%	$\left\lvert \frac{215}{16} \right\rvert$

Why is this page blank?

So you can cut out the cards on the other side.

JOURNAL

Define each term in your own words.

1 The set of rational numbers

2 The Density Property

> **REMEMBER**
>
> The set of integers includes the set of whole numbers with their opposites. The set of rational numbers includes all numbers that you can write in the form $\frac{a}{b}$, where a and b are integers and $b \neq 0$.

PRACTICE

1 Write all the sets of numbers to which each value belongs.

ⓐ The tundra covers about $\frac{1}{5}$ of Earth's surface.

ⓑ The average annual temperature is −18° Fahrenheit.

ⓒ There are 48 varieties of land mammals found in the tundra region.

ⓓ A layer of permafrost can extend below the Earth's surface to more than −3281 feet.

ⓔ During the summer months, the low temperature averages about 37.4°F.

2 Nadine collects data about some animals. Determine a rational number between each pair of rational numbers. Plot all three numbers on a number line.

ⓐ A mole's runway is between −3 and −12 inches in the ground.

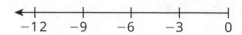

ⓑ The musky rat kangaroo weighs between $\frac{3}{4}$ and $\frac{3}{2}$ pound.

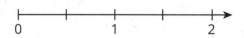

ⓒ The percent of change of the Alaskan polar bear population in the past year was between −0.33 and −0.32.

STRETCH Optional

Are there more integers or more natural numbers? Even though there are infinitely many of both, it seems like there should be more integers than natural numbers. But, actually, there are just as many integers as there are natural numbers!

❯ Show how to assign an integer to every natural number to demonstrate that the two sets of numbers are equal.

MIXED PRACTICE

❯ This Mixed Practice worksheet includes two sections: Spaced Review and End-of-Topic Review. **Use a separate piece of paper to show your work.**

Spaced Review

❯ Practice concepts from previous topics.

1 Perform the indicated operation.

    ⓐ $11\frac{4}{5} + 5\frac{2}{3}$ **ⓑ** $\frac{27}{4} \div \frac{3}{2}$

2 Solve each equation.

    ⓐ $\frac{t}{2} = 15$ **ⓑ** $y - 8 = 19$

3 Five employees work on the receiving dock at a factory. They divide the number of crates they unload from each truck equally. Define variables for the number of crates on a truck and for the number of crates each employee unloads. Write an equation that models the relationship.

4 Determine the better buy.

    ⓐ 6 car washes for $50 or 4 car washes for $36

    ⓑ 10 markers for $2.40 or 32 markers for $7.00

5 Plot each ordered pair on the coordinate plane.

    ⓐ (2, 4)

    ⓑ (5.5, 1.75)

    ⓒ $\left(4\frac{2}{5}, 5\frac{4}{5}\right)$

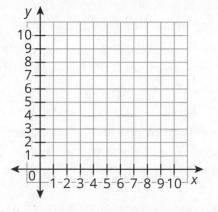

6 In Ms. Sobato's science class of 20 students, 3 of the students are in the school play. What percent of the class is in the school play?

7 Complete the table for the equation $w = \frac{m}{9.2}$.

m	w
27.6	
	5
74.52	
92	
	14

8 The table shows each class's portion of the total reading minutes for the reading contest. Order the classes from the greatest number of reading minutes to the least. Explain your reasoning.

Class	Portion of Reading Minutes
Mr. Karlie	$\frac{5}{12}$
Ms. Jacobs	$\frac{1}{18}$
Ms. Suarez	$\frac{4}{9}$
Mr. Mitchell	$\frac{1}{12}$

End-of-Topic Review

AVAILABLE ONLINE
1. A **Topic Summary** reviews the main concepts for the topic.
2. A video of the **Worked Example** is provided.

> Practice concepts you learned in **Signed Numbers**.

9 State the opposite of each number and plot both numbers on a number line.

(a) $2\frac{1}{8}$

(b) -5.97

10 Determine two rational numbers that are between the two given rational numbers.

(a) 3.4 and 3.5

(b) $\frac{12}{5}$ and $\frac{13}{5}$

11 Use the >, <, or = symbol to complete each statement.

(a) -5 ___ -8

(b) -3 ___ 0

(c) 5 ___ -5

12 Write the absolute value of each expression.

(a) $|-3.25|$

(b) $|250|$

(c) $|0|$

13 Write an absolute value expression to calculate the answer to each question.

(a) The temperature at 9:00 A.M. was 40°. The temperature at 2:00 P.M. was −10°. What was the change in temperature?

(b) You began your hike at 30 feet below sea level. You are now at 200 feet. How far have you hiked?

14 Write all the sets of numbers to which each value belongs.

(a) -6

(b) $-3\frac{1}{2}$

(c) 27

15 Order the numbers from least to greatest.

$0 \qquad \frac{2}{5} \qquad -1.2 \qquad 2.5 \qquad -\frac{5}{2} \qquad 1$

16 The table shown tracks the movements of people in a hotel. Complete the table to explain the changes.

Situation	Absolute Value Statement	Rational Number
Shane went from the 11th floor to the 3rd floor.	His position decreased by 8 floors.	
Frankie went from the 4th floor to the 13th floor.		9 floors
Ellie went from the 18th floor to the 8th floor.		

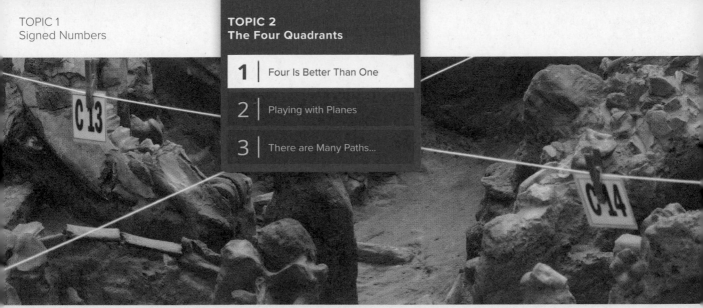

LESSON 1

Four Is Better Than One

Extending the Coordinate Plane

KEY TERM

quadrants

Learning Goals

- Identify the four quadrants of the coordinate plane and the characteristics of points located in each.

- Locate and plot ordered pairs of positive and negative rational numbers on the coordinate plane.

- Determine the relationship between the signs of coordinates of ordered pairs that are reflections across one or both axes.

- Use absolute value to determine distances on the coordinate plane.

- Solve problems by graphing points in all four quadrants of the coordinate plane.

REVIEW (1–2 minutes)

> Plot and label each point.

A (3, 5)   B (0, 4)

C (6, 1)   D (8, 0)

E (0, 0)

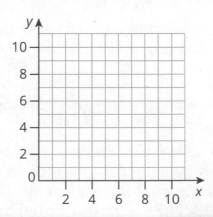

You can locate and plot ordered pairs of positive numbers on a coordinate plane.

How can you extend the plane to include ordered pairs of any rational numbers?

GETTING STARTED

The Four
Quadrants

TOPIC 2   LESSON 1

Getting
Started   Activity   Talk
1   2   3   4   the Talk

All About Extending

> Consider the coordinate plane that you have used to graph points where both the x- and y-coordinates were zero or positive numbers.

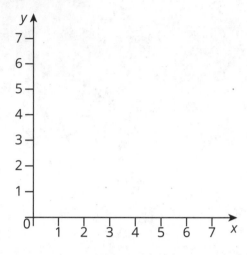

1 Based on what you have learned about number lines:

  (a) What do you know about the number line that makes up the x-axis? Extend that number line and label it appropriately.

  (b) What do you know about the number line that makes up the y-axis? Extend that number line and label it appropriately.

2 The point where the x-axis and y-axis intersect is known as the origin. Label the point of intersection with its coordinates.

By extending the number lines that form the axes, you have created the entire coordinate plane. You call the regions on the coordinate plane **quadrants** and number them with Roman numerals from one to four (I, II, III, IV) starting in the upper right-hand quadrant and moving counterclockwise.

3 Label each of the four quadrants on your coordinate plane.

DID YOU KNOW?

The coordinate plane is often called the Cartesian coordinate plane, named for René Descartes.

ACTIVITY 1

The Four
Quadrants

TOPIC 2 — LESSON 1

Getting
Started

Activity
1 2 3 4

Talk
the Talk

Human Coordinate Plane

HABITS OF MIND
• Look for and make use of structure.
• Look for and express regularity in repeated reasoning.

> Your teacher is going to direct students to stand at certain locations on the human coordinate plane.

1 For each student, plot and label the point where the student is standing on the coordinate plane. Then record the coordinates of that point in the table.

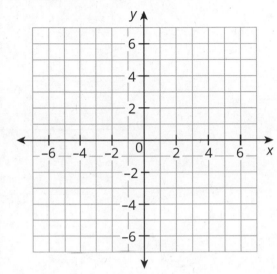

Student	Location	Student	Location
A		H	
B		I	
C		J	
D		K	
E		L	
F		M	
G		N	

2 Where did each student always start? How did each student know which direction to go first?

THINK ABOUT...
Help each other decide how to plot the ordered pairs.

3 What do you notice about the coordinates of points that are in the same quadrant?

TOPIC 2

❯ Your teacher is going to select students to plot ordered pairs that meet specific conditions. The students will select locations that satisfy those conditions.

4 For each student, plot and label the point where the student is standing on the coordinate plane. Then record the coordinates of that point in the table.

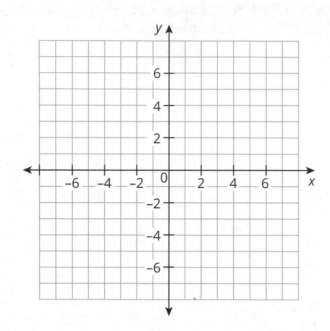

Student	Condition	Location
A	Negative *x*-coordinate	
B	Negative *y*-coordinate	
C	On an axis	
D	In QII	
E	In QIII	

5 Compare the ordered pairs you plotted and identified in this activity. What is similar about the points you graphed in each region or on each axis of the graph?

  ⓐ QI: _____   ⓑ QII: _____   ⓒ QIII: _____

  ⓓ QIV: _____   ⓔ *x*-axis: _____   ⓕ *y*-axis: _____

ACTIVITY 2
MATHia CONNECTION
• Exploring Symmetry on the Coordinate Plane

The Four Quadrants

TOPIC 2 — LESSON 1

Getting Started Activity 1 2 3 4 Talk the Talk

Investigating Reflections

In this activity, you will use patty paper to search for specific patterns on the coordinate plane.

Let's investigate reflecting across the *x*-axis.

❯ Place a sheet of patty paper over the coordinate plane and trace the axes.

1 For each ordered pair,

- Plot and label the point on patty paper.
- Fold the patty paper on the *x*-axis.
- Trace the point through the patty paper.
- Label the coordinates of the new point.

HABITS OF MIND
- Look for and make use of structure.
- Look for and express regularity in repeated reasoning.

DID YOU KNOW?

A′ is read "A prime."

ⓐ *A* (4, 1)   *A′* (_____, _____)

ⓑ *B* (−3, 4)   *B′* (_____, _____)

ⓒ *C* (5, −2)   *C′* (_____, _____)

ⓓ *D* (0, −7)   *D′* (_____, _____)

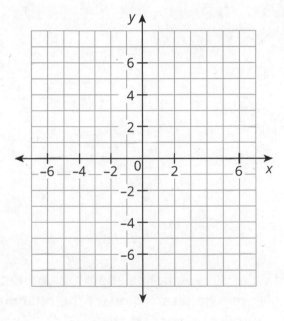

2 What did you notice about the coordinates of the original points and their reflections? **Write a generalization for the relationship between the coordinates of a point and its reflection across the *x*-axis.**

Now let's investigate reflecting across the *y*-axis.

❯ Place a new sheet of patty paper over the coordinate plane and trace the axes.

3 For each ordered pair,

- Plot and label the point on patty paper.
- Fold the patty paper on the *y*-axis.
- Trace the point through the patty paper.
- Label the coordinates of the new point.

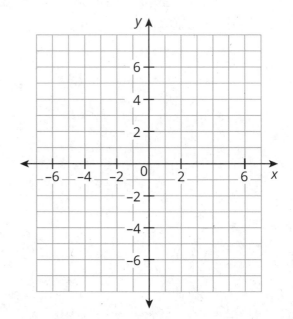

ⓐ *A* (4, 1) *A'* (_____ , _____)

ⓑ *B* (−3, 4) *B'* (_____ , _____)

ⓒ *C* (5, −2) *C'* (_____ , _____)

ⓓ *D* (−3, 0) *D'* (_____ , _____)

4 What did you notice about the coordinates of the original points and their reflections? **Write a generalization for the relationship between the coordinates of a point and its reflection across the *y*-axis.**

❯ Your teacher is going to select students to plot ordered pairs that meet specific conditions. The students will select locations that satisfy those conditions.

5 Plot and label the point where each student is standing on the coordinate plane. Then record the coordinates of that point in the table.

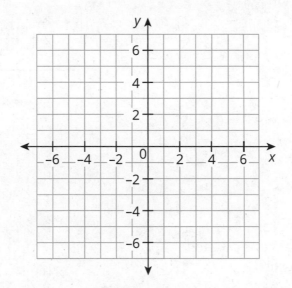

Student	Condition	Location
A	Quadrant II	
B	Reflection of A across the x-axis	
C	Reflection of B across the y-axis	

6 Compare the ordered pairs for A and C. What do you notice about their coordinates? **Write a generalization for the relationship between the coordinates of a point and its reflection across both axes.**

TOPIC 2

7 For each pair of conditions, plot and label two points. Record the coordinates of the points.

(a) One point is in Quadrant II. The two points are reflections of each other across the *x*-axis.

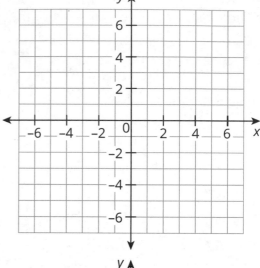

(b) One point is in Quadrant III. The points are reflections of each other across the *y*-axis.

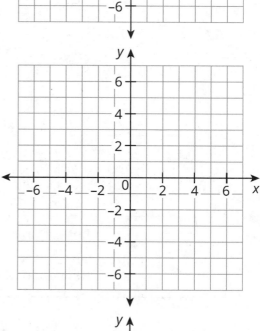

(c) One point is in Quadrant IV. The points are reflections of each other across both axes.

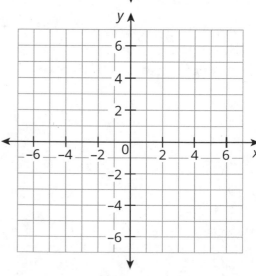

8 In general, how are points that are reflections across one or both axes similar to and different from each other?

ACTIVITY 3

MATHia CONNECTION
• Identifying and Interpreting Ordered Pairs
• Plotting Points

The Four
Quadrants

TOPIC 2   LESSON 1

Getting
Started   1   2   3   4

Activity

Talk
the Talk

Horizontal and Vertical Distance on the Coordinate Plane

HABITS OF MIND
• Look for and make use of structure.
• Look for and express regularity in repeated reasoning.

You can use absolute value and what you know about integers to determine distances between points on a coordinate plane.

1 Consider points A and B.

(a) Use the coordinate plane to determine the distance from point A to point B.

(b) Describe how the coordinates of points A and B are similar.

(c) Write an absolute value expression using the x-coordinates of the points to calculate the distance.

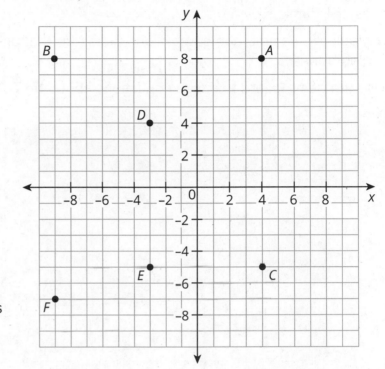

TOPIC 2

2 Consider points B and F.

(a) Use the coordinate plane to determine the distance from point B to point F.

(b) Describe how the coordinates of points B and F are similar.

(c) Write an absolute value expression using the y-coordinates of the points to calculate the distance.

3 Write an absolute value expression and calculate each distance.

(a) Point D to $(-3, -5)$

(b) $(-7, -4)$ to $(3, -4)$

(c) $(6, 2)$ to $(6, -5)$

(d) Point B to $(-9, 2)$

(e) $(8, -7)$ to point F

ACTIVITY 4

The Four
Quadrants

TOPIC 2 — LESSON 1

Getting
Started

Activity
1   2   3   4

Talk
the Talk

T-Rex Dig

In the T-Rex Dig game, players place the "bones" of their dinosaur horizontally or vertically on a coordinate grid. Players then take turns guessing the location of each other's dino bones using coordinates. Once a player has located all of the other player's dino bones, the game is over.

HABITS OF MIND
• Look for and make use of structure.
• Look for and express regularity in repeated reasoning.

Let's look at a sample game board and questions that players might ask to uncover all the dino bones.

❯ Use the game board to answer questions about the T-Rex fossils.

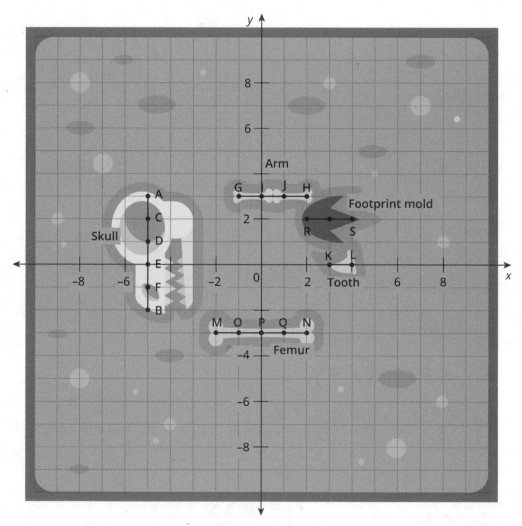

1. How long is the T-Rex's skull? **Write an absolute value expression to justify your answer**.

TAKE NOTE...
Each grid line is 1 foot long.

2 What is the minimum number of coordinates a player must guess to completely "uncover" the skull?

3 How long is the T-Rex's femur? **Write an absolute value expression to justify your answer**.

4 What is the greatest number of quadrants crossed by any one fossil?

5 Are any fossils on an axis? If so, identify the axis, the fossil, and the coordinates of the fossil(s).

Now it's your turn to play the T-Rex dig game!

> Use the game board provided on page 581. Use the bottom grid to plot and label your 5 fossils. You may want to label some of the coordinates to help you as you play the game. Use the top grid to record the coordinates you ask of your partner.

THINK ABOUT...

Ask your opponent mathematical questions:
Is the femur symmetric across an axis?
How many fossils are vertical?
Are any fossils on an axis? (But don't ask which axis!)
Do any fossils share an ending x-coordinate?

TOPIC 2

TALK THE TALK

The Four
Quadrants

TOPIC 2 — **LESSON 1**

Getting
Started

Activity
1 2 3 4

Talk
the Talk

Determining Coordinates

> Use the graph and information provided to answer each question.

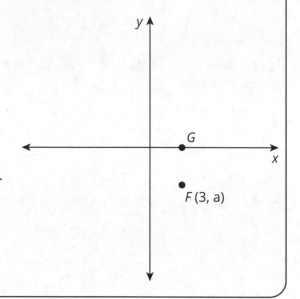

- The graph shows the locations of point *F* and point *G*.
- Point *G* is on the *x*-axis and has the same *x*-coordinate as point *F*.
- Point *H* is located at (−4, *a*).
- The distance from point *F* to point *G* is half the distance from point *F* to point *H*.

1 What is the value of *a*? **Explain how you determined this coordinate.**

2 Plot point *J* so that the distance from point *F* to point *J* is the same as the distance from point *F* to point *H*. **Explain how you decided where to plot point J.**

T-Rex Dig Game Board

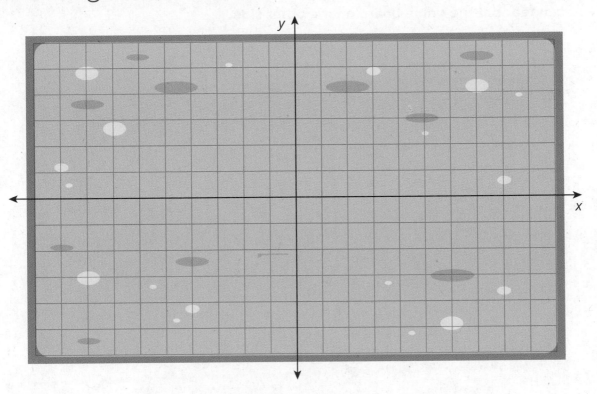

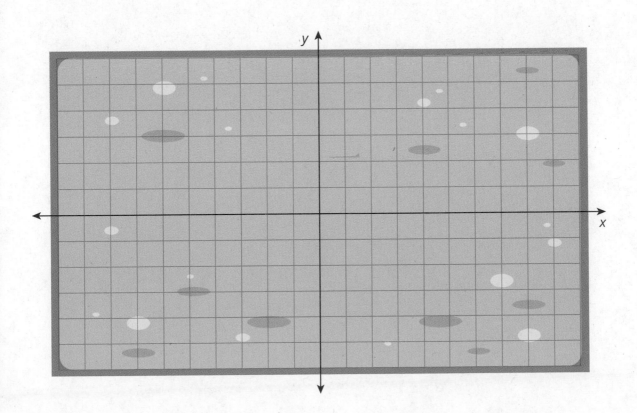

Why is this page blank?

So you can tear out the game board on the other side.

JOURNAL ▶

Use the terms *axis*, *quadrant*, and *coordinates* to explain the relationship between ordered pairs that differ only by sign.

REMEMBER

The Cartesian coordinate plane consists of two perpendicular number lines that intersect at the zeros, or the origin. The intersecting number lines divide the plane into four regions, called quadrants.

PRACTICE ▶

1 Plot and label the locations of points P through Z on a coordinate plane. Draw line segments from point to point, beginning and ending at point P. Describe the resulting figure.

P (0, 5)	Q (1, 3)	R (4, 3)
S (2, 1)	T (4, −3)	V (0, −1)
W (−4, −3)	X (−2, 1)	Y (−4, 3)

Z (−1, 3)

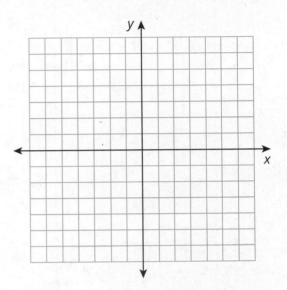

2 Consider point (a, b) located in Quadrant I and point (c, d) located in Quadrant III.

Plot and label each additional ordered pair. Explain how you knew where to plot each point.

ⓐ $(−a, b)$

ⓑ $(a, −b)$

ⓒ $(−a, −b)$

ⓓ $(−c, d)$

ⓔ $(c, −d)$

ⓕ $(−c, −d)$

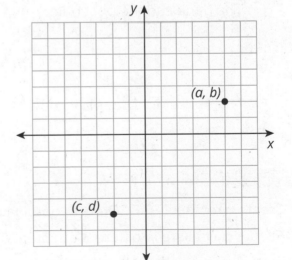

3 The coordinate plane shown represents a map of Paul's neighborhood. Each square represents one city block. Paul's house is at point *A*, which is the origin.

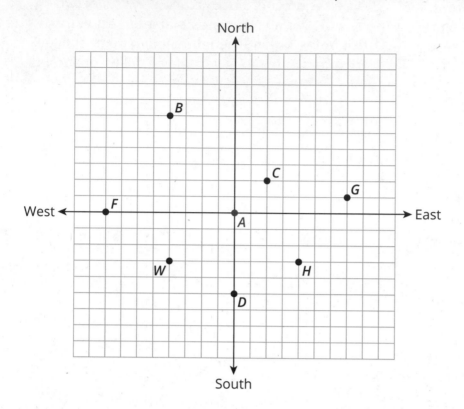

Write an absolute value expression using the *y*-coordinates of the points to calculate the distance between each location.

(a) The bank and the post office

(b) The middle school and the bakery

(c) The market and the playground

(d) The orthodontist and the post office

STRETCH Optional

❯ Create a rectangle *ABCD* on a coordinate plane that meets the following conditions:

- All four points are in different quadrants.
- Point *A* is in Quadrant II with coordinates (−*a*, *b*).
- The distance from point *A* to point *B* is 3*a*.
- The distance from point *A* to point *D* is 4*b*.
- Neither axis is a line of symmetry in the rectangle.

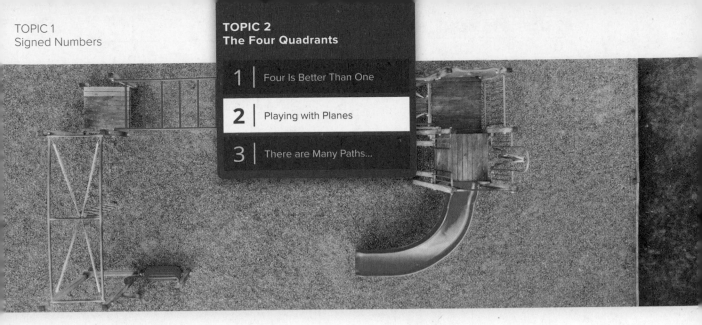

LESSON 2

Playing with Planes

Graphing Geometric Figures

Learning Goals

- Plot points in all four quadrants to form polygons.
- Draw polygons in the coordinate plane using coordinates for the vertices.
- Determine the area enclosed by a polygon on the coordinate plane.
- Use coordinates to determine the length of a side joining points with the same first or second coordinate.
- Solve real-world and mathematical problems with geometric shapes in all four quadrants on the coordinate plane.

REVIEW (1–2 minutes)

❯ Complete each drawing.

1 Draw a rectangle that is not a square.

2 Draw a rhombus that is also a rectangle.

3 Draw a trapezoid that is not a parallelogram.

You have determined area and perimeter of common polygons and the volume of right rectangular prisms.

How can you use the coordinate plane to determine the area, perimeter, and even volume of shapes and objects?

Shape Up!

❯ Your teacher will select students to participate in the activity and provide them with conditions to plot on the Human Coordinate Plane.

1 For each student, plot and label the point where the student is standing on the coordinate plane. Use a different color for each location. Then record the coordinates of the point where the student is standing in the table.

Student	Location 1	Location 2	Location 3
A			
B			
C			
D			

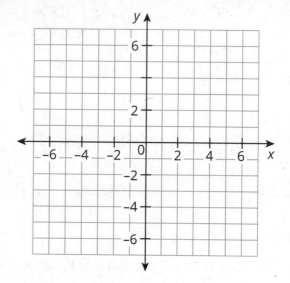

❯ Record the shape formed at each location.
Prove that your classmates formed the shape.

2 Location 1

3 Location 2

4 Location 3

ACTIVITY 1

The Four Quadrants

TOPIC 2   LESSON 2

Getting Started

Activity
1 2 3 4

Talk the Talk

Identifying Polygons on the Plane

The Cartesian coordinate plane allows mathematicians to use coordinates to analyze geometric figures.

1 Graph the points on the coordinate plane and connect them to form a polygon.

x	y
1	−2
−5	−2
−5	3
1	3

(a) What polygon did you form? **Justify your answer.**

(b) Determine the perimeter and area of the polygon.

2 Graph the points on the plane and connect them to form a polygon.

x	y
−2	5
−2	−3
3	−3
5	2

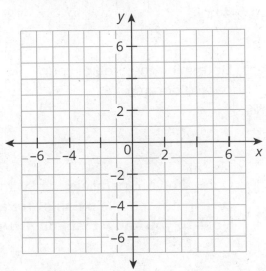

(a) What polygon did you form? **Justify your answer.**

(b) Determine the area of the polygon.

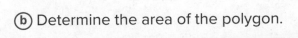

TOPIC 2

ACTIVITY 2

The Four
Quadrants

TOPIC 2 — LESSON 2

Getting
Started   1

Activity
2   3

4

Talk
the Talk

Completing Polygons on the Plane

Recall that a parallelogram is a quadrilateral in which both pairs of opposite sides are parallel.

1 Look at points A (−2, 4) and B (−2, −2) on the coordinate plane.

    (a) Plot and label points C, D, E, and F so that you form squares $ABCD$ and $ABEF$.

    (b) Determine the area of each square.

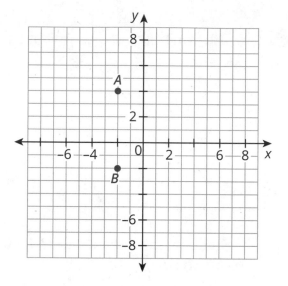

    (c) Compare your squares with your classmates' squares. Are all the squares the same or different? How do you know that you drew the squares correctly?

2 Look at line segment AB on the coordinate plane.

    (a) Plot and label points C and D to form parallelogram $ABCD$ with a height of 4 units.

    (b) Determine the area of your parallelogram.

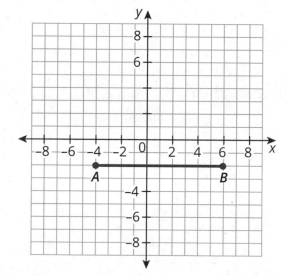

    (c) Compare your parallelogram with your classmates' parallelograms. Are all the parallelograms the same or different? **How do you know that you drew the parallelograms correctly?**

3 On the coordinate plane, the points *A* (−3, −3) and *B* (4, −3) form segment *AB*.

  (a) Plot and label point *C* so that you form a right triangle.

  (b) Plot and label point *D* so that you form an acute triangle.

  (c) Determine the areas of your triangles.

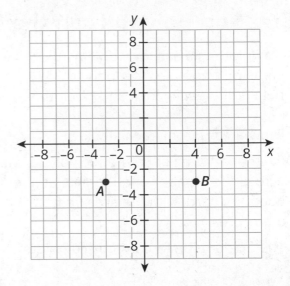

  (d) Compare your triangles with your classmates' triangles. Are all the triangles the same or different? **How do you know that you drew the triangles correctly?**

4 On the coordinate plane, points *A* and *B* form segment *AB*.

  (a) Plot and label two points to form trapezoid *ABCD* with a height of 5 units. Your trapezoid should cross into at least 3 quadrants.

  (b) Determine the area of your trapezoid.

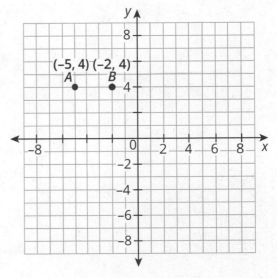

  (c) Compare your trapezoid with your classmates' trapezoids. Are all the trapezoids the same or different? **How do you know that you drew the trapezoids correctly?**

TOPIC 2

ACTIVITY 3

The Four
Quadrants

TOPIC 2 · LESSON 2

Getting
Started

Activity
1 2 3 4

Talk
the Talk

MATHia CONNECTION
• Drawing Polygons on the Coordinate Plane

Creating Polygons on the Plane

❯ Complete this activity with a partner. Cut out the cards on page 593. Keep the card types separate but shuffle each stack and place them face down.

• Draw a card from each stack.

• Each partner must create the polygon named, across the number of quadrants on the quadrant card, with the area from the area card.

• The first person to correctly complete the task gets a point.

• The first partner to earn 5 points wins the game.

❯ Record your polygons on the grid paper on page 595.

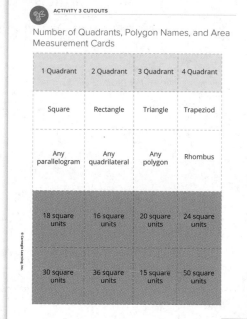

ACTIVITY 3 CUTOUTS

Number of Quadrants, Polygon Names, and Area Measurement Cards

1 Quadrant	2 Quadrant	3 Quadrant	4 Quadrant
Square	Rectangle	Triangle	Trapeziod
Any parallelogram	Any quadrilateral	Any polygon	Rhombus
18 square units	16 square units	20 square units	24 square units
30 square units	36 square units	15 square units	50 square units

Lesson 2 ❯ Playing with Planes   **593**

ACTIVITY 4

The Four
Quadrants

TOPIC 2 LESSON 2

Getting
Started 1

Activity
2 3 4

Talk
the Talk

Outfitting a Playground

An elementary school uses a grid to design a new playground. The grid for the playground has a unit of 1 foot.

The coordinates for the sandbox are (−18, −7), (−10, −7), (−18, −13), and (−10, −13).

1 Determine the volume of the sandbox when it is 0.75 foot deep.

TAKE NOTE...
You can use the grid paper on page 596 for this activity.

TOPIC 2

2 If the school fills the sandbox halfway up with sand, determine the volume of sand the school needs for the sandbox.

3 Each 50-pound bag of sand holds about 0.5 cubic foot of sand. Determine the number of bags of sand the school needs for the sandbox.

4 Each bag of sand costs $3.80. How much will the sand cost for the sandbox?

The coordinates for the swing set sandpit are (15, 2), (40, 2), (15, −8), and (40, −8).

5 Determine the volume of the swing set sandpit when the pit is 0.5 foot deep.

6 If the school has $250 to spend on the sand for the swing set sandpit, how much of it can they fill with sand?

TALK THE TALK

The Four
Quadrants

TOPIC 2   LESSON 2

Getting
Started   1   Activity   Talk
              2   3   4   the Talk

X-Ray Vision

> Consider the coordinates of parallelogram *ABCD*. Segment *AB* is parallel to the *x*-axis.

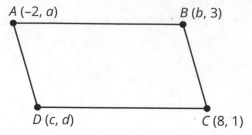

A (−2, a)   B (b, 3)

D (c, d)   C (8, 1)

1 Determine the values for *a*, *b*, *c*, and *d*, if possible.

2 Write an expression for the length of segment *AB*.

3 Determine the vertical height of the parallelogram.

4 Write an expression for the area of the parallelogram.

5 If *b* = 5, determine the values for *a*, *c*, and *d*. Then calculate the area of the parallelogram.

Number of Quadrants, Polygon Names, and Area Measurement Cards

1 Quadrant	2 Quadrant	3 Quadrant	4 Quadrant
Square	Rectangle	Triangle	Trapeziod
Any parallelogram	Any quadrilateral	Any polygon	Rhombus
18 square units	16 square units	20 square units	24 square units
30 square units	36 square units	15 square units	50 square units

Why is this page blank?

So you can cut out the cards on the other side

LESSON 2 ASSIGNMENT

> Use a separate piece of paper for your Journal entry.

JOURNAL

Explain how to use the coordinate plane and absolute value to determine perimeter and area of geometric shapes.

REMEMBER

One advantage of the Cartesian coordinate plane is that it allows mathematicians to use coordinates to analyze geometric figures. You can calculate the distance between two points on a coordinate plane by using the coordinates of the two points.

PRACTICE

1 Create and analyze a trapezoid.

(a) Plot and label four points on a coordinate plane that satisfy all the conditions listed:

- Each point is in a different quadrant.
- The four points form a trapezoid with only one pair of parallel sides.
- The trapezoid has a height of 9 units.
- One base of the trapezoid has a length of 6 units.
- The second base of the trapezoid has a length of 3 units.
- None of the points are on an axis.
- The trapezoid is not symmetric to either axis.

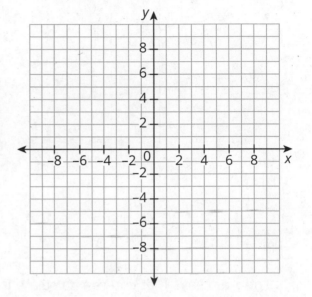

(b) Determine the area of the trapezoid.

(c) Is it possible to create a trapezoid that satisfies the conditions but has a different area? Explain your reasoning.

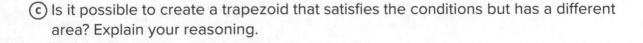

Go to LiveHint.com for help on the **PRACTICE** questions.

2 Plot the vertices of a parallelogram: (−1, 4), (−2, 2), (2, 2), (3, 4). Determine the area of the parallelogram.

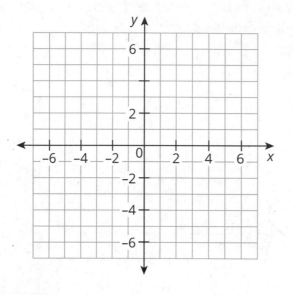

3 Plot the vertices of a rectangle: (1, 5), (1, −2), (3, −2), (3, 5). Determine the area of the rectangle.

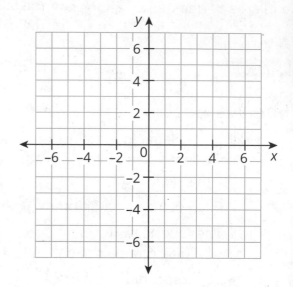

STRETCH Optional

Pick's Theorem says that you can calculate the area of a polygon that has its vertices on a lattice—a field of evenly spaced points—as follows:

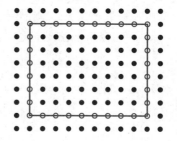

- Count the number of interior points.
- Add this to half the number of boundary points (circles).
- Subtract 1.

1 Determine the area of the figure on the coordinate plane using Pick's Theorem.

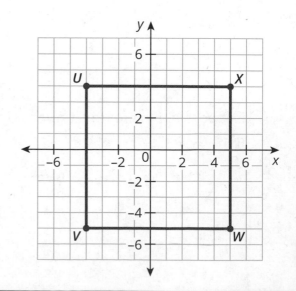

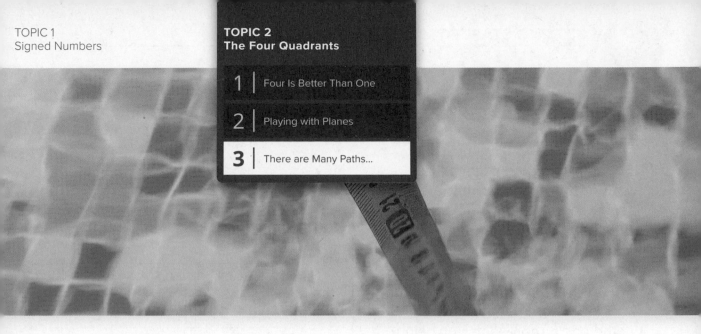

LESSON 3

There Are Many Paths...

Problem Solving on the Coordinate Plane

Learning Goals

- Solve real-world and mathematical problems by graphing points in all four quadrants of the coordinate plane.
- Interpret the meaning of points plotted on the coordinate plane.
- Use equations to solve real-world problems.
- Use graphs relating an independent and dependent quantity changing in relationship to one another to solve real-world problems.
- List advantages and disadvantages of different representations for solving real-world and mathematical problems on the coordinate plane.

REVIEW (1–2 minutes)

❯ Solve each equation.

1 $120 + h = 315$

2 $w - 17 = 38$

3 $\frac{c}{5} = 12$

4 $169 = 13w$

Now that you understand how to plot points in all four quadrants of the coordinate plane, you can solve many more types of problems than you could previously.

How can you use graphs and equations to solve problems?

GETTING STARTED

The Four Quadrants

TOPIC 2 — LESSON 3

Getting Started

Activity
1 2 3 4

Talk the Talk

No Place Like Home

Suppose this graph summarizes your day. The x-axis of this graph represents time in minutes from 12:00 P.M., and the y-axis represents your distance from home in miles. The locations north of your house are positive, and locations south of your house are negative. A point at the origin represents you being home at 12:00 P.M.

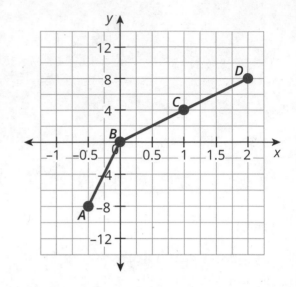

1 Describe the meaning of each of the four labeled points.

x	y	Meaning
−0.5	−8	
0	0	
1	4	
2	8	

2 Adrian and Sierra are discussing how the graph should look before $x = -\frac{1}{2}$ and after $x = 2$. Adrian thinks he should draw arrows to indicate that the graph continues to the left and right, respectively. Sierra disagrees and thinks they should draw segments that eventually connect back to the x-axis. Who is correct?

ACTIVITY 1

The Four
Quadrants

TOPIC 2 — LESSON 3

Getting
Started

Activity
1 2 3 4

Talk
the Talk

Pool Level

HABITS OF MIND
- Reason abstractly and quantitatively.
- Construct viable arguments and critique the reasoning of others.

Over a certain number of hours, the pool manager fills a pool at a constant rate with water until it reaches the desired level at 3:00 P.M.

The independent quantity, graphed on the *x*-axis, is the signed difference in hours between 3:00 P.M. and the current time. The dependent quantity, graphed on the *y*-axis, is the signed difference in inches between the desired water level and the current level.

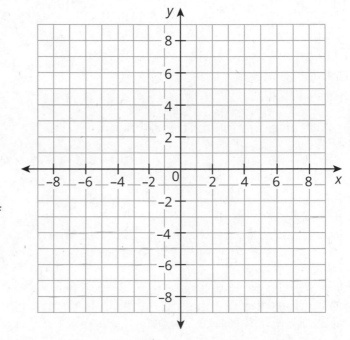

1 Create a table of values for each of the points described. Then plot the points.

TOPIC 2

x	y	Meaning
		At 6:00 A.M., the water level was 6 inches below the desired level.
		At 10:30 A.M., the water level was 3 inches below the desired level.
		At 3:00 P.M., the water level was perfect!
		At 9:00 P.M., the water level was 4 inches higher than desired.
		At midnight, the water level was 6 inches higher than desired.

2 At what rate did the water go into the pool? **Explain your reasoning.**

3 Describe a real-world situation that would match the graph.

4 Write an equation for this situation.

5 Why does the graph stop rather than continue infinitely?

6 Using any of your mathematical tools, determine the time when the pool was 3 inches above the desired fill level. Is your answer exact or approximate? **Explain your reasoning.**

ACTIVITY 2

The Four Quadrants

TOPIC 2   LESSON 3

Getting Started   Activity   Talk
1   **2**   3   4   the Talk

TOPIC 2

Water in the Bucket

HABITS OF MIND
- Reason abstractly and quantitatively.
- Construct viable arguments and critique the reasoning of others.

Damon collected water in a bucket in his backyard and is studying the evaporation. The first day he remembered to take measurements was Sunday, which was 4 days after the data collection was to begin. He collects the following data.

Number of Days Since Sunday	Height of Water (inches)
0	27
5	22
7	20
12	15

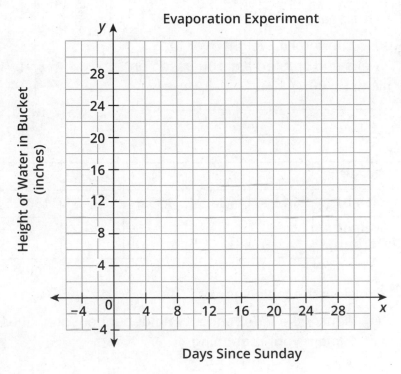

Evaporation Experiment

Height of Water in Bucket (inches)

Days Since Sunday

1 Graph the data. Connect the data values with a line. **Be sure to label your axes.**

2 Use your graph to determine the water level the day he was supposed to start data collection. Assume that the water evaporated at the same rate every day.

3 Assuming that the water evaporated at the same rate every day, use your graph to determine when the water level was at each height.

    (a) 30 inches   (b) 0 inches

4 Explain why you should or should not extend your graph into Quadrant IV.

Weigh In

You can also solve problems using a coordinate plane with data points where no graphed line is drawn.

Julio is a wrestler for his high school team. During this season he will wrestle in the 142-pound weight class. His coach would like him to stay around 140 pounds leading up to the season.

Julio charted his weight over 10 weeks and created a graph based on his data.

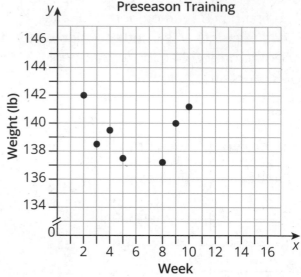

Preseason Training

Week	2	3	4	5	7	8	9	10
Weight	142.1	138.5	139.5	137.5	136.25	137.2	140	141.3
Weight Differential								

1 Consider the table shown.

(a) Identify the independent and dependent quantities. **Explain your reasoning.**

TAKE NOTE...
The break on the y-axis above shows that the interval from 0 to 134 is not equal to the rest of the intervals.

(b) What is the unit for each quantity?

2 The coach was impressed with Julio's data collection, but he was interested in how much Julio's weight varied from 140 pounds each week.

(a) Complete the last row: the differences of Julio's weight from 140 pounds. Use negative numbers when the weight is below 140 pounds and positive numbers when his weight is above 140 pounds.

(b) What is the dependent quantity in this situation?

(c) Which quadrant(s) will you need to plot Julio's data for the coach's request? Draw and label your axes, including the units. Then graph the data.

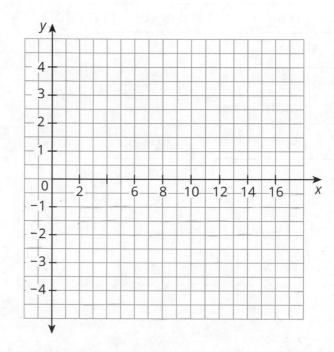

(d) Explain the meaning of the x-axis in the coach's graph.

3 Use the table and graphs to answer each question.

(a) Between which two recorded consecutive weeks did Julio's weight change the most? What was the weight change?

(b) What is the difference between Julio's highest and lowest recorded weights?

(c) Which representation—table, Julio's graph, the coach's graph—did you use to answer the questions? **Why did you make those choices?**

ACTIVITY 4
MATHia CONNECTION
- Writing an Expression from a Scenario, Table, or Graph
- Solving One-Step Equations Using Multiple Representations in Four Quadrants

The Four
Quadrants

TOPIC 2 — LESSON 3

Getting   ┌── Activity ──┐   Talk
Started   1   2   3   4   the Talk
○ ─── ○ ─── ○ ─── ● ─── ○

An Interesting Day in South Dakota

> **HABITS OF MIND**
> - Model with mathematics.
> - Use appropriate tools strategically.

An exciting day of temperature changes occurred in Rapid City, South Dakota, on January 22, 1943. The table shows the temperature changes that happened throughout the day.

REMEMBER...
0°C is 32°F.

Time	Temperature (°C)
10:30 A.M.	–6.7
10:35 A.M.	13.3
Noon	15.6
12:05 P.M.	–10.6
12:35 P.M.	–9.4
12:40 P.M.	10
2:20 P.M.	14.4
2:25 P.M.	–8.3

❯ Create a graph of the temperature changes.

1 Which quadrants do you need for your graph? **Explain your reasoning.**

2 Label the axes for the graph. Then graph the data and connect consecutive points.

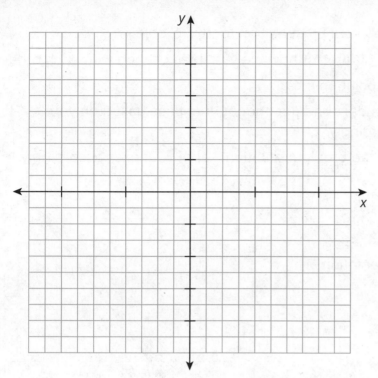

3 Between which two times was the temperature swing the greatest?

4 Describe the pattern. Why is this called an "interesting" day?

TOPIC 2

TALK THE TALK

The Four
Quadrants

TOPIC 2   LESSON 3

Getting
Started

Activity
1   2   3   4

Talk
the Talk

Your Turn!

> You and your group should prepare a presentation for this problem.

- Be sure to determine the ratio, or rate, for how the variables change with each other.

- Describe the meaning of each point on the graph.

- Define variables for the independent and dependent quantities based on your situation. Label your axes accordingly.

- Write an equation to represent the problem situation. Label your axes accordingly.

1 Create a situation that the graph can model.

Write at least 3 sentences for what you want to say during your presentation.

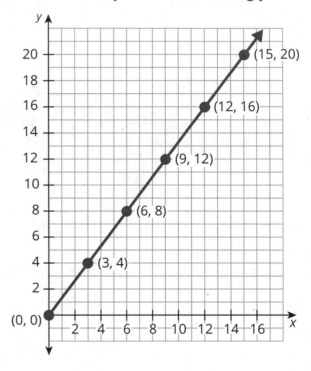

2 Describe how your situation would change if each *x*-value stayed the same, but each *y*-value was its opposite. For example, (3, 4) becomes (3, −4).

LESSON 3 ASSIGNMENT

> Use a separate piece of paper for your Journal entry.

JOURNAL

Give an example of when you might want to use an equation to answer a question and another example of when you might want to use a graph.

REMEMBER

Graphs, tables, equations, and scenarios provide different information and allow for various levels of accuracy when solving problems.

PRACTICE

1 The gravitational pull of the Moon is not as great as that of Earth. If a person checks his weight on the Moon, it will be only $\frac{1}{6}$ of his weight on Earth.

a Complete the table of values for a person's weight on Earth, weight on the Moon, and difference of the two weights. Use negative numbers when the weight is less than the person's weight on Earth.

Weight on Earth (lb)	186	168		198		
Weight on Moon (lb)			29		21	24
Weight Differential	–155					

b Graph the weight differential versus the weight on Earth. Be sure to label your axes.

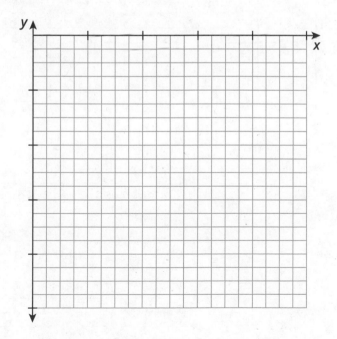

2 Sarina puts her dog Bruno on a plan of daily exercise and a special type of dog food. She estimates Bruno will lose $1\frac{1}{2}$ pounds per week on the plan.

(a) How many pounds does Sarina estimate Bruno will lose in 2 weeks? In $8\frac{1}{2}$ weeks?

(b) Write an equation for this situation. (Because Bruno is losing weight, the number of pounds he loses will be a negative value.)

(c) Create a table of values and graph for the situation.

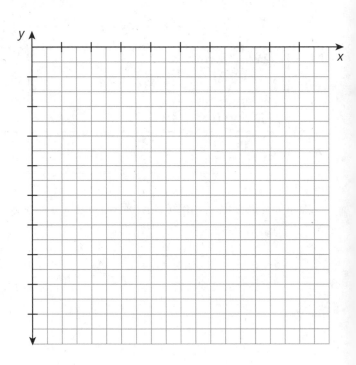

Independent Quantity	Dependent Quantity

STRETCH Optional

> Tell a story to describe the graph.

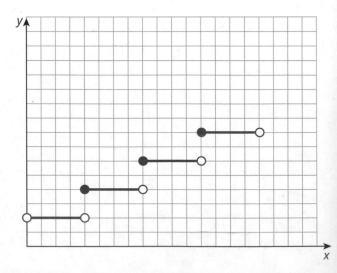

MIXED PRACTICE

❯ This Mixed Practice worksheet includes two sections: Spaced Review and End-of-Topic Review. **Use a separate piece of paper to show your work.**

Spaced Review

❯ Practice concepts from previous topics.

1 Calculate the distance of each number from 125. Use positive numbers to indicate the distance when the number is greater than 125 and negative numbers to indicate the distance when the number is less than 125.

(a) 107   (b) 161

(c) 87   (d) 232

2 Graph the solution set for each given inequality.

(a) $x > 7.75$

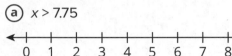

(b) $x \leq \frac{5}{2}$

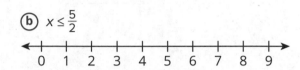

3 Calculate the area of each composite figure.

(a)
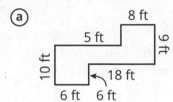

8 ft
5 ft
9 ft
10 ft
18 ft
6 ft   6 ft

(b)
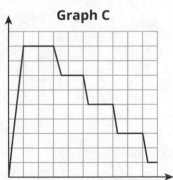

10 in.
8.5 in.
11 in.
24 in.

4 Evaluate each expression for the given values.

(a) $5.2r + 1.2$, when $r = 1.5$ and 4.1

(b) $\frac{1}{2}t + \frac{3}{4}$, when $t = \frac{2}{3}$ and $\frac{9}{5}$

5 Create a scenario to fit each numeric expression.

(a) $|-3| + |21|$

(b) $|8 - 3|$

6 Choose the graph that best represents the scenario. Explain your reasoning.
Carla fills a mug with tea. Every few minutes Carla takes a drink from the mug.

Graph A

Graph B

Graph C

End-of-Topic Review

AVAILABLE ONLINE

1. A **Topic Summary** reviews the main concepts for the topic.
2. A video of the **Worked Example** is provided.

> Practice concepts you learned in **The Four Quadrants**.

7 Label each of the four quadrants in the coordinate plane. Then identify and label the origin.

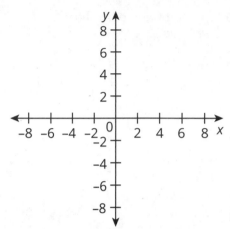

8 The point (x, y) is located in Quadrant II of a coordinate plane. Identify the quadrant each additional ordered pair is located in.

  ⓐ $(-x, y)$

  ⓑ $(x, -y)$

  ⓒ $(-x, -y)$

9 Plot and identify four points across at least 3 quadrants that form a right triangle. Determine the area of the triangle.

10 Label each point with its ordered pair.

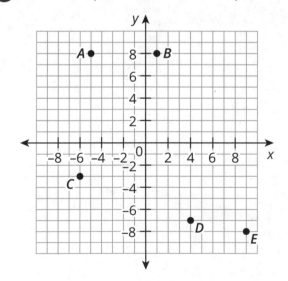

11 The vertices of a polygon are $(-4, -1)$, $(-3, -2)$, $(10, -2)$, $(3, 0)$ $(0, 4)$, and $(-2, 3)$.

Plot the points on a coordinate plane and connect the points in the order they are listed. Then determine the area of the polygon.

Describing Variability of Quantities

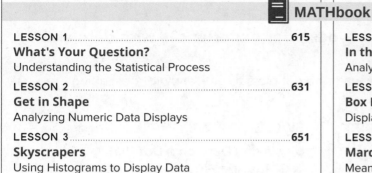
MATHia

Getting Ready for Module 5
Describing Variability of Quantities

You will expand your knowledge of statistics and develop an understanding of the statistical process and statistical questions. You will continue the work you have done with dot plots and explore other methods of displaying data. You will investigate how to summarize data using different measures of center and spread.

The lessons in this module build on your prior experiences with data and dot plots.

Review these key terms and strategies for analyzing dot plots to get ready for describing the variability of quantities.

KEY TERMS

data

Data is a collection of responses, numbers, or observations.

dot plot

A dot plot (sometimes called a line plot) is a data display that shows discrete data on a number line with dots, Xs, or other symbols.

The dot plot represents data set {1, 1, 3, 2, 1, 4, 5, 2, 1, 4}

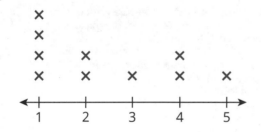

SKILLS YOU WILL NEED

Displaying Data on a Dot Plot

The dot plot shows data collected from a group of students.

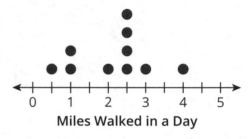

The response that appears the most, also called the mode, is 2.5 miles.

Adding all of the values, you can conclude the total number of miles walked is 21.5.

REVIEW

> Consider the dot plot.

1 Circle the value that appears most often.

2 List the values in order from least to greatest.

Amount of Trail Mix Eaten

(dot plot)

Cup

3 What is the total amount of trail mix eaten?

See the Appendix on page 719 for answers.

🖥 MATHia

Brush up on your skills.
You will practice these skills while working in workspaces already included in your sequence of MATHia.

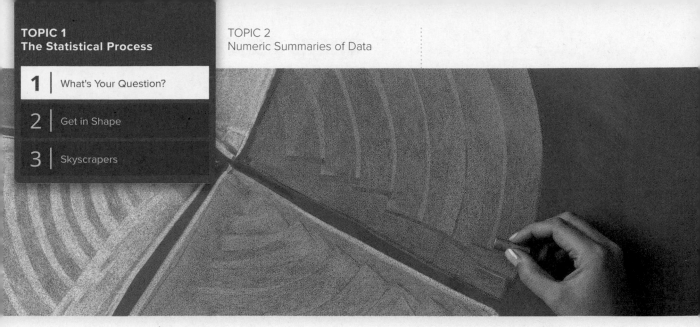

LESSON 1

What's Your Question?

Understanding the Statistical Process

Learning Goals

- Recognize statistical questions and anticipate variability in data related to the question.

- Describe the four stages of the statistical process.

- Discuss the different types of data that you can collect, display, and analyze.

- Differentiate between surveys, observational studies, and experiments.

- Analyze and interpret bar graphs and circle graphs.

KEY TERMS

variability
statistical process
statistical question
data
categorical data
quantitative data
population

sample
survey
observational study
experiment
bar graph
circle graph
frequency
mode

REVIEW (1–2 minutes)

❯ Use the bar graph to answer each question.

1 How many students in the class play basketball?

2 How many students in the class play football?

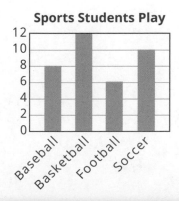

Sports Students Play

You have analyzed and interpreted various mathematical problems throughout this course. Now, you are going to study how to solve statistical problems.

What process do you use to solve statistical problems?

Statistical or Not, That Is the Question

Have you ever wondered, "How much money do professional athletes make?" Or, "How tall are the students in my class?" If so, you have asked a statistical question. If you have sought out the answer to your question, you have engaged in the statistical process.

> Cut out the survey questions provided on page 627. Read each question and sort them into at least two groups. Include at least two questions per group of questions.

1 Record your groups and the questions in each group.

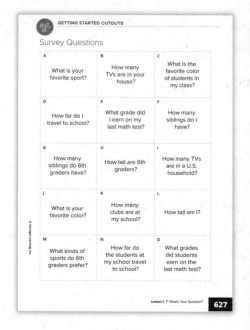

GETTING STARTED CUTOUTS

Survey Questions

A	B	C
What is your favorite sport?	How many TVs are in your house?	What is the favorite color of students in my class?

D	E	F
How far do I travel to school?	What grade did I earn on my last math test?	How many siblings do I have?

G	H	I
How many siblings do 6th graders have?	How tall are 6th graders?	How many TVs are in a U.S. household?

J	K	L
What is your favorite color?	How many clubs are at my school?	How tall am I?

M	N	O
What kinds of sports do 6th graders prefer?	How far do the students at my school travel to school?	What grades did students earn on the last math test?

Lesson 1 > What's Your Question?   627

Formulating Statistical Questions

In this module, you will begin your formal study of statistics and the *statistical process*. Statistics is a problem-solving process because the heart of statistics is about determining a possible answer to a question that has *variability*.

The **statistical process** has four components:

STEP 1 Formulate a statistical question.

STEP 2 Collect appropriate data.

STEP 3 Analyze the data graphically and numerically.

STEP 4 Interpret the results of the analysis.

Statistical problem solving begins with a *statistical question*. A **statistical question** is a question that anticipates an answer based on *data* that vary.

> Analyze the questions posed by Bianca and Rajan.

HABITS OF MIND
- Reason abstractly and quantitatively.
- Construct viable arguments and critique the reasoning of others.

TOPIC 1

TAKE NOTE...
In statistics, **variability** means that the value of the attribute you are studying can change from one person or thing to another.

Bianca

"What clubs am I in?"
"How many students are in the Chess Club?"

Rajan

"What clubs do my classmates belong to?"
"How many members do the clubs at my school have?"

1 Explain why Bianca's questions are not statistical questions but Rajan's are.

TAKE NOTE...
Data are categories, numbers, or observations gathered in response to a statistical question.

2 What kinds of answers do you expect from Rajan's questions?

Statistics is about posing interesting questions that you want to answer about varying attributes.

> Gather the survey questions from the Getting Started activity.

3 Which questions from your sort are statistical questions? **Explain how you would expect the answers to those questions to vary.**

TAKE NOTE...

Keep your questions. You will need them later in the lesson.

Answering a statistical question requires collecting variable data. You will learn about two types of data: *categorical data* and *quantitative data*.

4 Are the answers to Rajan's questions categorical or quantitative?

TAKE NOTE...

Categorical data, or *qualitative data*, fit into exactly one of several different groups or categories. You can place **quantitative data**, or *numeric data*, on a numeric scale and compare.

5 Which questions have categorical answers and which have quantitative answers? **Explain your reasoning.**

6 For each question, determine whether it is a statistical question. If it is not, rewrite it as a statistical question. Then, state whether the data would be categorical or quantitative.

    (a) How many text messages did you send and receive yesterday?

    (b) What school mascot do students at my school prefer?

    (c) How much time did you spend watching TV or playing video games last weekend?

    (d) How many hours do 6th graders sleep each night?

7 Write at least 2 additional statistical questions that you would have an interest in answering. State whether the data would be categorical or quantitative.

DID YOU KNOW?

Just as you can describe graphs as discrete or continuous, you can describe quantitative data as discrete or continuous.

ASK YOURSELF…

Don't worry about the answer to the question, if there even is one. What would you like to know?

TOPIC 1

Methods of Data Collection

In this activity, you will learn about the second component of the statistical process: collecting appropriate data.

What is the best way to collect the data to answer the statistical question?

> Suppose you want to collect data on the topic of school lunches.

1 Write three statistical questions that you can ask about school lunches.

ⓐ

ⓑ

ⓒ

You can answer a statistical question by collecting data from an entire *population* or, more commonly, from a *sample* of the population. A **population** is an entire set of items from which you collect data. A **sample** is a selection from a population.

❯ Consider the answer to the question, "How tall are 6th graders?"

WORKED EXAMPLE

To answer the question using the population of all 6th graders, you need to determine the heights of every 6th grader in the world.

To answer the question using a sample of 6th graders, you can collect data from just the 6th graders at your school.

Three common methods of data collection are *surveys, observational studies,* and *experiments.*

- In a **survey**, you ask people one or more questions.
- In an **observational study**, the researcher (you!) collects data by observing the variable of interest.
- In an **experiment**, the researcher imposes a condition and observes the results.

You could conduct an experiment to investigate whether sixth graders perform better on an assessment when they read a textbook or when they watch a video about the material. You would randomly assign half the students to read the text and half the students to watch the video. All students would then take the same assessment. You would compare the scores of the students in the two groups.

DID YOU KNOW?

If you have ever completed a science project, you have probably conducted an experiment.

2 For each statistical question you wrote in Question 1:

- Identify the population and sample of interest.
- State whether you would use a survey, observational study, or experiment to collect the data to answer your statistical questions. **Explain your reasoning.**

ⓐ

ⓑ

ⓒ

TOPIC 1

ACTIVITY 3

MATHia CONNECTION
• Analyzing Distributions with Shape, Center, and Spread

The Statistical Process

TOPIC 1 — LESSON 1

Getting Started | Activity 1 2 3 | Talk the Talk

Analyzing and Interpreting Data

In the statistical process, after you collect the data, it is time to analyze and interpret the results.

Analysis includes selecting the most appropriate graphical display and numeric summaries for your question and your method of data collection.

You already have experience displaying and summarizing categorical data using *bar graphs* and *circle graphs*.

A **bar graph** displays categorical data using either horizontal or vertical bars on a graph. The height or length of each bar indicates the value for that category.

A **circle graph**, often called a pie chart, displays categorical data using sectors, or "wedges," of a circle. It shows how parts of the whole relate to the whole and how parts of the whole relate to the other parts. The area of each sector corresponds to the ratio of the part in relation to the whole.

HABITS OF MIND
• Reason abstractly and quantitatively.
• Construct viable arguments and critique the reasoning of others.

TAKE NOTE...
Formulating a statistical question is **STEP 1** of the statistical process. Collecting data is **STEP 2** of the statistical process. Analyzing the collected data is **STEP 3** of the statistical process.

Nicole and Neal were interested in the favorite sports of 6th graders. They surveyed their class of 30 students. Then, they displayed their class's data in different ways.

❯ Analyze Nicole's graph and Neal's graph.

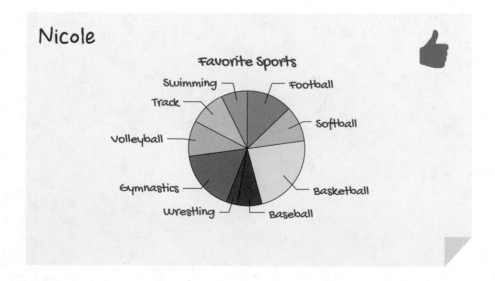

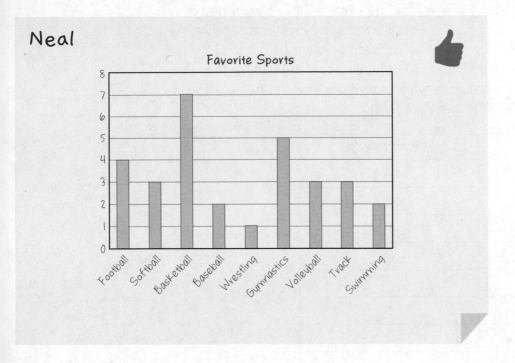

Neal

Favorite Sports

1 How are the graphs similar? How are they different?

To create the graphs, Nicole and Neal determined the *frequency* of each response and recorded the frequencies in a frequency table. A **frequency** is the number of times an item or number occurs in a data set. Once the frequency is known, you can determine the *mode*. The **mode** is the value or values that occur most frequently in a data set.

TAKE NOTE...
Interpreting the data, or drawing conclusions, is **STEP 4** of the statistical process.

Sport	Frequency (f)
Football	4
Softball	3
Basketball	7
Baseball	2
Wrestling	1
Gymnastics	5
Volleyball	3
Track	3
Swimming	2

2 What conclusions can you make about the most popular sport in Nicole and Neal's class? **Use the table and graphs to explain your reasoning.**

3 Choose one of the categorical statistical questions you wrote about school lunches and survey your class to obtain a sample.

4 Compile your class's responses to the survey question you asked in Question 3. Record the frequency of each response in a table.

5 Create a graphical display for your assigned survey question. What conclusions can you make about your class based on your graph?

ASK YOURSELF...
Would your conclusions be different if you changed the order of the categories?

TOPIC 1

(Graphically) Organizing the Process

This lesson provided an overview of the statistical process. You will continue to use the process throughout your study of statistics.

❯ Complete the graphic organizer for the statistical process. In each section, summarize what you know about the component and provide examples.

Statistical Process

1. Formulate a Statistical Question	2. Collect Data

3. Analyze the Data	4. Interpret the Results

Survey Questions

A

What is your favorite sport?

B

How many TVs are in your house?

C

What is the favorite color of students in my class?

D

How far do I travel to school?

E

What grade did I earn on my last math test?

F

How many siblings do I have?

G

How many siblings do 6th graders have?

H

How tall are 6th graders?

I

How many TVs are in a U.S. household?

J

What is your favorite color?

K

How many clubs are at my school?

L

How tall am I?

M

What kinds of sports do 6th graders prefer?

N

How far do the students at my school travel to school?

O

What grades did students earn on the last math test?

Why is this page blank?
So you can cut out the questions on the other side.

LESSON 1 ASSIGNMENT

> Use a separate piece of paper for your Journal entry.

JOURNAL

Explain the difference between a survey, an observational study, and an experiment in your own words.

REMEMBER

There are four components to the statistical process:

STEP 1 Formulate a statistical question.

STEP 2 Collect data.

STEP 3 Analyze the data using graphical displays and numeric summaries.

STEP 4 Interpret the results in terms of the original statistical question and context.

PRACTICE

1 Determine whether each given question is a statistical question. If not, rewrite it to make it a statistical question.

(a) How many people in your class like to play video games?

(b) Is pizza your favorite food?

(c) What time do you go to bed on school nights?

2 State whether you would use a survey, observational study, or experiment to answer each given statistical question.

(a) "How many of the students in your class ate breakfast this morning?"

(b) "Which students in your school can run a 40-meter sprint the fastest?"

(c) "Does listening to classical music while studying improve test scores?"

3 Determine whether each set of given data are categorical or quantitative. If the data are quantitative, determine whether they are discrete or continuous.

ⓐ Each student in your math class records their height.

ⓑ The members of the Horse Club list the types of horses they have.

ⓒ The members of the Horse Club list the numbers of horses they each have.

4 An online store asks the question, "Do the number of sales per customer increase when a promotional code is at the top of the website?"

ⓐ Is this a statistical question? Explain your reasoning.

ⓑ Explain how an experiment can answer this question.

STRETCH Optional

In 1945, George Polya published a book about mathematical problem solving. He outlined a four-step process for problem solving:

1. Understand the Problem

2. Devise a Plan

3. Carry out the Plan

4. Look Back

❯ Research the four steps and explain how the four-component statistical problem-solving process is similar to and different from Polya's four steps for mathematical problem solving.

TOPIC 1
The Statistical Process

1 | What's Your Question?

2 | Get in Shape

3 | Skyscrapers

TOPIC 2
Numeric Summaries of Data

LESSON 2

Get in Shape
Analyzing Numeric Data Displays

Learning Goals

- Create and interpret dot plots.
- Create and interpret stem-and-leaf plots.
- Describe the center, spread, and overall shape of a data distribution.

KEY TERMS

dot plot	gaps
distribution	peaks
symmetric	outliers
skewed right	uniform distribution
skewed left	stem-and-leaf plot
clusters	

REVIEW (1–2 minutes)

❯ Use the pictograph to answer each question.

1 How many dogs do the students in Mr. Garcia's class own?

2 How many fish and birds do the students own?

3 How many total pets do the students in Mr. Garcia's class own?

Pets Owned by Students in Mr. Garcia's Class
(each symbol represents 1 pet)

You know how to use picture graphs, bar graphs, and line plots to display categorical and numeric data.

What additional representations can you use to display and analyze numeric data?

GETTING STARTED

The Statistical Process
TOPIC 1 — LESSON 2

Getting Started

Activity
1   2   3   4

Talk
the Talk

Rock-Climbing Competition

Ms. Nicholson poses the question, **"Which grade has the fastest average rock-climbing time if each student attempts one climb?"**

To answer this question, Ms. Nicholson ran an experiment with one class from each grade level. She recorded the time it took for each student to climb the rock wall and created three different data displays.

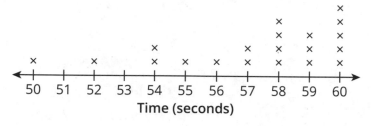

Rock-Climbing Times (6th Grade)

Sixth Grade Completion Times (seconds):
60, 50, 58, 59, 60, 54, 55, 58, 59, 60, 52, 54, 56, 57, 57, 58, 60, 60, 59, 58

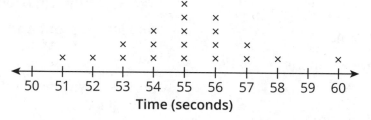

Rock-Climbing Times (7th Grade)

Seventh Grade Completion Times (seconds):
51, 52, 53, 53, 54, 54, 54, 55, 55, 55, 55, 55, 56, 56, 56, 56, 57, 57, 58, 60

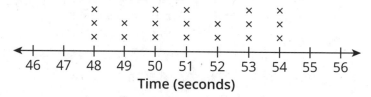

Rock-Climbing Times (8th Grade)

Eighth Grade Completion Times (seconds):
48, 54, 53, 50, 54, 52, 48, 49, 51, 54, 53, 48, 50, 50, 49, 51, 51, 52, 53

1 How are these data displays similar? How are they different?

2 What can you observe from a data display that you cannot see from looking at the numeric data?

ACTIVITY 1
MATHia CONNECTION
• Creating Dot Plots

The Statistical Process

TOPIC 1   LESSON 2

Getting Started   Activity 1 2 3 4   Talk the Talk

TOPIC 1

Creating and Analyzing Dot Plots

The 2018 Winter Olympics were in Pyeongchang, South Korea. While watching the Olympics, Jessica and Maurice decided to pose statistical questions about the Games.

HABITS OF MIND
• Model with mathematics.
• Use appropriate tools strategically.

1 Jessica asked, "How many medals did the United States win? How many of those were gold?" Maurice thought a better set of questions was, "What is the typical number of medals won? What is the typical number of gold medals won by a country?" Who's correct? **Explain your reasoning.**

The table located on page 645 lists the number of gold medals and the total medals won by all medal-winning countries for the 2018 Winter Olympics.

2 Analyze the data shown in the table.

ⓐ What conclusions can you make about the numbers of total medals won at the 2018 Winter Olympics?

ASK YOURSELF...
Do countries who win gold medals tend to win more medals in general?

ⓑ Are the data in the table categorical or quantitative? **Explain your reasoning.**

ⓒ Are the data in the table discrete or continuous? **Explain your reasoning.**

One way to describe a set of quantitative data is by drawing a graphical display of the data.

A **dot plot** is a data display that shows discrete data on a number line with dots, Xs, or other symbols. Dot plots help organize and display a small number of data points.

WORKED EXAMPLE

This dot plot shows the data for total medals won. The number line represents the total number of medals. Each X above a number represents the number of countries that won that many medals.

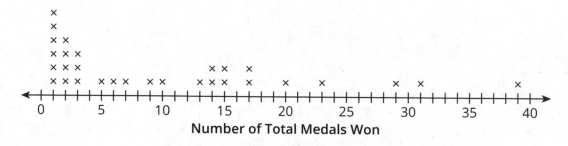

**Total Medals Won by Countries
at 2018 Winter Olympics**

Number of Total Medals Won

---

3 Use the dot plot in the worked example to answer each question.

   ⓐ What do the two Xs above the number 14 represent?

   ⓑ What do the six Xs above the number 1 represent?

   ⓒ Why are there no Xs above the number 4?

   ⓓ Use the dot plot to determine the number of countries that won medals in the 2018 Winter Olympics. **Explain your strategy.**

> Create a dot plot to display the number of gold medals won as listed in the 2018 Winter Olympics data table.

4 First, analyze the data set and set up the number line.

ⓐ What will you name your dot plot?

ⓑ What numbers will begin and end your number line? Why did you select these numbers?

ⓒ What interval will you use on your number line? Why did you select this interval?

5 Create your dot plot to display the data for the gold medals won at the 2018 Winter Olympics.

←——————————————————————————→

6 Write a brief summary to report the results of your data analysis back to Maurice and Jessica to help answer their questions about gold medals and all medals won at the 2018 Winter Olympics.

ACTIVITY 2
MATHia CONNECTION
- Interpreting Dot Plots

The Statistical Process

TOPIC 1 — **LESSON 2**

Getting Started | Activity 1 2 3 4 | Talk the Talk

Describing Distributions

When you analyze a graphical representation of numeric data, you can look at its shape, center, and spread to draw conclusions.

> **HABITS OF MIND**
> - Look for and make use of structure.
> - Look for and express regularity in repeated reasoning.

You call the overall shape of a graph the *distribution* of data. The way the data spreads out is its **distribution**. The most common distributions are *symmetric, skewed right,* and *skewed left.*

Shapes of Typical Distributions of Graphical Displays of Data

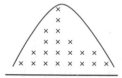

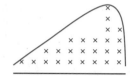

symmetric	**skewed right**	**skewed left**
• The peak of the data is in the middle.	• The peak of the data is to the left side of the graph.	• The peak of the data is to the right side of the graph.
• The left and right halves of the graph are mirror images, or almost mirror images, of each other.	• There are only a few data points to the right side of the graph.	• There are only a few data points to the left side of the graph.

1 Miko says that the dot plot for the number of gold medals won is skewed right. Do you agree with her statement? **Explain your reasoning.**

**Gold Medals Won by Countries
at the 2018 Winter Olympics**

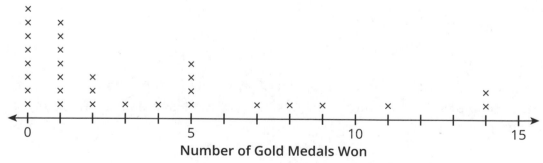

Number of Gold Medals Won

❯ Analyze the dot plot.

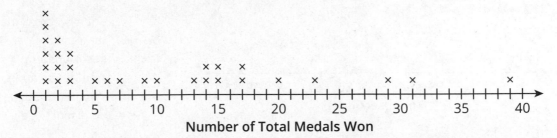

Total Medals Won by Countries
at 2018 Winter Olympics

Number of Total Medals Won

2 What is the distribution of the dot plot? **Explain what this means in terms of the total number of medals won.**

When analyzing a graphical display of data, you can also look for any interesting patterns. Some of these patterns include:

- **clusters**—areas where data group close together

- **gaps**—areas where there are no data

- **peaks**—values that contain more data points than the values on either side of it

- **outliers**—data values that lie a large distance from the other data. Outliers usually accompany gaps in data.

TAKE NOTE...
Gaps usually span multiple possible data values.

3 Identify any clusters, gaps, peaks, or outliers in the dot plot Total Medals Won by Countries at the 2018 Winter Olympics, located above. **Explain what this means in terms of the total number of medals won.**

4 Identify any clusters, gaps, peaks, or outliers in the plot for the Gold Medals Won by Countries at the 2018 Winter Olympics, located in Question 1. **Explain what this means in terms of the number of gold medals won.**

ACTIVITY 2 Continued

Another common shape for data distribution is a *uniform distribution*.

❯ Analyze the dot plots from the Getting Started activity.

5 Describe the shape of each dot plot, including its overall shape and any relevant patterns.

DID YOU KNOW?

A **uniform distribution** describes the shape of data spread equally across the range of the data set. A uniform distribution appears symmetric, but has no distinct peaks.

ⓐ

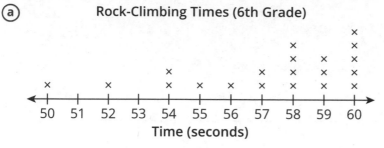

Rock-Climbing Times (6th Grade)

ⓑ

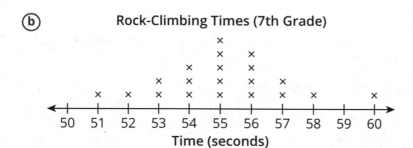

Rock-Climbing Times (7th Grade)

ⓒ

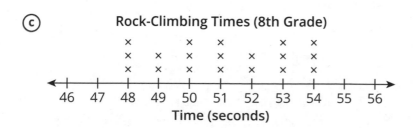

Rock-Climbing Times (8th Grade)

Stem-and-Leaf Plots

In this activity, you will learn about a different graphical display for numeric data.

HABITS OF MIND
• Model with mathematics.
• Use appropriate tools strategically.

TOPIC 1

> At the 2018 Winter Olympics, 92 countries competed in the events, but only 30 won medals. The 2016 Summer Olympics had 207 countries compete in the events. Athletes from 80 countries won medals, but only 44 countries won at least 5 medals.

The table located on page 648 lists the total number of medals won by the top-performing countries in the 2016 Summer Olympics.

> Compare this data set to the data set for the total number of medals won at the 2018 Winter Olympics.

1 Do you think using a dot plot would be a good way to organize and analyze the data in the Summer Olympics table? **Explain your reasoning.**

A numeric data display that can easily display data sets with a larger range of data values would be helpful to plot the 2016 Summer Olympic data.

A **stem-and-leaf plot** is a graphical method used to represent ordered numeric data.

> Create a stem-and-leaf plot displaying the number of medals won in the 2016 Summer Olympics.

WORKED EXAMPLE

STEP 1 Determine the **stems** and **leaves**. Typically, the stem is all the digits in a number except the rightmost digit, which is the leaf. For data that have only a ones place, the stem is 0.

STEP 2 Draw the stem-and-leaf plot. Place the stems in the left column and the leaves in numeric order in the right column.
Title the display and include a key indicating what the stems and leaves represent.

Total Medals Won by Countries 2016 Summer Olympics

0	5 5 5 6 6 6 7 7 7 8 8 8 8 8 9 9
1	0 0 0 1 1 1 1 1 3 3 5 5 7 8 8 8 9 9
2	2 8 9
3	
4	1 2 2
5	6
6	7
7	0
8	
9	
10	
11	
12	1

Key: $4 \mid 1 = 41$ medals won.

> Analyze the stem-and-leaf plot in the worked example.

2 What does 7 | 0 mean in the stem-and-leaf plot?

Total Medals Won by Countries 2016 Summer Olympics

0	5 5 5 6 6 6 7 7 7 8 8 8 8 8 9 9
1	0 0 0 1 1 1 1 1 3 3 5 5 7 8 8 8 9 9
2	2 8 9
3	
4	1 2 2
5	6
6	7
7	0
8	
9	
10	
11	
12	1

Key: 4 | 1 = 41 medals won.

3 What does 0 | 5 mean?

4 How many stems are in the stem-and-leaf plot?

5 How many leaves are in the stem-and-leaf plot? Why are there that many leaves?

6 Why would a stem have more than one leaf?

TOPIC 1

7 Why do some stems have no leaves?

8 Why do some stems have the same leaf repeated?

9 Carlos claims that he should write 0s as leaves after the stems 3, 8, 9, 10, and 11 to show that there are no countries that have an amount of medals in the 30s, 80s, 90s, 100s, or 110s. Is Carlos correct? **Explain your reasoning.**

10 What is the most common number of medals won? How can you determine this from the stem-and-leaf plot?

11 Describe the distribution and any interesting patterns you notice in the stem-and-leaf plot. Interpret your findings in terms of the number of medals won in the 2016 Summer Olympics.

TAKE NOTE...
To see the distribution better, rotate the stem-and-leaf plot so that the stems resemble a horizontal number line.

ACTIVITY 4

The Statistical
Process

TOPIC 1   LESSON 2

Getting
Started   Activity   Talk
    1   2   3   4   the Talk

Creating and Analyzing Data Displays

You can display numeric data using a graphical display to better analyze the data.

During a presidential election, media reports sometimes call attention to the ages of the candidates. Alicia wondered, "Are the candidates too old to be president?" Because she wanted to collect and analyze data, she revised her question: **"At what age do presidents take office?"**

1 Explain why Alicia's question is a statistical question.

To answer her question, Alicia collected data on the ages of the presidents of the United States at their first inauguration. Her data appear in the table on page 649.

To analyze the data, let's create a data display of the presidents' ages at inauguration.

2 Create a dot plot or stem-and-leaf plot to display the age of each president at their first inauguration.

3 Describe the distribution of the ages of presidents at their first inaugurations.

4 The minimum age to become president of the United States is 35 years old. How is this requirement reflected in your data display?

5 What was the most common age for presidents upon inauguration? **Explain using your data display.**

6 Write a brief summary to report the results of your data analysis back to Alicia in response to her question about the ages of presidents at their inaugurations.

TALK THE TALK

The Statistical Process

TOPIC 1 — **LESSON 2**

Getting Started

Activity 1 2 3 4

Talk the Talk

Peaks, Gaps, and Clusters...Oh, My!

> Analyze the data displays shown.

Plot A

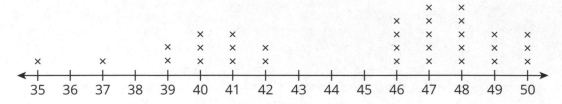

Plot B

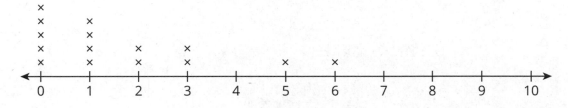

Plot C

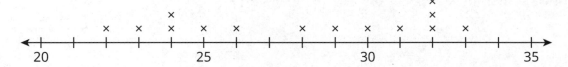

Plot D

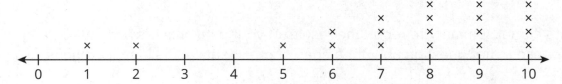

1 Which plot or plots appear to illustrate each graphical feature?

ⓐ cluster(s)　　　ⓑ gap(s)　　　ⓒ outlier(s)　　　ⓓ skewness

2 Select a symmetric distribution and explain how you can make it skewed left or skewed right.

2018 Winter Olympics All Countries with Medal Wins

TOPIC 1

Country	Gold Medals	Total Medals	Country	Gold Medals	Total Medals
Norway	14	39	Finland	1	6
Germany	14	31	Great Britain	1	5
Canada	11	29	Belarus	2	3
United States	9	23	Slovakia	1	3
Netherlands	8	20	Australia	0	3
Olympic Athletes from Russia	2	17	Poland	1	2
South Korea	5	17	New Zealand	0	2
France	5	15	Slovenia	0	2
Switzerland	5	15	Spain	0	2
Austria	5	14	Hungary	1	1
Sweden	7	14	Ukraine	1	1
Japan	4	13	Belgium	0	1
Italy	3	10	Kazakhstan	0	1
China	1	9	Latvia	0	1
Czech Republic	2	7	Liechtenstein	0	1

Total Number of Medals Won by Top-Performing Countries, 2016 Summer Olympics

Country	Medals Won	Country	Medals Won
United States	121	Ukraine	11
China	70	Poland	11
Great Britain	67	Sweden	11
Russian Federation	56	Croatia	10
Germany	42	Czech Republic	10
France	42	South Africa	10
Japan	41	Cuba	9
Australia	29	Belarus	9
Italy	28	Columbia	8
Canada	22	Iran	8
Netherlands	19	Ethiopia	8
Brazil	19	Serbia	8
South Korea	18	Turkey	8
New Zealand	18	Georgia	7
Azerbaijan	18	North Korea	7
Kazakhstan	17	Switzerland	7
Hungary	15	Belgium	6
Denmark	15	Thailand	6
Kenya	13	Greece	6
Uzbekistan	13	Romania	5
Spain	11	Malaysia	5
Jamaica	11	Mexico	5

Ages of Presidents at First Inauguration

President	Age at First Inauguration	President	Age at First Inauguration
Washington	57	Harrison	55
Adams, J.	61	Roosevelt, T.	42
Jefferson	57	Taft	51
Madison	57	Wilson	56
Monroe	58	Harding	55
Adams, J.Q.	57	Coolidge	51
Jackson	61	Hoover	54
Van Buren	54	Roosevelt, F.D.	51
Harrison	68	Truman	60
Tyler	51	Eisenhower	62
Polk	49	Kennedy	43
Taylor	64	Johnson, L.B.	55
Fillmore	50	Nixon	56
Pierce	48	Ford	61
Buchanan	65	Carter	52
Lincoln	52	Reagan	69
Johnson, A.	56	Bush, G.H.W.	64
Grant	46	Clinton	46
Hayes	54	Bush, G.W.	54
Garfield	49	Obama	47
Arthur	50	Trump	70
Cleveland	47	Biden	78
McKinley	54		

Wins and Losses by Atlanta Hawks Over 44 Seasons

Season	Wins	Losses	Season	Wins	Losses
2019–2020*	20	47	1997–1998	50	32
2018–2019	29	53	1996–1997	56	26
2017–2018	24	58	1995–1996	46	36
2016–2017	43	39	1994–1995	42	40
2015–2016	48	34	1993–1994	57	25
2014–2015	60	22	1992–1993	43	39
2013–2014	38	44	1991–1992	38	44
2012–2013	44	38	1990–1991	43	39
2011–2012	40	26	1989–1990	41	41
2010–2011	44	38	1988–1989	52	30
2009–2010	53	29	1987–1988	50	32
2008–2009	47	35	1986–1987	57	25
2007–2008	37	45	1985–1986	50	32
2006–2007	30	52	1984–1985	34	48
2005–2006	26	56	1983–1984	40	42
2004–2005	13	69	1982–1983	43	39
2003–2004	28	54	1981–1982	42	40
2002–2003	35	47	1980–1981	31	51
2001–2002	33	49	1979–1980	50	32
2000–2001	25	57	1978–1979	46	36
1999–2000	28	54	1977–1978	41	41
1998–1999	31	19	1976–1977	31	51

*Shortened season

LESSON 2 ASSIGNMENT

> Use a separate piece of paper for your Journal entry.

JOURNAL

Write a definition for each term in your own words.

1 symmetric

2 skewed right

3 skewed left

REMEMBER

You can describe data sets according to the shape of their distribution.

Dot plots are ideal for small data sets.

Stem-and-leaf plots are ideal for moderately sized data sets, especially when you need to see the actual data values.

PRACTICE

The data table on page 648 shows the number of wins and losses the Atlanta Hawks have had in 44 seasons in Atlanta.

1 Create a dot plot or a stem-and-leaf plot for the number of wins by the Atlanta Hawks. Be sure to name your plot and provide a key if necessary.

2 Describe the distribution of the data. Include any specific graphical features or patterns. Explain what your answer means in terms of the number of wins by the Hawks.

3 Create a dot plot or a stem-and-leaf plot for the number of losses by the Atlanta Hawks. Be sure to name your plot and provide a key if necessary.

4 Describe the distribution of the data. Include any specific graphical features or patterns. Explain what your answer means in terms of the number of losses by the Hawks.

5 Propose a win-loss record for an upcoming season that changes the overall distribution of both plots.

STRETCH Optional

Another type of display used to compare two data sets is a side-by-side or back-to-back stem-and-leaf plot.

1 Describe the distribution of each data set.

2 Then, use the key and the plot to list the numeric data values in each data set.

Data Set One		Data Set Two
8 6	4	
9 3 1	5	9
9 8 6 5 1 1 0	6	2 7
7 3 2	7	0 0 3 6 6 8 9
5 3	8	0 1 2 2
2 1	9	

Key: 1|5|9 = 5.1 and 5.9

TOPIC 1
The Statistical Process

TOPIC 2
Numeric Summaries of Data

1 | What's Your Question?

2 | Get in Shape

3 | Skyscrapers

LESSON 3

Skyscrapers

Using Histograms to Display Data

KEY TERMS

histogram

range

grouped
frequency table

Learning Goals

- Display and interpret numeric data in histograms.

- Compare data displays.

REVIEW (1–2 minutes)

❯ Use the bar graph to answer each question.

1 Who found the most sharks' teeth? How many did that person find?

2 How many total sharks' teeth did the friends find?

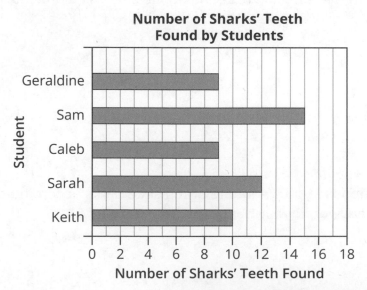

Number of Sharks' Teeth Found by Students

You have used dot plots and stem-and-leaf plots, which are good for small data sets.

How can you display data sets with a larger number of observations?

State Parks

There are over 6000 state parks in the United States. The table shows how many state parks there are in each of the states listed.

1 Create a bar graph using the data in the table.

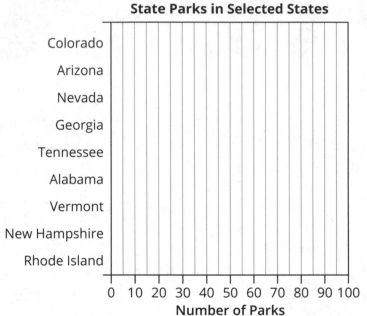

State Parks in Selected States

State	Number of Parks
Colorado	42
Arizona	31
Nevada	23
Georgia	50
Tennessee	56
Alabama	21
Vermont	21
New Hampshire	93
Rhode Island	15

2 Is there benefit in rearranging the states in alphabetical order? **Why or why not?**

3 Suppose you wanted to graph state parks according to the region of the country. **How would your bar graph be different?**

ACTIVITY 1
MATHia CONNECTION
• Introduction to Histograms

The Statistical Process
TOPIC 1   LESSON 3

Getting Started   Activity 1 2 3   Talk the Talk

Histograms

In the remainder of this lesson, you will analyze and create *histograms*, which look similar to bar graphs but do not display the same type of data.

HABITS OF MIND
• Model with mathematics.
• Use appropriate tools strategically.

Minneapolis and St. Paul are known as the Twin Cities. Both cities are home to flourishing downtowns with tall buildings.

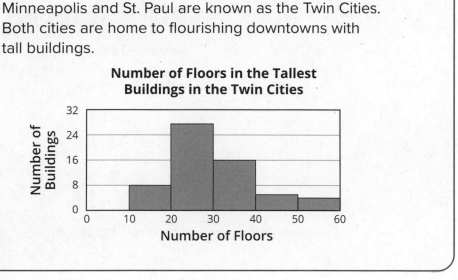

Number of Floors in the Tallest Buildings in the Twin Cities

TAKE NOTE...
A **histogram** is a graphical way to display quantitative or numeric data using vertical bars.

1 Analyze the histogram.

(a) How is this graph different from the bar graphs you have used previously?

(b) What information does the histogram display? Describe the data represented in the histogram shown. Look at the title and the labels on the axes.

TAKE NOTE...
The width of a bar in a histogram represents an interval of data known as a bin. The height of the bar indicates the frequency, or the number of data values included in any given bin.

(c) Are the data represented in the histogram discrete or continuous? **Explain your reasoning.**

(d) Describe the distribution of the data, such as the overall shape and the existence of peaks, clusters, and gaps.

2 Let's think about the bars in the histogram.

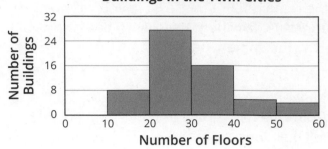

Number of Floors in the Tallest Buildings in the Twin Cities

(a) How many bins are there?

(b) Are all the bins the same size?

(c) What does the height of each bar represent?

3 Describe the range of floors included in each of the remaining bins shown on the horizontal axis.

(a) 2nd bin: interval 20–30

THINK ABOUT...
In the second bin, the *bounds* are the numbers 20 and 30. What are the bounds of the 5th bin?

(b) 3rd bin: interval 30–40

(c) 4th bin: interval 40–50

(d) 5th bin: interval 50–60

4 Suppose a new building has 20 floors. Which bin would change? **How would it change?**

5 Tell whether you can determine each number, using the histogram. **Explain why or why not.**

(a) The total number of buildings

(b) The number of buildings that have 31 floors

(c) The *range* of the data set

6 Write a summary to report the results of your data analysis about the number of floors in the Twin Cities' tallest buildings.

ACTIVITY 2
MATHia CONNECTION
• Creating Histograms
• Exploring Histograms

The Statistical Process

TOPIC 1   LESSON 3

Getting Started   Activity 1   **2**   3   Talk the Talk

Creating and Analyzing Histograms

You can analyze the histograms of two different data sets to compare the displays.

New York City has over 5800 tall buildings and is home to the ninth tallest building in the United States, the Empire State Building, which is 1250 feet tall, or 1454 feet to its tip. Not to be outdone, Chicago is home to the Willis Tower, formerly known as Sears Tower. It stands an impressive 1450 feet tall, or 1729 feet to its tip.

The table shows the number of floors in the 15 tallest buildings in New York City.

Number of Floors in New York City's Tallest Buildings				
104	75	77	54	70
89	74	52	80	59
103	66	76	82	52

To create a histogram, organize data into a *grouped frequency table*. A **grouped frequency table** organizes data according to how many times the data values within a given range of values occur.

WORKED EXAMPLE

You can create a histogram of the data in a table.

Number of Floors	Frequency (*f*)
50–60	||||
60–70	|
70–80	⫣⫣⫣
80–90	|||
90–100	
100–110	||

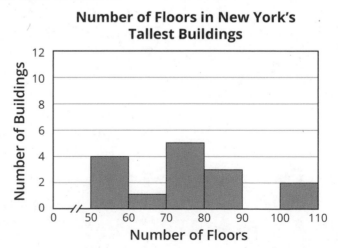

Number of Floors in New York's Tallest Buildings

The slashes on the horizontal axis of the histogram indicate a break in the range of data values.

The table shows the number of floors in the 15 tallest buildings in Chicago.

1 Complete the grouped frequency table for the number of floors in Chicago's buildings. Then complete the histogram. **Make sure that you name your table and histogram.**

Number of Floors in Chicago's Tallest Buildings				
108	60	64	100	67
98	74	65	61	73
83	82	57	60	66

Number of Floors	Frequency (f)
50–60	
60–70	
70–80	
80–90	
90–100	
100–110	

2 What is similar about the histograms? What are the differences between the two histograms?

3 Use what you know about the distributions and patterns of a graphical display to describe what the histograms say about the number of floors in each city's buildings.

ACTIVITY 3

The Statistical
Process

TOPIC 1   LESSON 3

Getting
Started

Activity
1   2   3

Talk
the Talk

Creating a Histogram with Continuous Data

You can display both discrete and continuous numeric data using a histogram.

Each year, the Empire State Building Run-Up (ESBRU) challenges runners to race up its stairs. You surveyed runners about their times at the end of the Run-Up. The table shows the results.

Amount of Time to Complete the ESBRU (minutes)					
10.4	11.25	15.76	9.81	12.05	18.2
10.52	13.73	13.01	12.75	14.99	11.24
15.0	15.57	16.6	14.8	13.35	12.22

1 Are the data in the table discrete or continuous? **Explain your reasoning.**

Shania and Trinh decide to make a histogram for the data set. They want to use these intervals for the histogram.

Trinh 👎

9–10
11–12
13–14
15–16
17–18

Shania 👎

9   10.9
11 12.9
13 14.9
15 16.9
17 18.9

2 Explain why both Trinh's and Shania's intervals are incorrect. **Use a data value from the table to explain.**

3 Use the frequency table to create a histogram for the amount of time to complete the ESBRU.

Time to Complete ESBRU (minutes)	Frequency (*f*)
9–11	3
11–13	5
13–15	5
15–17	4
17–19	1

4 When the bin size changes, how will the histogram change?

THINK ABOUT...
Changing the size of the intervals allows you to manipulate how the data display appears.

5 What conclusions can you make about the amount of time it takes to complete the Empire State Building Run-Up? **Use what you know about distributions and patterns of graphical displays.**

TOPIC 1

Which Plot Is Best?

Throughout this topic, you have created and analyzed a variety of numeric data displays.

1 List at least one advantage and one disadvantage of using each type of plot to display numeric data.

	Advantage (or Use)	Disadvantage (or Limitation)
Dot Plot		
Stem-and-Leaf Plot		
Histogram		

LESSON 3 ASSIGNMENT

> Use a separate piece of paper for your Journal entry.

REMEMBER

You use histograms with larger sets of numeric data. Histograms represent numeric data continuously in intervals.

The intervals in a histogram must all be the same size. The width of the bar represents the interval. The height of the bar indicates the frequency of values in the interval.

PRACTICE

Every summer, Ben's town has a yard-sale day. The values shown are the dollar amounts earned from 20 different yard sales that day.

50, 199, 246, 356, 89, 210, 391, 325, 273, 260,

100, 172, 123, 167, 194, 172, 23, 426, 75, 239

1 Create a frequency table and a histogram to display the amounts earned. Be sure to name your histogram.

Amount Earned ($)	Frequency (f)

2 Describe the distribution of the data. Include any specific graphical features or patterns. Explain what your answer means in terms of the dollar amounts earned at yard sales.

3 Create a second frequency table and histogram to provide a different view of the data distribution.

Amount Earned ($)	Frequency (f)

STRETCH Optional

Aviana claims that she can turn any stem-and-leaf plot into a histogram. Is she correct?

> Provide an example or a counterexample.

MIXED PRACTICE

❯ This Mixed Practice worksheet includes two sections: Spaced Review and End-of-Topic Review. **Use a separate piece of paper to show your work.**

Spaced Review

❯ Practice concepts from previous topics.

1 Determine the absolute value of each number.

    ⓐ $|-4.2|$ ⓑ $\left|11\frac{7}{8}\right|$

2 Use long division to determine each quotient. Write the quotient as a decimal.

    ⓐ $247 \div 8$ ⓑ $894 \div 12$

3 Use absolute value equations to determine each distance.

    ⓐ Between the horizontal lines that contain points A (7, 5) and B (−4, −8).

    ⓑ Between the vertical lines that contain points A (7, 5) and B (−4, −8).

4 A free diver is diving at a constant rate of 0.75 feet per second. Write and graph an equation that represents the situation.

5 Insert a >, <, or = symbol to make each number sentence true.

    ⓐ $-9\frac{1}{8}$ _____ -9.4

    ⓑ 0.006 _____ 1%

6 Tell a story to describe the graph.

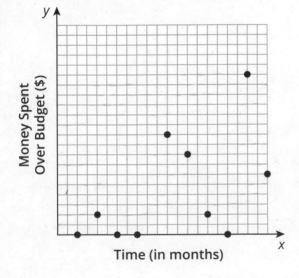

7 Plot and identify 4 points on the coordinate plane that are vertices of a parallelogram. Include points in more than one quadrant. Draw the parallelogram. Write absolute value statements for the length of the base and height of your parallelogram. Then, determine the area of the parallelogram.

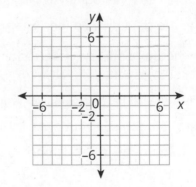

End-of-Topic Review

AVAILABLE ONLINE
1. A **Topic Summary** reviews the main concepts for the topic.
2. A video of the **Worked Example** is provided.

❯ Practice concepts you learned in **The Statistical Process**.

8 Write a statistical question about each situation.

    ⓐ vacation destinations   ⓑ books

9 Describe the graphical features or patterns of the data displayed in the dot plot.

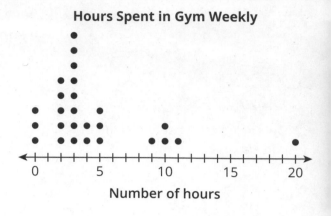

Hours Spent in Gym Weekly

Number of hours

10 Describe the shape of the distribution of the data shown.

(a)

Amount of Money Collected by Each Student for Fundraiser

Frequency vs. Amount collected ($)

(b)

40 Yard Dash Times

4	2
5	3 7 8
6	0 1 4 4
7	1 3 4 7
8	0 9 9
9	6

Key: 4|1 = 4.1

11 The scores for Mr. Watson's math test are:
98, 62, 87, 94, 75, 79, 82, 90, 86, 68, 70, 93, 67, 88, 86, 94, 90, 89, 65, 78, 82, 73, 89, 91, 76, 86, 78, 99

(a) Create and title a histogram to display the test scores.

(b) Describe the data distribution.

12 Determine whether a survey, observational study, or experiment is the best way to answer each statistical question.

(a) Do students who listen to classical music while studying perform better on tests?

(b) How many students in your class listen to classical music while studying?

(c) How many students wear earphones while riding the bus?

13 Analyze the histogram to answer each question.

(a) How many cities have between 20 and 29 parks and zoos?

(b) How many cities have only 1 park or zoo?

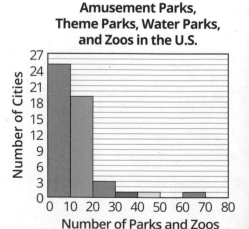

Amusement Parks, Theme Parks, Water Parks, and Zoos in the U.S.

Number of Cities vs. Number of Parks and Zoos

TOPIC 1
The Statistical Process

TOPIC 2
Numeric Summaries of Data

1	In the Middle
2	Box It Up
3	March MADness
4	You Chose...Wisely

LESSON 1

In the Middle

Analyzing Data Using Measures of Center

KEY TERMS

measure of
center

median

balance point

mean

Learning Goals

- Define the three measures of center: mode, median, and mean.

- Recognize that a measure of center for a numeric data set is a
  single value that summarizes all of its values.

- Give quantitative measures of center for a data set, including mean
  or median, and interpret the mode, median, and mean for a data set.

REVIEW (1–2 minutes)

> Evaluate each numeric expression.

1 $(13 + 17) \div 2$

2 $(29 + 36) \div 2$

3 $(48 + 9) \div 2$

4 $(27 + 31) \div 2$

You have created, analyzed, and interpreted data displays
such as dot plots, stem-and-leaf plots, and histograms.
You have described shapes and patterns in distributions of
data displays.

**How can you describe a
numeric data set using a
single value?**

GETTING STARTED

Numeric
Summaries of Data
TOPIC 2 → **LESSON 1**

Getting
Started

Activity
1   2   3   4

Talk
the Talk

Describing Data

> Analyze each display. Identify the mode and estimate the middle data value in each.

1

Pencils in Backpack

```
        ×
        ×   ×
    ×   ×   ×
    ×   ×   ×       ×   ×   ×           ×
    ×   ×   ×   ×   ×   ×   ×           ×   ×               ×
◄───┼───┼───┼───┼───┼───┼───┼───┼───┼───┼───┼───┼───┼───┼───┼──►
    0   1   2   3   4   5   6   7   8   9  10  11  12  13  14
```
Number of Pencils

REMEMBER....

The mode is the data value or values that occur most frequently in a data set.

2

Ages of U.S. First Ladies (20th Century)

```
3 │ 1
4 │ 0 3 4 5 7 8 9
5 │ 0 2 4 6 6 6 9
6 │ 0 0 3
```

Key │ 6|0 means 60

THINK ABOUT...

What patterns do you notice in the data?

3

Hours Spent Playing Video Games on Weekends

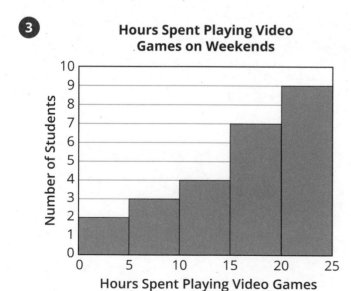

Hours Spent Playing Video Games

ACTIVITY 1

Numeric
Summaries of Data

TOPIC 2   LESSON 1

Getting
Started

Activity
1   2   3   4

Talk
the Talk

Measures of Center

When you analyze a set of data, you often want to describe it numerically. One way to numerically describe a data set is to use a *measure of center*.

Three measures that describe the center of a data center are the *mean*, the *median*, and the *mode*.

The **median** is the middle number in a data set when you place the values in order from least to greatest or greatest to least.

- When a data set has an odd number of data values, you can determine which number is exactly in the middle of the data set.

- When there is an even number of data values, then you calculate the median by adding the two middle numbers and dividing by 2.

TAKE NOTE...
A **measure of center** tells you how data values cluster, or where the "center" of the data is.

TOPIC 2

The Olive Street Middle School girls' basketball team has a chance to be in the league playoffs. Coach Harris must determine whether Josephine, Shelly, or Chanice should get more playing time in the first playoff game.

In the past six games:

- Josephine scored 12, 12, 6, 26, 4, and 12 points.

- Shelly scored 3, 2, 8, 17, 10, and 20 points.

- Chanice scored 15, 12, 13, 10, 8, and 14 points.

1 Determine each measure of center.

(a) Determine the mode for the number of points scored by each player.

DID YOU KNOW?
A data set can have more than one mode or no mode.

(b) Determine the median number of points scored by each player.

ⓒ Which of these two measures of center, mode or median, would be better for Coach Harris to use in making her decision? **Explain your reasoning.**

Abana scored 5, 6, 10, 4, and 9 points in her last five games.

❯ Analyze Abana's statement.

> ## Abana
>
> The median number of points I scored is 10.

② Explain what Abana did incorrectly to determine that the median was 10. Then determine the correct median.

ACTIVITY 2

Numeric Summaries of Data

TOPIC 2 · LESSON 1

Getting Started

Activity
1 2 3 4

Talk the Talk

Mean as Fair Share

When you level off or create fair shares using the values in a data set, you determine another measure of center, the *mean*.

> Create two equal stacks of cubes using the stacks shown.

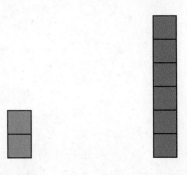

HABITS OF MIND
- Model with mathematics.
- Use appropriate tools strategically.

WORKED EXAMPLE

Subtract two cubes from the greater stack, and add the two cubes to the lesser stack.

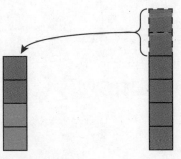

Each stack now has 4 cubes.

---

1 For each stack of cubes, create four equal stacks. Record which operations you performed.

(a)

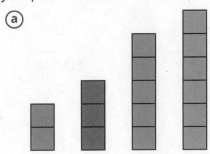

(b)

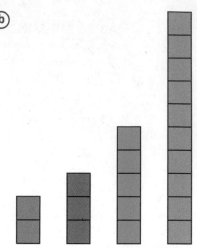

2 Compare your results from parts (a) and (b). How did the number of cubes in each equal stack change in part (b)? **Explain why this happened.**

THINK ABOUT...
You have to keep the number of stacks the same.

ACTIVITY 3
MATHia CONNECTION
• Calculating Mean, Median, Mode, and Range

Numeric
Summaries of Data

TOPIC 2   LESSON 1

Getting
Started
1   2   **3**   4
Activity

Talk
the Talk

Mean as Balancing

In the previous activity, stacks of cubes represented data values. You rearranged the stacks to create equal stacks, or fair shares. You can also represent quantities on a number line and create a *balance point*.

> **HABITS OF MIND**
> • Model with mathematics.
> • Use appropriate tools strategically.

WORKED EXAMPLE

Consider the data set: 2, 6. Determine the balance point of the set.

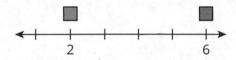

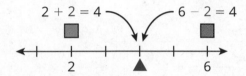

The value 2 was moved to the right from 2 to 4. To maintain balance, 6 was moved 2 to the left from 6 to 4. The balance point is 4.

> **TAKE NOTE...**
> When you have all the points at the same value, you balance the number line. You call this value the **balance point**.

TOPIC 2

When you attempt to create a balance on a number line:

• When you move a value to the right a certain amount, then you must also move a value to the left that amount.

• You can move a data value left and right as much as you need as long as you do the opposite to another data value.

• You can start however you like.

1 What do you think the ▲ in the worked example represents?

You can also determine the balance point of a number line with more than two data points.

2 Kathryn determined the balance point of the data set. Record the operations she used in the rectangles in each step. **Label the balance point in Step 3.**

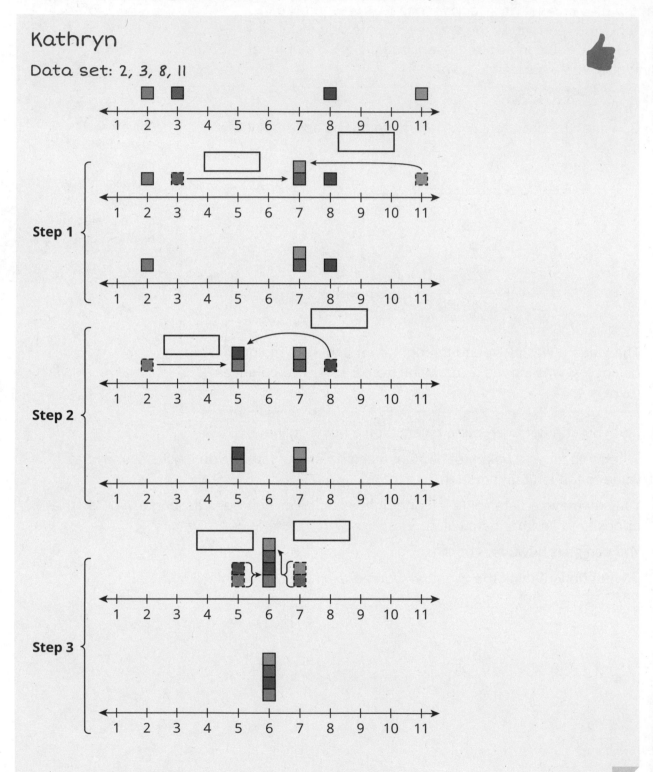

> Recall the data sets for the number of points each player scored for the Olive Street Middle School basketball team.

3 For each data set, determine the balance point on the number lines shown. Record the steps you used to determine the balance point.

    ⓐ Josephine

       Data set: 12, 12, 6, 26, 4, 12

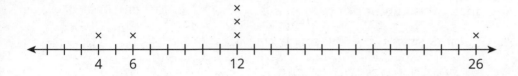

    ⓑ Shelly

       Data set: 3, 2, 8, 17, 10, 20

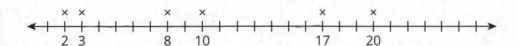

    ⓒ Chanice

       Data set: 15, 12, 13, 10, 8, 14

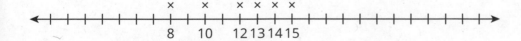

TOPIC 2

You can also call the balance point the *mean*. The **mean** is the arithmetic average of the numbers in a data set.

You calculate the mean by adding all of the values in the data set and dividing the sum by the number of values.

WORKED EXAMPLE

Calculate the mean number of points scored by Josephine.

STEP 1 Add the data points. 12 + 12 + 6 + 26 + 4 + 12 = 72

STEP 2 Divide the sum by the number of data points. $\frac{72}{6}$ = 12

The mean number of points scored by Josephine was 12.

THINK ABOUT...

The expression 72 ÷ 6 takes the 72 total points and divides them evenly into 6 games, for 12 points in each game.

4 Calculate the mean number of points scored by each player.

a) Shelly

Data set: 3, 2, 8, 17, 10, 20

b) Chanice

Data set: 15, 12, 13, 10, 8, 14

ACTIVITY 4
MATHia CONNECTION
● Determining Measures of Center
● Measuring the Effects of Changing Data Sets

Numeric
Summaries of Data
TOPIC 2   LESSON 1

Getting
Started   Activity
    1   2   3   4   Talk
the Talk

In the Middle

You can interpret the different measures of center for a data set based on the situation.

HABITS OF MIND
- Reason abstractly and quantitatively.
- Construct viable arguments and critique the reasoning of others.

A corporation awards grants to local schools to purchase fitness equipment. The principal at Sharpe Middle School would like to apply for the grant. If awarded the money, the school would like to add fitness equipment to the gym.

Before she applies, the principal wants to understand how much time the students at Sharpe Middle School spend exercising each weekday. She decides to give a survey to 15 anonymous students.
Here are the results.

0 min	40 min	60 min	30 min	60 min
15 min	45 min	30 min	120 min	90 min
30 min	120 min	60 min	0 min	20 min

1 Identify the statistical question posed in this situation. Create a display from the survey data. Calculate and interpret each measure of center. **Then write a summary statement based on your findings.**

REMEMBER...
The Statistical Process
- Formulate a question
- Collect data
- Graph and analyze the data
- Interpret the results

TOPIC 2

TALK THE TALK

Numeric
Summaries of Data

TOPIC 2   **LESSON 1**

Getting
Started

Activity
1   2   3   4

Talk
the Talk

Center of Attention

In this lesson, you learned about three measures of center: mode, median, and mean.

1 Describe how you can use each measure of center to describe a data set.

2 What are the most important differences between each of the measures of center?

3 Which measure do you think is more or less meaningful than the others?
Explain your reasoning.

LESSON 1 ASSIGNMENT

> Use a separate piece of paper for your Journal entry.

JOURNAL

Use the key terms from the lesson to best complete each sentence.

REMEMBER

The three most common measures of center are the mode, median, and mean. Measures of center are numeric ways of determining where the center of data is.

1 A _____ for a numeric data set summarizes all of its values with a single number.

2 The _____ is the arithmetic average of the numbers in a data set.

3 When you have all the points on a number line at the same value after moving data values, you call this value the _____.

4 The _____ is the middle number in a data set when you place the values in order from least to greatest.

PRACTICE

1 Temperature affects the rate at which crickets chirp. You can estimate the outside temperature by counting cricket chirps. As a homework assignment, Mr. Ortega asks each of his students to count the number of chirps they hear in 15 seconds at 8:00 P.M. Here are the results.

36	37	41	39	35	39	35	39
42	37	40	35	36	37	42	35
37	37	38	42	41	37	41	

ⓐ Determine the mode for the number of chirps heard in 15 seconds.

ⓑ What does the mode tell you about the number of chirps heard in 15 seconds?

(c) Determine the median number of chirps heard in 15 seconds.

(d) What does the median tell you about the number of chirps heard in 15 seconds?

(e) Calculate the mean number of chirps heard by the students in 15 seconds.

(f) What does the mean tell you about the number of chirps heard in 15 seconds?

STRETCH Optional

1 Create a data set where the mean is greater than the median.

2 Create a data set where the mean is less than the median.

LESSON 2

Box It Up

Displaying the Five-Number Summary

Learning Goals

- Calculate and interpret measures of variation for a data set, including range, quartiles, interquartile range, and the five-number summary.

- Display numeric data in box plots.

- Describe an overall pattern of data with reference to the context in which you gathered the data.

KEY TERMS

quartile

measure of variation

interquartile range (IQR)

box-and-whisker plot

REVIEW (1–2 minutes)

❯ Use the stem-and-leaf plot to answer each question.

1 What is the median of the data?

2 What does the median describe in the problem situation?

Quiz Scores

4	0
5	8
6	1
7	2
8	3 4 5
9	2 3

Key: $5|8 = 58\%$

You have used the measures of center—mean, median, and mode—to describe a data set. Other characteristics, such as how much the data varies from that center, are also important.

How can you describe the variation in a data set?

GETTING STARTED

Numeric
Summaries of Data

TOPIC 2   LESSON 2

Getting
Started

Activity
1   2   3

Talk
the Talk

Human Box Plot

❯ Your teacher will provide you with an index card and a penny. On the index card, write the date imprinted on the penny.

1 Consider the data from the class and predict the shape of the data set.

ⓐ Do you think that it will be skewed right, skewed left, or symmetrical?

ⓑ Do you think that there will be any clusters or gaps?

When you arrange data in a set in order, **quartiles** are the numbers that split data into quarters (or fourths).

❯ On your teacher's signal, line up with your index card from the oldest date to the most recent date. As a class, discuss how to determine the following measures: minimum, lower quartile, median, upper quartile, maximum.

2 Complete the table for your data set.

Minimum	Lower Quartile (Q1)	Median (Q2)	Upper Quartile (Q3)	Maximum

TAKE NOTE...

Quartiles are often denoted by the letter Q followed by a number that indicates which fourth it represents. Since the median is the second quartile, you can represent it using Q2. The other quartiles are Q1 and Q3.

3 Describe the variation of the data.

ACTIVITY 1

Numeric
Summaries of Data

TOPIC 2   LESSON 2

Getting   ┌─ Activity ─┐   Talk
Started   1   2   3   the Talk

The Five-Number Summary

HABITS OF MIND
• Attend to precision.

To summarize and describe the spread of the data values, you can use the five-number summary. The five-number summary includes these 5 values from a data set:

• Minimum: the least value in the data set

• Q1: the first quartile

• Median: the median of the data set

• Q3: the third quartile

• Maximum: the greatest value in a data set.

A **measure of variation** describes the spread of data values. One measure of variation is the range.

> Given the collection of pennies provided by your teacher, line up the pennies from the earliest imprinted date to the most recent.

1 Calculate the range for the penny data.

REMEMBER...
The range is the difference between the maximum and minimum values of a data set.

The quartiles are another set of values that help to describe variation in a data set.

2 How do you calculate the quartiles for a data set?

3 How many quartiles does it take to divide the data into fourths?

TOPIC 2

4 For each quartile of the penny data, identify the value of the quartile. Then, identify the percent of the data below the quartile and the percent of the data above the quartile.

Quartile	Value of Quartile	Percent of Data Below	Percent of Data Above
Q1			
Q2			
Q3			

5 What percent of the data is between Q1 and Q3?

The **interquartile range (IQR)** is the difference between the third quartile and the first quartile, or Q3 − Q1. The IQR indicates the range of the middle 50 percent of the data.

6 What do you think "the middle 50 percent" means?

7 Do you think it is possible for two sets of data to have the same range but different IQRs? **Explain your reasoning.**

8 What is the IQR for your penny data?

9 Determine the 5-number summary and IQR for each data set. **Explain the process you used to calculate the values and what they tell you about the data.**

(a) 24, 32, 16, 18, 30, 20

(b) 200, 150, 260, 180, 300, 240, 280

ACTIVITY 2

MATHia CONNECTION
• Introduction to Box Plots
• Creating Box Plots

Numeric
Summaries of Data

TOPIC 2   LESSON 2

Getting   Activity   Talk
Started   1   2   3   the Talk

Box-and-Whisker Plots

There is a special type of graph that displays the variation in a data set. A **box-and-whisker plot**, or just box plot, is a graph that displays the five-number summary of a data set.

❯ Examine the box-and-whisker plot shown.

WORKED EXAMPLE

Recall that the five-number summary consists of:

• **minimum value in the data set**

• **Q1**

• **median**

• **Q3**

• **maximum value in the data set**

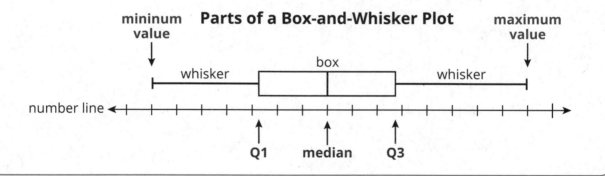

Parts of a Box-and-Whisker Plot

---

1 What does the "box" in the box-and-whisker plot represent? What do the "whiskers" represent?

TAKE NOTE...
You can represent box-and-whisker plots horizontally and vertically.

> Use the box-and-whisker plot shown to answer each question.

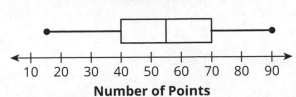

Number of Points Scored on a Math Test

Number of Points

2 Identify the given values for the points scored on the math test. **Explain what those values tell you about the scores on the test.**

(a) minimum:

(b) Q1:

(c) median:

(d) Q3:

(e) maximum:

(f) range:

3 Determine the IQR for the test scores. **Explain what the IQR represents in this problem situation.**

4 How many students took the math test? **Explain your answer.**

ASK YOURSELF....

What percent of the test scores are between Q1 and Q3?

TOPIC 2

5 Karyn says the median is 50 because it is in the middle of the number line. Is Karyn's claim correct? **Explain how you determined your answer.**

6 Jamal claims that more students scored between 15 and 40 than between 70 and 90 because the lower whisker is longer than the upper whisker. Is Jamal's claim correct? **Explain your reasoning.**

You can describe the distribution of a box plot in the same way you described the shapes of stem-and-leaf plots or histograms.

7 How would you describe the distribution of the box plot displaying the number of points scored on the math test? **Why?**

8 Use the number line shown to complete a box-and-whisker plot for the penny data.

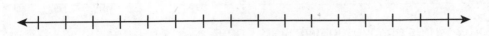

9 Describe the distribution of the box plot.

10 The data set lists the amount of rainfall in inches San Francisco gets on average each month.

4.4, 3.3, 3.1, 1.4, 0.3, 0.1, 0.0, 0.1, 0.3, 1.3, 2.9, 3.1

ⓐ Construct a box-and-whisker plot for the average monthly rainfall in San Francisco.

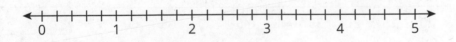

ⓑ Describe the distribution of the box plot.

ⓒ Interpret the IQR for the rainfall in San Francisco.

Building a Box Plot
- Label the number line. Include the maximum and minimum values.
- Place dots above the minimum and maximum values.
- Place vertical lines above the median and quartile values. Draw the box around them.
- Draw lines, or whiskers, to connect the box to the minimum and maximum values.
- Name the box-and-whisker plot.

TOPIC 2

ACTIVITY 3
MATHia CONNECTION
• Exploring Box Plots
• Interpreting Box Plots

Numeric
Summaries of Data

TOPIC 2   LESSON 2

Getting   Activity   Talk
Started   1 2 3   the Talk

Comparing Box-and-Whisker Plots

You can construct box-and-whisker plots for different data sets on the same number line to compare the data sets.

A newspaper reporter writes an investigative story about the wait time at two local restaurants. With the help of her assistant, the reporter randomly selected 11 patrons at each restaurant and recorded how many minutes they had to wait before being served. The tables show the results.

The Captain's Corner	
Wait Time (minutes)	
16	60
22	15
12	24
20	18
16	23
22	

1 Create a box-and-whisker plot for the wait times at each of the restaurants. Use the same number line for each representation so you can compare them.

The First Deck	
Wait Time (minutes)	
34	60
44	10
27	52
26	31
47	48
45	

Time (minutes)

2 Describe the distributions of each box plot.

3 What is the range of wait times? What does the five-number summary tell you about the spread of the data that the range does not tell you?

4 What do the IQR values tell you about the time spent waiting at each restaurant?

5 How does the mean wait time compare to the median wait time for each restaurant?

6 Assume the food prices and service were the same in both restaurants. Write a brief summary to share the results of your data analysis with the newspaper reporter to help answer her question about wait times in The Captain's Corner and The First Deck restaurants.

TALK THE TALK

Numeric
Summaries of Data

TOPIC 2 **LESSON 2**

Getting
Started Activity
1 2 3

Talk
the Talk

Build a Box

> Analyze the box-and-whisker plots shown.

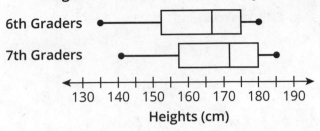

Heights of Students on the Volleyball Team

6th Graders

7th Graders

130 140 150 160 170 180 190

Heights (cm)

1 Determine whether each statement is true or false and provide a reason for your decision.

ⓐ On average, the 6th-grade players are taller.

ⓑ The range of heights is greater for the 7th-grade players.

ⓒ Half the 6th-grade players are over 165 cm tall.

ⓓ Half the 7th-grade players are below 172 cm tall.

ⓔ The shortest person is a 7th-grade player.

2 Use the given information to determine a five-number summary and construct a box-and-whisker plot. Is your data set the only possible solution? **Why or why not?**

- The data set has a range of 30.
- The maximum value is 50.
- The IQR is 10.
- The median is closer to Q1 than to Q3.

LESSON 2 ASSIGNMENT

❯ Use a separate piece of paper for your Journal entry.

JOURNAL

Explain the difference between quartiles and interquartile range.

REMEMBER

You can describe variation in a data set using the range or the interquartile range. The interquartile range, or IQR, is the difference between the third and first quartiles of a data set and indicates the range of the middle 50 percent of the data.

PRACTICE

1 The box-and-whisker plot shows the distribution of scores on a history quiz.

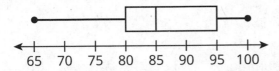

(a) Identify the median of the data and interpret its meaning.

(b) Identify the range of the data and interpret its meaning.

2 Answer each question using the following data set.

0, 5, 5, 15, 30, 30, 45, 50, 50, 60, 75, 110, 140, 240, 330

(a) Sketch a box-and-whisker plot of the data.

(b) What is the median for the data set?

(c) What is Q3 for the data set?

3 The residents of a small town worry about people speeding through it on the main road. The police monitored the speed of the cars that pass through the town. The data show the recorded speeds in miles per hour of 23 cars that passed through the town one morning.

73, 68, 72, 61, 51, 68, 70, 53, 72, 71, 46, 51, 55, 53, 65, 57, 65, 57, 58, 68, 61, 48, 83

(a) Construct a box-and-whisker plot of the data.

(b) Interpret each number in the five-number summary.

(c) What does the IQR value tell you about the speeds of the cars?

(d) Suppose the speed limit through the town is 50 miles per hour. Should the collected data concern the residents?

STRETCH Optional

1 Create a data set to represent the box-and-whisker plot shown. Is your data set the only possible solution? Why or why not?

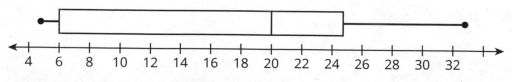

(a) Data set with 11 numbers.

(b) Data set with 8 numbers.

LESSON 3

March MADness

Mean Absolute Deviation

Learning Goals

- Determine the absolute deviations of data points in a data set.

- Give quantitative measures of variation, including mean absolute deviation, for a data set.

- Use the mean absolute deviation as a measure of variation to describe and interpret data.

- Compare data sets using variation and the mean absolute deviation.

- Summarize numeric data sets in relation to their context.

REVIEW (1–2 minutes)

❯ Determine the absolute value of each number.

1 $|-4|$

2 $|12.5|$

3 $|-1.09|$

4 $\left|4\frac{2}{3}\right|$

You use the interquartile range as a measure of variation when the median is the measure of center.

How can you measure the variation when mean is the measure of center?

GETTING STARTED

Numeric
Summaries of Data

TOPIC 2   LESSON 3

Getting
Started

Activity
1   2

Talk
the Talk

We Are the Champions

Coach Harris's basketball team advances to the district championship. Tamika and Lynn are possible starters for the game. The dot plots display each player's scoring over the past six games.

Number of Points Scored by Tamika

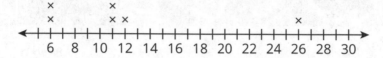

Number of Points Scored by Lynn

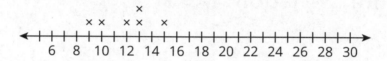

1 Determine the mean of each data set. **Explain what this number tells you.**

2 How are the two data sets similar and different?

Coach Harris needs to choose between Tamika and Lynn to start the championship game.

3 Based on the dot plots, which player do you think Coach Harris should choose?

ASK YOURSELF...

What does it mean for both players to have the same mean? Does it matter who Coach Harris puts in the game?

ACTIVITY 1
MATHia CONNECTION
• Calculating Mean Absolute Deviation

Numeric
Summaries of Data
TOPIC 2   LESSON 3

Getting   Activity   Talk
Started   1   2   the Talk

TOPIC 2

Exploring Variation and Deviation

In the Getting Started, you examined the dot plots of the points scored by Tamika and Lynn in their past six games. Are there measures other than the mean that can help Coach Harris choose between Tamika and Lynn for starters for the championship game?

When analyzing a data set, measures of center give you an idea of a typical data value. Measures of variation describe the spread of the data values. Just as there are several measures of central tendency, there are also several measures of variation.

The **deviation** of a data value indicates the distance of a data value from the mean.

To calculate the deviation, use reasoning to determine how far the data point is from the mean.

- When the data value is greater than the mean, the deviation is positive.
- When the data value is less than the mean, the deviation is negative.

HABITS OF MIND
- Reason abstractly and quantitatively.
- Construct viable arguments and critique the reasoning of others.

REMEMBER....
The mean number of points scored by both Tamika and Lynn is 12.

1 Complete each table by describing the deviation of each data point from the mean.

Tamika			Lynn		
Points Scored	Deviation from the Mean		Points Scored	Deviation from the Mean	
	Description	Value		Description	Value
11	1 less than the mean	−1	15		
11			12		
6			13		
26			10		
6			9		
12			13		

2 Describe how the data point relates to the mean for each deviation.

    ⓐ A positive deviation

    ⓑ A negative deviation

    ⓒ A deviation of 0

3 What do you notice about the deviations for each player?

4 Carly claims that the sum of the deviations for a data set will always be 0. Is she correct? **Why or why not?**

Because the mean is the balance point, the sums of the data points on either side of the balance point are equal. The sum of all the deviations less than 0 equals the sum of the deviations greater than 0.

To get an idea of the spread of the data values, you can take the absolute value of each deviation and then determine the mean of those absolute values. You call the absolute value of each deviation the **absolute deviation**. The **mean absolute deviation** (MAD) is the mean of the absolute deviations.

5 Record the absolute deviations for the points scored in the tables.

Tamika			Lynn		
Points Scored	Deviation from the Mean	Absolute Deviation	Points Scored	Deviation from the Mean	Absolute Deviation
11	−1		15	3	
11	−1		12	0	
6	−6		13	1	
26	14		10	−2	
6	−6		9	−3	
12	0		13	1	

6 Calculate the mean absolute deviation for the points scored for each player.

7 What does the mean absolute deviation tell you about the points scored by each player?

8 If you were Coach Harris, which player would you choose to play in the championship game? **Justify your decision.**

ACTIVITY 2
MATHia CONNECTION
• Using Mean Absolute Deviation

Numeric
Summaries of Data
TOPIC 2 — LESSON 3

Getting
Started

Activity
1   2

Talk
the Talk

Applying Mean Absolute Deviation

HABITS OF MIND
- Reason abstractly and quantitatively.
- Construct viable arguments and critique the reasoning of others.

Draven wants to know whether the heights of players on an NBA basketball team vary more or less than the heights of the players on his 6th-grade basketball team.

The dot plots show the heights in inches of ten NBA players and ten 6th-grade players.

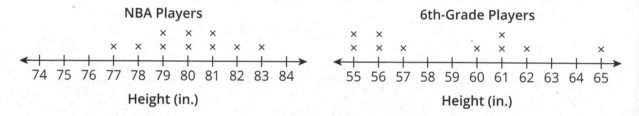

NBA Players

74 75 76 77 78 79 80 81 82 83 84
Height (in.)

6th-Grade Players

55 56 57 58 59 60 61 62 63 64 65
Height (in.)

❯ Complete the tables for the NBA players and the 6th-grade players.

1

NBA Players		
Height (in.)	**Describe the Deviation from the Mean**	**Absolute Deviation**
77		
78		
79		
79		
80		
80		
81		
81		
82		
83		

THINK ABOUT...

Mean absolute deviation and interquartile range are both measures of variation.

2

6th-Grade Players		
Height (in.)	Describe the Deviation from the Mean	Absolute Deviation
55		
55		
56		
56		
57		
60		
61		
61		
62		
65		

3 Compare the mean absolute deviations of the data sets and interpret your results.

TOPIC 2

TALK THE TALK

Numeric
Summaries of Data

TOPIC 2 — LESSON 3

Getting
Started

Activity
1   2

Talk
the Talk

GPA and MAD

Sometimes you can change non-numeric data into numeric data to analyze it.

❯ Consider the report cards shown. The categories of grades for the courses are
A, B, C, D, and F, with A being the highest grade.

Luca's Grades	
Science	B
Cultural Literacy	A
Music	C
Math	A
English	B

Eric's Grades	
Math	A
English	B
Cultural Literacy	C
Science	A
Music	A

1 Explain how you can change the report card data into numeric data.

2 Determine the mean of each data set. What does each mean tell you?

3 Determine the mean absolute deviation for each data set.

Luca's Grades		Eric's Grades	
Data Value	Absolute Deviation	Data Value	Absolute Deviation

4 Interpret each of the mean absolute deviations.

LESSON 3 ASSIGNMENT

> Use a separate piece of paper for your Journal entry.

JOURNAL

Use one of the key terms provided to complete each sentence.

┌──────WORD BANK──────┐
Deviation
Absolute deviation
Mean absolute deviation
└─────────────────────┘

REMEMBER

To calculate the mean absolute deviation:

- Determine the mean of the data.
- Determine the deviations by calculating the distance that each data point is from the mean.
- Record the absolute value of each deviation.
- Determine the mean of the absolute deviations.

1 _____ indicates how far the data value is from the mean.

2 _____ is the absolute value of each deviation.

3 _____ is the average, or mean, of the absolute deviations.

PRACTICE

> Calculate the mean absolute deviation for each data set.

1 Data set: 4, 5, 9, 4, 8

Mean = 6

2 Data set: 7, 11, 8, 35, 14

Mean = 15

Go to LiveHint.com for help on the **PRACTICE** questions.

3 Data set: 60, 65, 66, 67, 67, 65

Mean = 65

4 Data set: 22, 26, 29, 23, 26, 21, 28, 24, 25, 26

Mean = 25

5 Data set: 180, 210, 155, 110, 230, 90, 400, 35, 190, 0, 10, 100, 90, 130, 200

Mean = 142

6 Data set: 55, 74, 90, 20, 47, 59, 26, 83, 77, 62, 58, 33, 57, 44, 31

Mean = 54.4

STRETCH Optional

1 Create a data set of 5 numbers that has a mean absolute deviation of 1. Explain how you arrived at your solution.

2 Create a data set of 6 numbers that has a mean absolute deviation of 10. Explain how you arrived at your solution.

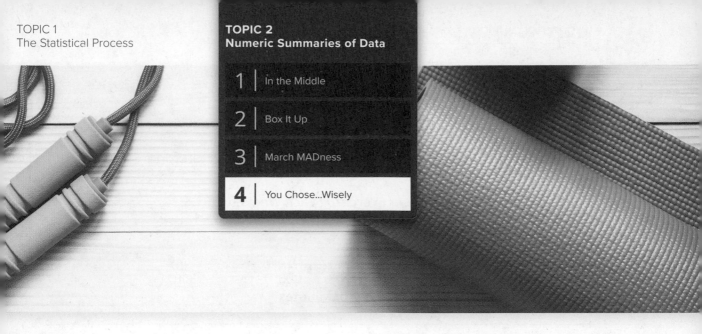

TOPIC 1
The Statistical Process

TOPIC 2
Numeric Summaries of Data

1 | In the Middle

2 | Box It Up

3 | March MADness

4 | You Chose...Wisely

LESSON 4

You Chose...Wisely

Choosing Appropriate Measures

Learning Goals

- Determine whether the mean or median most appropriately represents a typical value in a data set.

- Understand how the distribution of a data set affects the different measures of central tendency and relate the choice of measures of center and variability to the context.

- Determine when to use the interquartile range and the mean absolute deviation to describe the variation of a data set.

REVIEW (1–2 minutes)

❯ Determine each measure for the data set 2, 3, 6, 6, 7, 10, 22.

1 mean

2 median

You have learned about different measures of center and different measures of variation.

Which of these measures are appropriate to use for data with different characteristics?

GETTING STARTED

Numeric
Summaries of Data

TOPIC 2   LESSON 4

Getting
Started

Activity
1   2   3   4

Talk
the Talk

An Exercise in Data Analysis

The dot plot shows the amount of time Ben's friends spend exercising on weekends.

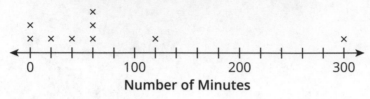

Time Spent Exercising Each Weekend

Number of Minutes

1 Ben says, "The mean is greater than the median in this data set." Is Ben correct? **Explain your reasoning.**

2 Determine the median and mean for the exercise data set. **Explain how you determined each.**

3 Is the mean or the median the better measure to describe a typical value in the exercise data? **Explain your reasoning.**

ACTIVITY 1

Numeric
Summaries of Data

TOPIC 2   LESSON 4

Getting
Started

Activity
1   2   3   4

Talk
the Talk

Choosing Median or Mean

In this activity, you will analyze the mean and median to determine which best characterizes a data set.

HABITS OF MIND
- Model with mathematics.
- Use appropriate tools strategically.

The stem-and-leaf plot shown displays the scores of students on a 100-point math test.

**Student Scores on a
100-Point Test**

5	6 8
6	0 1
7	0 0 1 6 9
8	1 2 2 5 6 7 7 7 8 9
9	0 1 3 4 5 6

Key: 7|1 = 71 points

1 Consider the data given.

(a) How many students do the data represent?

(b) Describe the shape of the distribution of the data.

(c) Do you think the mean test score is greater than, less than, or about the same as the median score?
Explain your reasoning.

ASK YOURSELF...
Does the skew of the data affect the difference between the median and the mean?

(d) Determine the median and mean. Identify which measure better represents a typical value in the data. **Explain your reasoning.**

TOPIC 2

The histogram shown displays the number of hours students spend playing video games each week.

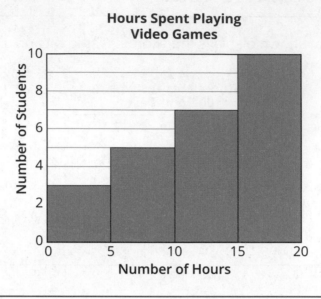

2 Consider the data given.

   ⓐ How many students do the data represent?

   ⓑ Describe the shape of the distribution of the data.

   ⓒ Identify which measure—median or mean—would better represent a typical value in the data. **Explain your reasoning.**

ACTIVITY 2

Numeric
Summaries of Data
TOPIC 2 — LESSON 4

Getting
Started
1

Activity
2 3 4

Talk
the Talk

Mean or Median: Which Is Greater?

You have learned about three common distributions of data: skewed left, skewed right, and symmetric. You have also learned that the distribution of data can affect the measures of center.

HABITS OF MIND
- Model with mathematics.
- Use appropriate tools strategically.

❭ Study the diagrams.

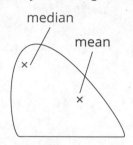

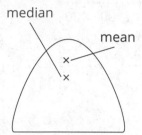

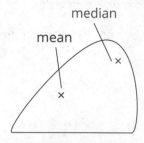

skewed right

The mean of a data set is greater than the median when the distribution is skewed right.

The median is the best measure of center because very large data values do not affect it.

symmetric

The mean and median are equal when the distribution is symmetric.

skewed left

The mean of a data set is less than the median when the distribution is skewed left.

The median is the best measure of center because very small data values do not affect it.

TAKE NOTE...

When you use the median to describe the center of a data set, you need to use the IQR to describe the range. When you use the mean to describe the center of a data set, you need to use the MAD to describe the range.

Very large or very small data values do not affect the median, but these large and small values do affect the mean.

1 For each plot shown, first describe the distribution of data. Then, determine whether the mean is less than, greater than, or about equal to the median.

(a) **Height of Students in Room 201**

```
5 | 4 6 6 8 8 9
6 | 0 0 1 2 3 3 4 5 6 6 6 8 8 9 9
7 | 0 0 1 1 1
```

Key: 6|3 = 63 inches

TOPIC 2

(b) **Number of Text Messages Sent by 6th Graders**

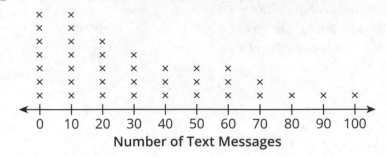

Number of Text Messages

(c) **Rock-Climbing Times of 6th-Grade Students**

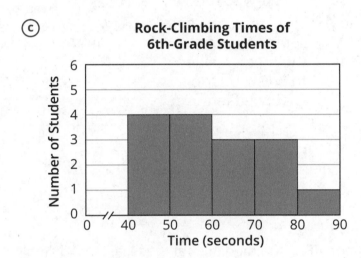

2 For each part in Question 1, determine whether you should use the median or mean to describe the center of the data.

ACTIVITY 3

Numeric
Summaries of Data

TOPIC 2   LESSON 4

Getting
Started

Activity
1   2   3   4

Talk
the Talk

Choosing IQR or MAD

In this activity you will analyze a data set to determine whether or not you should describe its variation using the IQR or MAD.

> **HABITS OF MIND**
> • Model with mathematics.
> • Use appropriate tools strategically.

When a participant takes part in the Special Olympics, they receive a number. The table represents the first 18 people labeled by their participation number and the number of gold medals each participant won.

> Analyze the data.

1 Create a display to visualize the distribution of the data. Describe the distribution.

Participation Number	Gold Medals Won
001	6
002	14
003	1
004	6
005	0
006	0
007	9
008	1
009	1
010	9
011	5
012	10
013	1
014	2
015	2
016	5
017	4
018	3

TOPIC 2

2 Shelly says that she should use the median and mean absolute deviation to describe the data because the mean absolute deviation is less than the interquartile range. Is Shelly correct? **Explain why or why not.**

3 Which measure of central tendency and measure of variation should you use to describe the data? **Explain your reasoning.**

4 What conclusions can you draw about the number of gold medals participants won?

Numeric
Summaries of Data

TOPIC 2   LESSON 4

Getting
Started

Activity
1   2   3   4

Talk
the Talk

ACTIVITY 4

MATHia CONNECTION
• Choosing Appropriate Measures

Using Center and Variation to Compare

You should use the same measure of center and variation to compare data sets.

HABITS OF MIND
• Model with mathematics.
• Use appropriate tools strategically.

> A travel agent collected data from two airlines measuring the difference in the stated departure times and the times the flights actually departed. He recorded the average departure time differences for each month for one year.

❯ Consider the two stem-and-leaf plots that display the travel agent's data.

1 Describe the distribution of each data set.

Difference in Departure Time (minutes)

My Air Airlines		Fly High Airlines	
0	0 5	0	7 8
1	1 5 9	1	4 5 6
2	0 0 6	2	4 7 9
3	3 3 4	3	0 2
4	0	4	5 9

Key: 1|5 = 15 minutes

2 Determine an appropriate measure of central tendency and measure of variation for each data set. Then calculate each measure.

3 What conclusions can you draw from the measure of central tendency and measure of variation you chose?

4 You need to schedule a flight for an important meeting and you must be there on time. Which airline would you schedule with? **Explain your reasoning.**

TOPIC 2

TALK THE TALK

Numeric
Summaries of Data
TOPIC 2   LESSON 4

Getting
Started   Activity   Talk
                1 2 3 4   the Talk

All Together Now!

> For each data set, calculate the median, mean, IQR, and MAD, if possible. **Explain which measure of center and which measure of variation best describe the data set.**

1   **Pencils in Backpacks**

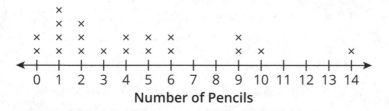

2 **Ages of U.S. First Ladies (20th Century)**

```
3 | 1
4 | 0 3 4 5 7 8 9
5 | 0 2 4 6 6 6 9
6 | 0 0 3
```

Key: 6|0 means 60

3 Prepare a presentation of your analysis of the data from Question 2 to give to the class.

LESSON 4 ASSIGNMENT

> Use a separate piece of paper for your Journal entry.

JOURNAL >

In your own words, describe how you would decide whether to use the median or mean to represent the center of a data set.

REMEMBER

When a data set is skewed right, the mean is greater than the median.
When a data set is skewed left, the mean is less than the median.
When a data set is symmetric, the mean and median are approximately equal.

PRACTICE >

Branson Creek Middle School has decided to make fitness a key message to their students in the upcoming school year. As a result, they will participate in a national fitness program. To participate, they must randomly select 15 students in the 5th grade and record their exercise time each day. Here are the data (in minutes).

85, 80, 76, 78, 82, 88, 80, 80, 110, 85, 85, 82, 83, 88, 76

1 Construct a dot plot of the data.

2 Describe the distribution of the data.

3 Determine the median and mean of the data. Explain which measure better represents a typical value in the data set.

4 Determine which measure of variation to use to describe the spread of the data. Then calculate this measure.

5 Interpret the measure of variation you calculated.

STRETCH Optional

Cecile applies for a job. She notices that the average salary is really high and says that it must be a great place to work.

> Explain to Cecile why this average might be misleading. Provide an example set of data to justify your argument.

> ❯ This Mixed Practice worksheet includes two sections: Spaced Review and End-of-Topic Review. **Use a separate piece of paper to show your work.**

Spaced Review

❯ Practice concepts from previous topics.

1 Evaluate each expression.

   (a) $\dfrac{(8+2)^2}{2}$

   (b) $10 + 5^2 - 3 \cdot 2^2$

2 Determine each quotient.

   (a) $\dfrac{3}{5} \div \dfrac{4}{5}$

   (b) $\dfrac{7}{8} \div 1\dfrac{1}{2}$

3 Order the integers in each group from least to greatest.

   (a) 0, 115, −35, 32, −116, 92

   (b) −2, 31, −5, 27, 0, 90

4 Determine each difference.

   (a) $2\dfrac{4}{5} - 1\dfrac{1}{2}$

   (b) $3 - 1\dfrac{1}{3}$

5 Write the coordinates of each point described. Identify the quadrant in which the point is located.

   (a) This point is a reflection across the *y*-axis of the point at (7, 1.5).

   (b) This point is a reflection across the *x*-axis of the point at (3, 9).

6 The number of items purchased by a number of randomly chosen customers at a toy store is 2, 4, 3, 7, 12, 3, 1, 5, 6, 3, 4, 2, 4, 3, 7, 14, 10, 3, 5, and 9. Display the data in a dot plot and describe the distribution.

7 The graph represents the total distance traveled in miles.

   (a) Write an equation to represent the graph. Define each variable.

   (b) If you know the number of hours, how can you use the graph to determine any total distance? How many hours did it take to travel 120 miles?

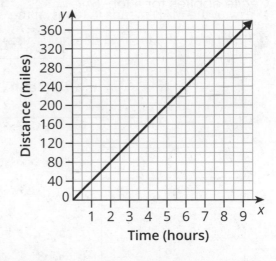

End-of-Topic Review

AVAILABLE ONLINE
1. A **Topic Summary** reviews the main concepts for the topic.
2. A video of the **Worked Example** is provided.

❯ Practice concepts you learned in **Numeric Summaries of Data**.

8 Construct a dot plot for each.

   (a) The number of items purchased by a number of randomly chosen customers at a toy store are 2, 4, 3, 7, 12, 3, 1, 5, 6, 3, 4, 2, 4, 3, 7, 14, 10, 3, 5, and 9. Describe the distribution.

   (b) The scores on a recent math quiz are 12, 14, 8, 13, 12, 14, 5, 13, 14, 3, 15, 15, 10, 13, 12, 0, 14, 11, 14, 13, and 10. Describe the distribution.

9 Determine the five-number summary and IQR for each data set.

   (a) 45, 58, 37, 41, 22, 49

   (b) 525, 480, 540, 505, 730, 500, 450

10 Determine the mean, median, mode, and range of the set of data.

   (a) 14, 19, 8, 22, 11, 19, 4, 18, 12, 10, 21

   (b) 55, 24, 73, 108, 39, 46, 72, 100, 92, 32

11 Analyze the box-and-whisker plot.

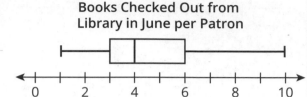

Books Checked Out from Library in June per Patron

Number of books

   (a) Describe the distribution of the box plot.

   (b) What percent of patrons checked out less than 3 books in June?

   (c) Interpret the IQR of the books checked out from the library in June per patron.

12 Determine whether the mean or median would best describe a typical value in each data set. Explain your reasoning.

   (a)

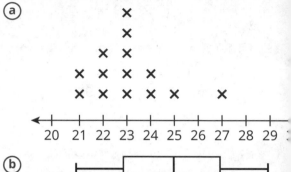

   (b)

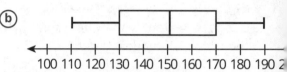

13 Yana recorded the number of hours she slept each night for a month. She calculated the mean of her data to be 9.5 hours and the mean absolute deviation of her data as 1.5 hours. Describe what the MAD means in terms of the data.

14 Complete the table to determine the mean absolute deviation.

Data	Mean	Deviation From the Mean	Absolute Value of the Deviation From the Mean
35			
18			
58			
65			
29			
Mean Absolute Deviation			

Appendix

Getting Ready for Module 1
Review Answers

Composing and Decomposing

1 4

2 $\frac{35}{11}$

3 $\frac{20}{9}$

4 $\frac{1}{40}$

Getting Ready for Module 2
Review Answers

Relating Quantities

Hours	2	5	8	15
Minutes	120	300	480	900

Getting Ready for Module 3
Review Answers

Determining Unknown Quantities

1 $\frac{11}{13}$

2 $\frac{7}{9}$

3 $\frac{1}{3}$

4 $\frac{17}{20}$

Getting Ready for Module 4
Review Answers

Moving Beyond Positive Quantities

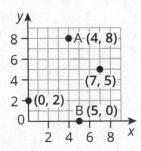

Getting Ready for Module 5
Review Answers

Describing Variability of Quantities

1 Amount of Trail Mix Eaten

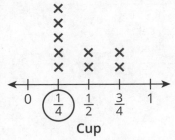

2 $\frac{1}{4}, \frac{1}{4}, \frac{1}{4}, \frac{1}{4}, \frac{1}{4}, \frac{1}{2}, \frac{1}{2}, \frac{3}{4}, \frac{3}{4}$

3 $3\frac{3}{4}$ cups of trail mix

Glossary

A

absolute deviation

The absolute value of a deviation is called the absolute deviation.

EXAMPLE

$$11 - 12 = -1$$
data   mean   deviaton

$$|-1| = 1$$
deviation   absolute
deviation

absolute value

The absolute value, or magnitude, of a number is its distance from zero on a number line.

EXAMPLE

The absolute value of -3 is the same as the absolute value of 3 because they are both a distance of 3 from zero on a number line.

$$|-3| = |3|$$

Addition Property of Equality

The Addition Property of Equality states that if two values a and b are equal, when you add the same value c to each, the sums are equal.

EXAMPLES

$12 = 12$ and $12 + 7 = 12 + 7$

If $a = b$, then $a + c = b + c$.

additive reasoning

Additive reasoning focuses on the use of addition and subtraction for comparisons.

EXAMPLE

Vicki is 40 years old and Ben is 10 years old. In 5 years, Vicki will be 45 and Ben will be 15. Vicki will always be 30 years older than Ben. This is additive reasoning.

algebraic expression

An algebraic expression is a mathematical phrase that has at least one variable, and it can contain numbers and operation symbols.

EXAMPLES

a $2a + b$ xy $\dfrac{4}{p}$ z^2

algorithm

An algorithm is a process or description of steps you can follow to complete a mathematical calculation.

EXAMPLES

The algorithm for multiplying two fractions is to multiply across the numerators and denominators.

$$\frac{2}{3} \cdot \frac{4}{5} = \frac{2 \cdot 4}{3 \cdot 5} = \frac{8}{15}$$

area

The number of square units needed to cover a two-dimensional shape or the surface of an object is the area.

EXAMPLE

The rectangle has an area of 24 square units.

Glossary

area model

An area model is a rectangular diagram used to represent multiplication and division problems. The factors are the length and width and the product is the area.

EXAMPLE

The area model shows that 7(13) is equivalent to 7(3) + 7(10). Both expressions are equal to 91.

	3	10
7	21	70

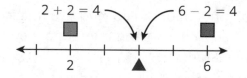

B

balance point

When you have all the points on a number line at the same value, you balance the number line. You call this value the balance point.

EXAMPLE

Consider the data set: 2, 6.

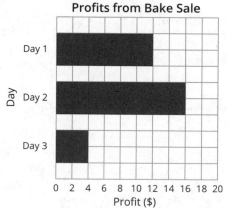

The balance point is 4.

bar graph

A bar graph displays categorical data using either horizontal or vertical bars on a graph. The height or length of each bar indicates the value for that category.

EXAMPLES

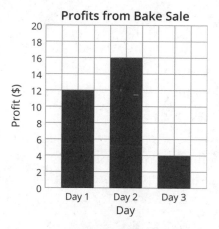

base

The base of a power is the factor that is multiplied repeatedly in the power.

EXAMPLES

$$2^3 = 2 \times 2 \times 2 = 8 \qquad 8^0 = 1$$

base   base

benchmark percents

A benchmark percent is a commonly used percent, such as 1%, 5%, 10%, 25%, 50%, and 100%.

box-and-whisker plot

A box-and-whisker plot, or just box plot, is a graph that displays the five-number summary of a data set: the median, the upper and lower quartiles (Q1 and Q3), and the minimum and maximum values.

EXAMPLE

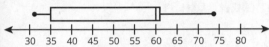

Data: 32, 35, 35, 53, 55, 60, 60, 61, 61, 74, 74

Minimum = 32

Q1 = 35

Median = 60

Q3 = 61

Maximum = 74

C

categories

Categories are groups of things that have some quality or qualities in common.

categorical data

Categorical data, or qualitative data, are data for which each piece of data fits into exactly one of several different groups or categories.

EXAMPLES

Animals: lions, tigers, bears, etc.

Colors: blue, green, red, etc.

circle graph

A circle graph, often called a pie chart, displays categorical data using sectors, or "wedges," of a circle. The area of each sector corresponds to the ratio of the part in relation to the whole.

EXAMPLE

Favorite Ways to Travel

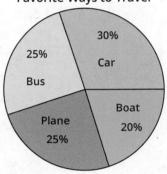

clusters

Clusters are areas of the graph where data group close together.

EXAMPLE

Number of Pets

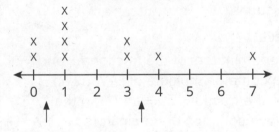

There are clusters of data from 0 to 1 and from 3 to 4.

coefficient

You call a number multiplied by a variable in an algebraic expression a coefficient.

EXAMPLES

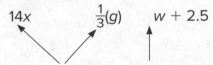

$14x$ $\frac{1}{3}(g)$ $w + 2.5$

coefficient   The coefficient is 1 even though it is not shown.

Glossary <small>Continued</small>

coordinate plane

A plane formed by the intersection of a vertical number line called the *y*-axis, and a horizontal number line called the *x*-axis is a coordinate plane.

EXAMPLE

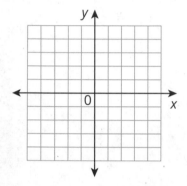

common denominators

When two or more fractions have the same denominator, they have common denominators. You can write fractions with common denominators by determining a common multiple of the denominators of the fractions.

EXAMPLE

The denominators of the fractions $\frac{1}{2}$ and $\frac{2}{3}$ have a common multiple of 6. You can rewrite the fractions as $\frac{2}{6}$ and $\frac{4}{6}$ so that they have common denominators.

common factor

A common factor is a factor shared between two or more numbers.

EXAMPLE

factors of 60: **1**, **2**, **3**, **4**, 5, **6**, 10, **12**, 15, 20, 30, 60

factors of 24: **1**, **2**, **3**, **4**, **6**, 8, **12**, 24

common factors of 60 and 24: 1, 2, 3, 4, 6, and 12

Commutative Property of Multiplication

The Commutative Property of Multiplication states that for any numbers *a* and *b*, the product $a \cdot b$ is equal to the product $b \cdot a$.

EXAMPLES

$$\begin{array}{r}29\\\times\ 3\\\hline 87\end{array} = \begin{array}{r}3\\\times 29\\\hline 27\\+\ 60\\\hline 87\end{array}$$

$$\frac{1}{5}\cdot\frac{2}{3}=\frac{2}{3}\cdot\frac{1}{5}$$
$$\frac{2}{15}\qquad\frac{2}{15}$$

complex fraction

A complex fraction is a fraction that has a fraction in either the numerator, the denominator, or both the numerator and denominator.

EXAMPLES

$\dfrac{\frac{3}{4}}{3}$, $\dfrac{7}{\frac{2}{1}}$, and $\dfrac{\frac{1}{4}}{\frac{2}{3}}$ are all complex fractions.

composite

A number is composite if it has more than 2 factors.

EXAMPLES

The number 4 has three factors: 1, 2, and 4.

The number 6 has four factors: 1, 2, 3, and 6.

These are composite numbers.

composite figure

A composite figure is a figure made up of more than one geometric figure.

EXAMPLE

The composite figure is made up of two rectangles and a triangle.

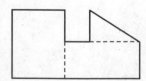

composite solid

A composite solid is made up of more than one geometric solid.

EXAMPLE

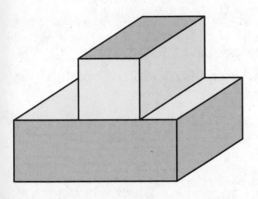

continuous graph

A continuous graph is a graph with no breaks in it.

EXAMPLES

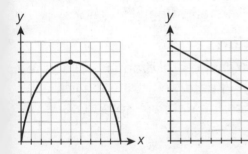

conversion table

A conversion table is a table of equivalent measures for changing from one unit of measure to another.

EXAMPLE

The conversion table shows equivalent customary lengths.

Conversion Table
1 foot = 12 inches
1 yard = 3 feet
1 mile = 5280 feet

convert

To convert a measurement means to change it to an equivalent measurement in different units.

EXAMPLE

To convert 36 inches to feet, you can multiply:

$$36 \text{ in.} \left(\frac{1 \text{ ft}}{12 \text{ in.}} \right) = \frac{36 \text{ ft}}{12}$$
$$= 3 \text{ ft}$$

cube

A cube is a polyhedron that has congruent squares as faces.

EXAMPLE

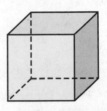

D

data

Data are categories, numbers, or observations gathered in response to a statistical question.

EXAMPLES

favorite foods of sixth graders, heights of different animals at the zoo

decimal notation

Decimal notation is an equivalent form of a number using a decimal point.

EXAMPLE

$$\frac{107}{100} = 1 + \frac{7}{100} \quad \text{Decimal Notation}$$
$$= 1 + 0.07 = 1.07$$

denominator

The bottom number in a fraction is the denominator. It indicates how many equal parts are in the whole.

EXAMPLE

$\frac{3}{4}$ ← denominator

Density Property

The Density Property states that between any two rational numbers there is another rational number.

dependent quantity

The dependent quantity is the quantity that depends on another in a problem situation.

EXAMPLE

Max just got a new hybrid car that averages 51 miles to the gallon. How far does the car travel on 15 gallons of fuel?

number of gallons $\cdot \frac{\text{miles}}{\text{gallon}}$ = miles traveled

The dependent quantity is the total miles traveled. The number of miles traveled depends on the gallons of fuel.

dependent variable

The variable that represents the dependent quantity is called the dependent variable.

EXAMPLE

Max just got a new hybrid car that averages 51 miles to the gallon. How far does the car travel on 15 gallons of fuel?

number of gallons $\cdot \frac{\text{miles}}{\text{gallon}}$ = miles traveled

$$g \cdot m = t$$

The dependent quantity is the total miles traveled. Since t represents total miles traveled in the equation, t is the dependent variable.

deviation

The deviation of a data value indicates how far that data value is from the mean.

EXAMPLE

deviation = data value − mean

discrete graph

A discrete graph is a graph of isolated points.

EXAMPLES

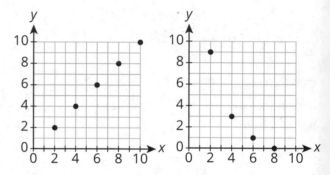

distribution

The overall shape of a graph is called the distribution of data. A distribution is the way in which the data are spread out.

Distributive Property

The Distributive Property states that for any numbers a, b, and c, $a(b + c) = ab + ac$.

EXAMPLES

$$4(2 + 15) = 4 \cdot 2 + 4 \cdot 15$$
$$= 8 + 60$$
$$= 68$$

Division Property of Equality

The Division Property of Equality states that when you divide equal values a and b by the same value c and $c \neq 0$, the quotients are equal.

EXAMPLES

$12 = 12$ and $12 \div 7 = 12 \div 7$

If $a = b$ and $c \neq 0$, then $\frac{a}{c} = \frac{b}{c}$.

dot plot

A dot plot is a data display that shows discrete data on a number line with dots, Xs, or other symbols.

EXAMPLE

Number of Pets

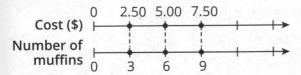

double number line

A double number line is a model that is made up of two number lines used together to represent the ratio between two quantities.

EXAMPLE

Cost ($)   0   2.50   5.00   7.50

Number of muffins   0   3   6   9

E

edge

An edge is the intersection of two faces of a three-dimensional figure.

EXAMPLE

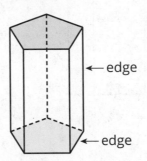

← edge

← edge

ellipsis

An ellipsis is a set of three periods used to represent infinity in a number set.

EXAMPLE

$\{..., -2, -1, 0, 1, 2, ...\}$

↑ ellipsis   ↑ ellipsis

equation

An equation is a mathematical sentence that uses an equals sign to show that two expressions are the same as one another. An equation can contain numbers, variables, or both in the same mathematical sentence.

EXAMPLES

$$y = 2x + 4$$
$$6 = 3 + 3$$
$$2(8) = 26 - 10$$
$$\frac{1}{4} \cdot 4 = \frac{8}{4} - \frac{4}{4}$$

equivalent fractions

Fractions that represent the same part-to-whole relationship are equivalent fractions.

EXAMPLE

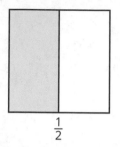 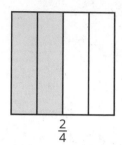

$\frac{1}{2}$ $\frac{2}{4}$

equivalent number

An equivalent number has the same value as another expression.

EXAMPLE

$2 + 2 = 4$

$\frac{3}{10} = 0.3$

equivalent ratios

Equivalent ratios are ratios that represent the same part-to-part or part-to-whole relationship.

evaluate an algebraic expression

To evaluate an algebraic expression means to determine the value of the expression for a given value of each variable.

EXAMPLE

Evaluate the expression
$\frac{4x + (2^3 - y)}{p}$ for $x = 2.5$, $y = 8$, and $p = 2$.

- First replace the variables with numbers: $\frac{4(2.5) + (2^3 - 8)}{2}$.

- Then, evaluate the expression: $\frac{10 + 0}{2} = \frac{10}{2} = 5$.

evaluate a numeric expression

To evaluate a numeric expression means to rewrite the expression as a single numeric value.

EXAMPLE

$$19 - 4 \times 3$$
$$19 - 12$$
$$7$$

experiment

An experiment is one method of collecting data in which a researcher imposes a condition and observes the results.

EXAMPLE

A researcher conducts an experiment to investigate whether 6th graders perform better on an assessment when they read a textbook or watch a video about the material. The researcher randomly assigns half the students to read the text and half the students to watch the video. The researcher then gives all students the same assessment and compares the scores of the students in the two groups.

exponent

The exponent of the power is the number of times the base is used as a factor.

EXAMPLES

$2^3 = 2 \times 2 \times 2$

↑
exponent

$8^4 = 8 \times 8 \times 8 \times 8$

↑
exponent

F

face

A face is one of the polygons that makes up a polyhedron.

EXAMPLE

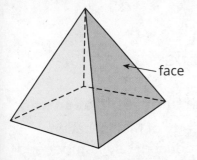

face

frequency

A frequency is the number of times an item or number occurs in a data set.

EXAMPLE

Number Rolled	Tally	Frequency
2	IIII II	7

The number 2 was rolled 7 times, so its frequency was 7.

G

gaps

Gaps are areas of the graph where there are no data.

EXAMPLE

Number of Pets

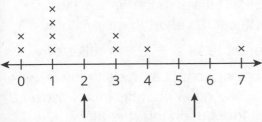

There are gaps between 1 and 3 and between 4 and 7.

geometric solid

A geometric solid is a bounded three-dimensional geometric figure.

EXAMPLE

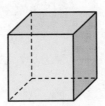

graph of an inequality

The graph of an inequality in one variable is the set of all points on a number line that make the inequality true.

EXAMPLE

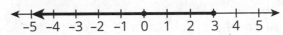

$x \leq 3$

grouped frequency table

A grouped frequency table is a table used to organize data according to how many times data values with a given range of values occur.

EXAMPLE

Floor Intervals	Frequency (f)
10–20	8
20–30	27
30–40	16
40–50	5
50–60	4

Glossary Continued

greatest common factor (GCF)

The greatest common factor, or GCF, is the largest factor two or more numbers have in common.

EXAMPLE

factors of 16: **1**, **2**, **4**, 8, 16

factors of 12: **1**, **2**, 3, **4**, 6, 12

common factors: 1, 2, 4

greatest common factor: 4

H

histogram

A histogram is a graphical way to display quantitative or numeric data using vertical bars. The width of a bar represents an interval of data and is often referred to as a bin. The height of the bar indicates the frequency, or the number of data values included in any given bin.

EXAMPLE

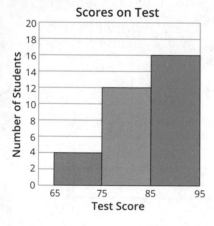

I

Identity Property of Addition

The Identity Property of Addition states that the sum of any number and 0 is the number.

EXAMPLES

$6 + 0 = 6$ $\frac{3}{4} + 0 = \frac{3}{4}$

$5^2 + 0 = 5^2$ $0.125 + 0 = 0.125$

Identity Property of Multiplication

The Identity Property of Multiplication states that the product of any number and 1 is the number.

EXAMPLES

$6 \times 1 = 6$ $\frac{3}{4} \times 1 = \frac{3}{4}$

$5^2 \cdot 1 = 5^2$ $0.125(1) = 0.125$

improper fraction

An improper fraction is a fraction in which the numerator is greater than the denominator.

EXAMPLES

$\frac{3}{1}$, $\frac{5}{4}$, and $\frac{325}{129}$ are improper fractions.

independent quantity

The independent quantity is the quantity the dependent quantity depends on.

EXAMPLE

Max just got a new hybrid car that averages 51 miles to the gallon. How far does the car travel on 15 gallons of fuel?

$$\text{number of gallons} \cdot \frac{\text{miles}}{\text{gallon}} = \text{miles traveled}$$

The independent quantity is the number of gallons. The other quantity (miles traveled) is dependent upon this quantity.

independent variable

The variable that represents the independent quantity is called the independent variable.

EXAMPLE

Max just got a new hybrid car that averages 51 miles to the gallon. How far does the car travel on 15 gallons of fuel?

number of gallons $\cdot \frac{\text{miles}}{\text{gallon}} =$ miles traveled

$$g \cdot m = t$$

The independent quantity is the number of gallons. Since g represents the number of gallons in the equation, g is the independent variable.

inequality

An inequality is a comparison of two values that shows that one value is greater than ($>$), less than ($<$), or not equal to ($\neq$) the second value.

EXAMPLES

$0.3 > 0.28$	0.3 is greater than 0.28.
$\frac{3}{8} < \frac{3}{4}$	$\frac{3}{8}$ is less than $\frac{3}{4}$.
$7 \neq 11$	7 is not equal to 11.

infinity

Infinity, represented by the symbol ∞, means a quantity with no end or bound.

EXAMPLE

Negative infinity   Positive infinity

$-\infty$ ← ─┼─┼─┼─┼─┼─┼─┼─┼─┼─┼─ → ∞
     -5 -4 -3 -2 -1 0 1 2 3 4 5

integers

Integers are the set of whole numbers with their opposites.

EXAMPLE

The set of integers can be represented as $\{\ldots -3, -2, -1, 0, 1, 2, 3, \ldots\}$

interquartile range (IQR)

The interquartile range, abbreviated IQR, is the difference between the third quartile, Q3, and the first quartile, Q1. The IQR indicates the range of the middle 50 percent of the data.

EXAMPLE

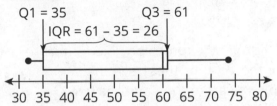

Q1 = 35   Q3 = 61

IQR = 61 – 35 = 26

30 35 40 45 50 55 60 65 70 75 80

inverse operations

Inverse operations are pairs of operations that reverse the effects of each other.

EXAMPLES

Addition and subtraction are inverse operations: $351 + 25 - 25 = 351$.

Multiplication and division are inverse operations: $351 \times 25 \div 25 = 351$.

K

kite

A kite is a quadrilateral with two pairs of consecutive congruent sides. A square is a special type of kite.

EXAMPLE

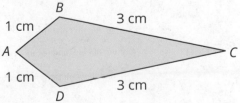

least common multiple (LCM)

The least common multiple, or LCM, is the smallest multiple (other than zero) that two or more numbers have in common.

EXAMPLE

multiples of 60: 60, **120**, 180, **240**, 300, 360, 420, 480 . . .

multiples of 24: 24, 48, 72, 96, **120**, 144, 168, 192, 216, **240** . . .

some common multiples of 60 and 24: 120, 240, . . .

least common multiple of 60 and 24: 120

like terms

In an algebraic expression, like terms are two or more terms that have the same variable raised to the same power.

EXAMPLES

like terms

$4x + 3p + x + 2 = 5x + 3p + 2$

like terms

$24a^2 + 2a - 9a^2 = 13a^2 + 2a$

no like terms

$m + m^2 - x + x^3$

line of symmetry

A line of symmetry is an imaginary line that passes through a shape or object and divides it into two identical halves.

EXAMPLE

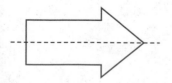

linear relationship

When a set of points graphed on a coordinate plane forms a straight line, a linear relationship exists.

EXAMPLE

The points graphed show a linear relationship.

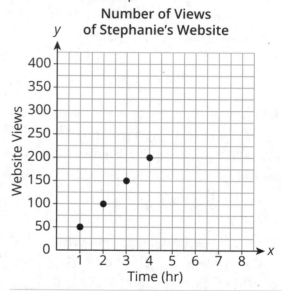

Number of Views of Stephanie's Website

literal equation

A literal equation is an equation in which the variables represent specific measures.

EXAMPLES

$A = lw \qquad A = \frac{1}{2}bh \qquad d = rt$

mean

The mean is the arithmetic average of the numbers in a data set.

EXAMPLE

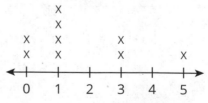

Number of Pets

$$\text{Mean} = \frac{0 + 0 + 1 + 1 + 1 + 1 + 3 + 3 + 5}{9}$$

$$= \frac{15}{9} = 1\frac{2}{3} \text{ pets}$$

mean absolute deviation

The mean absolute deviation is the average or mean of the absolute deviations.

measure of center

A measure of center tells you how data values cluster, or the location of the "center" of the data.

EXAMPLES

Mean, median, and mode are each a measure of center for data.

measure of variation

A measure of variation describes the spread of data values.

EXAMPLE

Range is a measure of variation for data.

median

The median is the middle number in a data set when you place the values in order from least to greatest or greatest to least.

EXAMPLE

Number of Pets

```
    X
    X
X   X       X
X   X       X       X
+---+---+---+---+---+--->
0   1   2   3   4   5
```

0, 0, 1, 1, 1̲, 1, 3, 3, 5

median

mode

The mode is the value or values that occur most frequently in a data set.

EXAMPLE

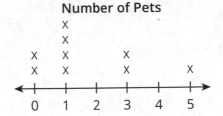

Number of Pets

0, 0, 1, 1, 1, 1, 3, 3, 5

The mode of the data is 1.

multiple

A multiple is the product of a given whole number and another whole number.

EXAMPLE

multiples of 10:

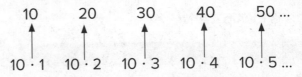

$10 \cdot 1 \quad 10 \cdot 2 \quad 10 \cdot 3 \quad 10 \cdot 4 \quad 10 \cdot 5 \ldots$

Multiplication Property of Equality

The Multiplication Property of Equality states that if two values a and b are equal, when you multiply each by the same value c, the products are equal.

EXAMPLES

$12 = 12$ and $12(7) = 12(7)$

If $a = b$, then $ac = bc$.

multiplicative inverse

The multiplicative inverse of a number $\frac{a}{b}$ is the number $\frac{b}{a}$, where a and b are nonzero numbers. The product of any nonzero number and its multiplicative inverse is 1.

EXAMPLES

The multiplicative inverse of

$\frac{3}{7}$ is $\frac{7}{3}$. $\frac{3}{7} \cdot \frac{7}{3} = \frac{21}{21} = 1$

The multiplicative inverse of

5 is $\frac{1}{5}$. $\frac{5}{1} \cdot \frac{1}{5} = \frac{5}{5} = 1$

multiplicative reasoning

Multiplicative reasoning focuses on the use of multiplication and division.

EXAMPLE

Vicki is 40 years old and Ben is 10 years old. Vicki is 4 times as old as Ben. In 5 years, Vicki will be 3 times as old as Ben.

This is multiplicative reasoning.

N

negative numbers

Negative numbers are to the left of 0 on a number line.

EXAMPLE

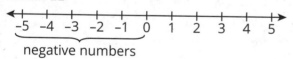

negative numbers

net

A net is a two-dimensional representation of a three-dimensional geometric figure.

EXAMPLE

This is a net of a cube.

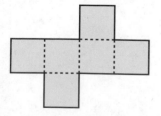

number line

A number line is a line on which numbers are marked at equal intervals along its length.

EXAMPLE

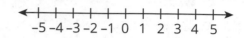

numerator

The top number in a fraction is the numerator. It indicates how many equal parts of the whole to count.

EXAMPLE

$\frac{3}{4}$ ← numerator

numeric expression

A numeric expression is a mathematical phrase that contains numbers and operations.

EXAMPLE

$5 \times 4 - 9$

numeric pattern

A numeric pattern is a sequence, or ordered set, of numbers that is created by following a given rule.

EXAMPLE

Rule: Multiply by 2.

Input	1	2	3	4
Output	2	4	6	8

O

observational study

An observational study is one method of collecting data in which a researcher collects data by observing the variable of interest.

EXAMPLE

A researcher wants to determine whether more men or women prefer a certain store. The researcher observes the number of men and women who visit the store over a number of hours and compares the values of the two groups.

one-step equation

A one-step equation is an equation you can solve using only one operation.

Order of Operations

The Order of Operations is a set of rules that ensures the same result every time anyone evaluates an expression.

EXAMPLE

$44 + (6 - 5) - 2 \cdot 75 \div 5^2$ Parentheses

$44 + 1 - 2 \cdot 75 \div 5^2$ Exponents

$44 + 1 - 2 \cdot 75 \div 25$ Multiplication and Division (from left to right)

$44 + 1 - 150 \div 25$

$44 + 1 - 6$ Addition and Subtraction (from left to right)

$45 - 6$

39

ordered pair

A pair of real numbers of the form (x, y) used to locate a point on a coordinate plane is an ordered pair. The first number is the x-coordinate, and the second number is the y-coordinate.

EXAMPLE

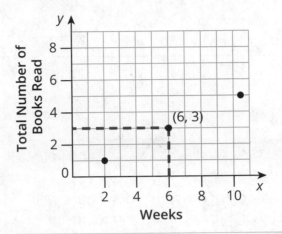

origin

The origin is the point on a coordinate plane where the x- and y-axes intersect. It has the coordinates $(0, 0)$.

EXAMPLE

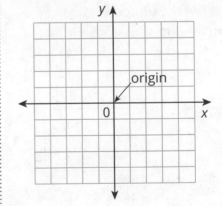

outliers

Outliers are data values that lie a large distance from the other data in a graph. Outliers usually accompany gaps in data.

EXAMPLE

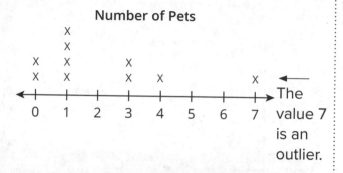

Number of Pets

The value 7 is an outlier.

P

parallelogram

A parallelogram is a four-sided figure with two pairs of parallel sides and opposite sides that are equal in length.

EXAMPLES

In parallelogram *ABCD*, opposite sides *AB* and *CD* are parallel and equal in length; opposite sides *AD* and *BC* are parallel and equal in length.

In parallelogram *EFGH*, opposite sides *EF* and *GH* are parallel and equal in length; opposite sides *FG* and *EH* are parallel and equal in length.

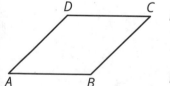 

peaks

Peaks are values on a graph that contain more data points than the values on either side of it.

EXAMPLE

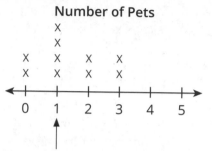

Number of Pets

The value 1 is a peak.

percent

A percent is a part-to-whole ratio where the whole is equal to 100. Percent is another name for hundredths. The percent symbol "%" means "per 100," or "out of 100."

perfect cube

A perfect cube is the product of three equal whole numbers.

EXAMPLE

64 is a perfect cube: $4 \times 4 \times 4 = 64$

perfect square

A perfect square is the product of two equal whole numbers.

EXAMPLES

9 is a perfect square: $3 \times 3 = 9$

25 is a perfect square: $5 \times 5 = 25$

point

A point is a location in space. A point has no size or shape, but it is often represented by using a dot and is named by a capital letter.

EXAMPLES

Points *A* and *B* are shown.

A•

　　•*B*

polyhedron

A polyhedron is a three-dimensional solid figure that has polygons as faces.

EXAMPLE

A cube is a polyhedron. It has six square faces.

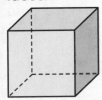

population

A population is an entire set of items from which you collect data.

EXAMPLE

If you wanted to determine the average height of the students at your school, the number of students at the school would be the population.

positive rational number

A positive rational number is a number you can write in the form $\frac{a}{b}$, where a and b are both whole numbers greater than 0.

EXAMPLES

$0.75 = \frac{75}{100}$, where $a = 75$ and $b = 100$

$6 = \frac{6}{1}$, where $a = 6$ and $b = 1$

$\frac{9}{11}$, where $a = 9$ and $b = 11$

power

A power has two elements: the base and the exponent.

EXAMPLE

base $\longrightarrow 6^2 \longleftarrow$ exponent

power

prime

A number is prime if it has exactly two distinct factors: 1 and the number itself.

EXAMPLES

2, 3, 5, 7, and 11 are the first five prime numbers.

proportion

A proportion is an equation that states that two ratios are equal.

EXAMPLE

$\frac{1}{2} = \frac{4.5}{9}$

pyramid

A pyramid is a polyhedron with one base and the same number of triangular faces as there are sides of the base.

EXAMPLE

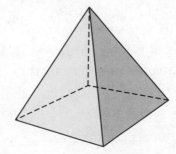

Glossary Continued

Q

quadrants

The x- and y-axes divide the coordinate plane into four regions called quadrants. You number these quadrants with Roman numerals from one (I) to four (IV), starting in the upper right-hand quadrant and moving counterclockwise.

EXAMPLE

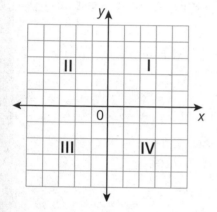

qualitative reasoning

When you compare ratios without measuring or counting quantities, you use qualitative reasoning.

EXAMPLE

A race car travels more laps in less time than it did yesterday. You can use qualitative reasoning to determine that the speed of the race car is faster today because the ratio of laps to time increased.

quantitative data

Quantitative data, or numeric data, are data you can place on a numeric scale and compare.

EXAMPLES

The zoo has 4 lions, 3 tigers, and 6 bears.

In 2006, Los Angeles had a population of about 3,849,378. In the same year, Atlanta had a population of about 429,500.

quantitative reasoning

When you compare ratios by measuring or counting quantities, you use quantitative reasoning.

EXAMPLE

Homeroom A uses 3 tablespoons of cocoa powder and 2 cups of milk to make hot chocolate. Homeroom B uses 8 tablespoons of cocoa powder and 5 cups of milk to make hot chocolate. You can use quantitative reasoning to determine that Homeroom B's mix has a stronger chocolate taste because $\frac{8}{5} > \frac{3}{2}$.

quartiles

Quartiles are a set of values that describe variation in a data set. When data in a set are arranged in order, quartiles are the numbers that split data into quarters (or fourths).

EXAMPLE

first quartile (Q1)   third quartile (Q3)

32, 35, 35, 53, 55, 60, 60, 61, 61, 74, 74

second quartile/median (Q2)

R

range

The range is the difference between the maximum and minimum values of a data set.

EXAMPLE

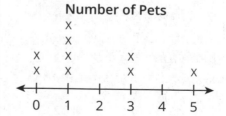

0, 0, 1, 1, 1, 1, 3, 3, 5

$5 - 0 = 5$

The range of the data is 5.

rate

A rate is a ratio that compares two quantities that are measured in different units.

EXAMPLE

The speed of 60 miles in two hours is a rate:

$$\frac{60 \text{ mi}}{2 \text{ h}} = \frac{30 \text{ mi}}{1 \text{ h}}$$

ratio

A ratio is a comparison of two quantities that uses division.

EXAMPLES

The ratio of stars to circles is $\frac{3}{2}$, or 3:2, or 3 to 2.

The ratio of circles to stars is $\frac{2}{3}$, or 2:3, or 2 to 3.

rational numbers

Rational numbers are the set of numbers that you can write in the form $\frac{a}{b}$, where a and b are integers and $b \neq 0$.

EXAMPLES

-4, $\frac{1}{2}$, $\frac{2}{3}$, 0.67, and $\frac{22}{7}$ are examples of rational numbers.

reciprocal

The reciprocal of a number is also known as the multiplicative inverse of the number. (See *multiplicative inverse*.)

EXAMPLES

The reciprocal of $\frac{3}{7}$ is $\frac{7}{3}$. $\frac{3}{7} \cdot \frac{7}{3} = \frac{21}{21} = 1$

The reciprocal of 5 is $\frac{1}{5}$. $\frac{5}{1} \cdot \frac{1}{5} = \frac{5}{5} = 1$

Reflexive Property of Equality

The Reflexive Property of Equality states that a number is always equal to itself. So, when both sides of an equation look exactly the same, their values are equal.

EXAMPLES

$7 = 7$

$a = a$

relatively prime

Two numbers that do not have any common factors other than 1 are called relatively prime.

EXAMPLES

Positive whole number pairs that have a difference of 1 (4 and 5, 10 and 11, 15 and 16) are always relatively prime.

repeating decimal

When you rewrite a fraction as a decimal using division, and a digit or a group of digits repeats without end in the quotient, the resulting decimal is a repeating decimal.

EXAMPLES

$\frac{1}{9} = 0.111...$ $\frac{7}{12} = 0.58333...$

$\frac{22}{7} = 3.142857142857...$

right rectangular prism

A right rectangular prism is a polyhedron with three pairs of congruent and parallel rectangular faces.

EXAMPLE

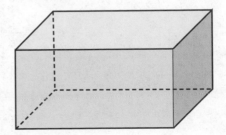

Glossary _{Continued}

sample

A sample is a selection from a population.

EXAMPLE

If you wanted to determine the average height of the students in your school, you could choose a certain number of students and measure their heights. The heights of the students in this group would be your sample.

scaling down

Scaling down means to divide both parts of the ratio by the same factor greater than 1, or multiply both parts of the ratio by the same factor less than 1.

EXAMPLE

$$\frac{3}{6} = \frac{1}{2}$$

scaling up

Scaling up means to multiply both parts of a ratio by the same factor greater than 1.

EXAMPLE

$$\frac{1}{2} = \frac{3}{6}$$

skewed left distribution

In a skewed left distribution of data, the peak of the data is to the right side of the graph. There are only a few data points to the left side of the graph.

EXAMPLE

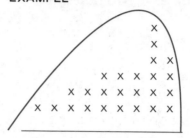

skewed right distribution

In a skewed right distribution of data, the peak of the data is to the left side of the graph. There are only a few data points to the right side of the graph.

EXAMPLE

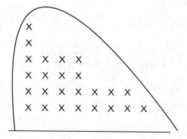

slant height

A slant height of a pyramid is the distance measured along a triangular face from the vertex of the pyramid to the midpoint, or center, of an edge of the base.

EXAMPLE

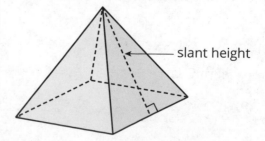

slant height

solution

A solution to an equation is any value for a variable that makes the equation true.

EXAMPLE

The solution to the equation $2x + 4 = 8$ is $x = 2$.

solution set of an inequality

The set of all points that make an inequality true is the solution set of the inequality.

EXAMPLES

$x \geq 7$

The solution set for $x \geq 7$ is all the numbers greater than or equal to 7.

$x < 7$

The solution set for $x < 7$ is all the numbers less than 7.

statistical process

The statistical process has four components:

- Formulating a statistical question.
- Collecting appropriate data.
- Analyzing the data graphically and numerically.
- Interpreting the results of the analysis.

statistical question

A statistical question is a question that anticipates an answer based on data that vary.

EXAMPLE

"What sport is the most popular in your school?" is a statistical question. It anticipates that the answers will vary since not everyone at your school is likely to have the same favorite sport.

"How many students are in Chess Club?" is NOT a statistical question because there is only one answer to the question.

stem-and-leaf plot

A stem-and-leaf plot is a graphical method used to represent ordered numeric data. Once you order the data, you determine the stems and leaves. Typically, the stem is all the digits in a number except the rightmost digit, which is the leaf.

EXAMPLE

Books Read in Mr. Brown's Class

```
0 | 3 6
1 | 0 1 5
2 |
3 | 9 9
4 | 0 0 0
```

Key: 1|0 = 10

straightedge

A straightedge is a tool to draw straight lines.

Glossary Continued

Subtraction Property of Equality

The Subtraction Property of Equality states that when you subtract the same value c from equal values a and b, the differences are equal.

EXAMPLES

$12 = 12$ and $12 - 7 = 12 - 7$

If $a = b$, then $a - c = b - c$.

surface area

The surface area of a polyhedron is the total area of all its two-dimensional faces.

EXAMPLE

The surface area of a unit cube is 6 square units. The cube has 6 faces and the area of each face is 1 square unit.

survey

A survey is one method of collecting data in which you ask people one or more questions.

EXAMPLE

A restaurant may ask its customers to complete a survey with the following question:

On a scale of 1–5, with 1 meaning "poor" and 5 meaning "excellent," how would you rate the food you ate?

☐ 1 ☐ 2 ☐ 3 ☐ 4 ☐ 5

symmetric distribution

In a symmetric distribution of data, the left and right halves of the graph are mirror images, or almost mirror images, of each other. The peak is in the middle because there are many data values in the center.

EXAMPLE

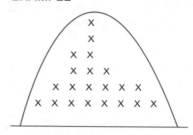

Symmetric Property of Equality

The Symmetric Property of Equality states that if $a = b$, then $b = a$.

EXAMPLE

$x = 3$ is the same as $3 = x$.

T

tape diagram

A tape diagram illustrates number relationships by using rectangles to represent ratio parts.

EXAMPLE

A bakery sells packs of muffins in the ratio of 3 blueberry muffins : 2 pumpkin muffins : 1 bran muffin. The tape diagram represents the ratio of each type of muffin.

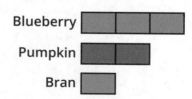

term

A term of an algebraic expression is a number, variable, or product of numbers and variables.

EXAMPLE

The expression has four terms.

$$3y + 5xy + \tfrac{1}{2}x + 6$$

terms

terminating decimal

When you rewrite a fraction as a decimal using division, and the denominator divides evenly into the numerator, the resulting decimal is a terminating decimal. It has a finite number of digits and all following decimal places have a value of 0.

EXAMPLES

$$\frac{9}{10} = 0.9 \qquad \frac{15}{8} = 1.875 \qquad \frac{193}{16} = 12.0625$$

trapezoid

A trapezoid is a quadrilateral with two parallel bases often labeled b_1 and b_2.

EXAMPLE

Quadrilateral $ABCD$ is a trapezoid. Side BC is parallel to side AD.

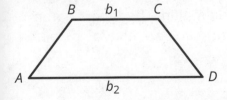

---

uniform distribution

A uniform distribution describes the shape of data spread equally across the range of the data set. A uniform distribution appears symmetric, but has no distinct peaks.

EXAMPLE

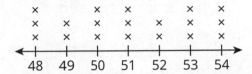

unit cube

A unit cube is a cube whose sides are all 1 unit long.

EXAMPLES

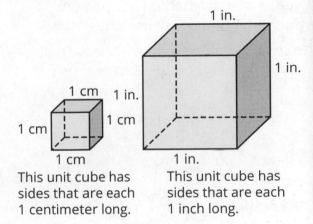

This unit cube has sides that are each 1 centimeter long.

This unit cube has sides that are each 1 inch long.

unit rate

A unit rate is a comparison of two different measurements in which the numerator or denominator has a value of one unit.

EXAMPLE

The speed 60 miles in 2 hours can be written as a unit rate:

$$\frac{60 \text{ mi}}{2 \text{ h}} = \frac{30 \text{ mi}}{1 \text{ h}}.$$

The unit rate is 30 miles per hour.

Glossary Continued

<table>
<tr><td>

V

variability

In statistics, variability means that the value of the attribute being studied can change from one person or thing to another.

variable

A variable is a letter used to represent a number.

EXAMPLES

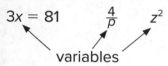

$3x = 81 \qquad \dfrac{4}{p} \qquad z^2$

variables

vertex

A vertex of a polyhedron is a point at which three or more of its edges meet.

EXAMPLE

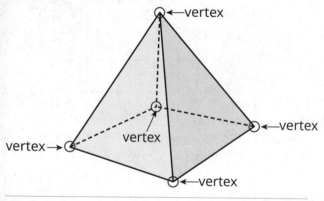

vertex

vertex

vertex → vertex

vertex

volume

Volume is the amount of space occupied by an object. You measure the volume of an object in cubic units.

</td><td>

Z

Zero Property of Multiplication

The Zero Property of Multiplication states that the product of any number and 0 is 0.

EXAMPLES

$6 \times 0 = 0 \qquad\qquad \dfrac{3}{4} \times 0 = 0$

$5^2 \cdot 0 = 0 \qquad\qquad 0.125(0)\, 0 = 0$

</td></tr>
</table>

Index

E

Q

R

S

Photo Credits